ELECTROMAGNETICS

VOLUME 2

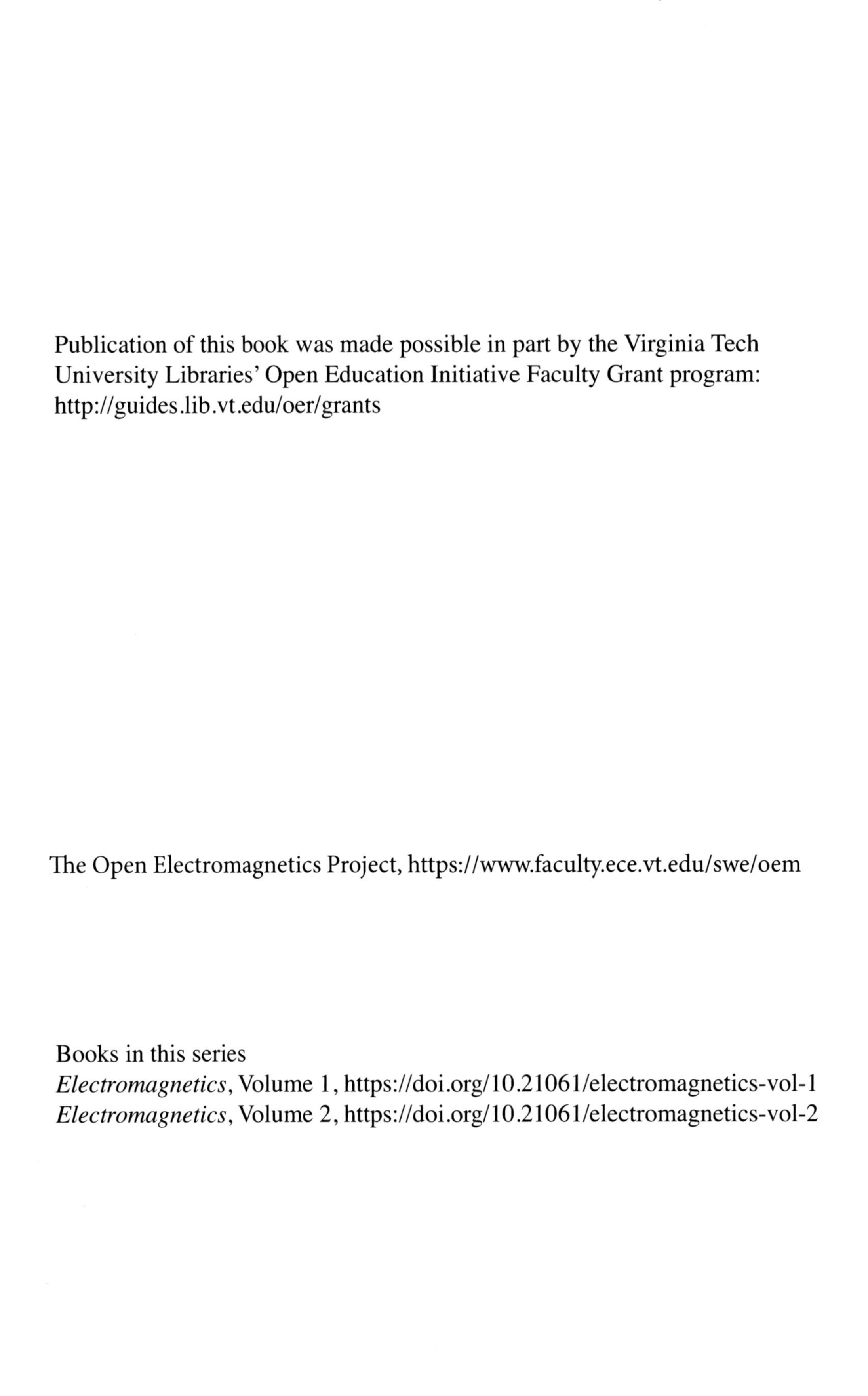

Publication of this book was made possible in part by the Virginia Tech University Libraries' Open Education Initiative Faculty Grant program: http://guides.lib.vt.edu/oer/grants

The Open Electromagnetics Project, https://www.faculty.ece.vt.edu/swe/oem

Books in this series
Electromagnetics, Volume 1, https://doi.org/10.21061/electromagnetics-vol-1
Electromagnetics, Volume 2, https://doi.org/10.21061/electromagnetics-vol-2

ELECTROMAGNETICS

STEVEN W. ELLINGSON

VOLUME 2

Copyright © 2020 Steven W. Ellingson

This textbook is licensed with a Creative Commons Attribution Share-Alike 4.0 license: https://creativecommons.org/licenses/by-sa/4.0. You are free to copy, share, adapt, remix, transform, and build upon the material for any purpose, even commercially, as long as you follow the terms of the license: https://creativecommons.org/licenses/by-sa/4.0/legalcode.

This work is published by Virginia Tech Publishing, a division of the University Libraries at Virginia Tech, 560 Drillfield Drive, Blacksburg, VA 24061, USA (publishing@vt.edu).

Suggested citation: Ellingson, Steven W. (2020) *Electromagnetics*, Vol. 2. Blacksburg, VA: Virginia Tech Publishing. https://doi.org/10.21061/electromagnetics-vol-2. Licensed with CC BY-SA 4.0. https://creativecommons.org/licenses/by-sa/4.0.

Peer Review: This book has undergone single-blind peer review by a minimum of three external subject matter experts.

Accessibility Statement: Virginia Tech Publishing is committed to making its publications accessible in accordance with the Americans with Disabilities Act of 1990. The screen reader–friendly PDF version of this book is tagged structurally and includes alternative text which allows for machine-readability. The LaTeX source files also include alternative text for all images and figures.

Publication Cataloging Information
Ellingson, Steven W., author
Electromagnetics (Volume 2) / Steven W. Ellingson
Pages cm
ISBN 978-1-949373-91-2 (print)
ISBN 978-1-949373-92-9 (ebook)
DOI: https://doi.org/10.21061/electromagnetics-vol-2
1. Electromagnetism. 2. Electromagnetic theory.
I. Title
QC760.E445 2020
621.3

The print version of this book is printed in the United States of America.

Cover Design: Robert Browder
Cover Image: © Michelle Yost. *Total Internal Reflection* (https://flic.kr/p/dWAhx5) is licensed with a Creative Commons Attribution-ShareAlike 2.0 license: https://creativecommons.org/licenses/by-sa/2.0/ (cropped by Robert Browder)

Features of This Open Textbook

Additional Resources

The following resources are freely available at http://hdl.handle.net/10919/93253

Downloadable PDF of the book
LaTeX source files
Slides of figures used in the book
Problem sets and solution manual
Print edition ordering details
Links to collaborator portal and listserv
Links to other books in the series
Errata

Review / Adopt /Adapt / Build upon

If you are an instructor reviewing, adopting, or adapting this textbook, please help us understand your use by completing this form: http://bit-ly/vtpublishing-update.

You are free to copy, share, adapt, remix, transform, and build upon the material for any purpose, even commercially, as long as you follow the terms of the license: https://creativecommons.org/licenses/by-sa/4.0/legalcode.

You must:

Attribute — You must **give appropriate credit, provide a link to the license, and indicate if changes were made.** You may do so in any reasonable manner, but not in any way that suggests the licensor endorses you or your use.

Suggested citation: Adapted by _[your name]_ from (c) Steven W. Ellingson, *Electromagnetics*, Vol 2, https://doi.org/10.21061/electromagnetics-vol-2, CC BY SA 4.0, https://creativecommons.org/licenses/by-sa/4.0.

ShareAlike — If you remix, transform, or build upon the material, you must distribute your contributions under the same license as the original.

You may not:

Add any additional restrictions — You may not apply legal terms or technological measures that legally restrict others from doing anything the license permits.

If adapting or building upon, you are encouraged to:

Incorporate only your own work or works with a CC BY or CC BY-SA license. Attribute all added content. Have your work peer reviewed. Include a transformation statement that describes changes, additions, accessibility features, and any subsequent peer review. If incorporating text or figures under an informed fair use analysis, mark them as such and cite them. Share your contributions in the collaborator portal or on the listserv. Contact the author to explore contributing your additions to the project.

Suggestions for creating and adapting
Create and share learning tools and study aids.
Translate. Modify the sequence or structure.
Add or modify problems and examples.
Transform or build upon in other formats.

Adaptation resources
LaTeX source files are available.
Adapt on your own at https://libretexts.org.
Guide: Modifying an Open Textbook
https://press.rebus.community/otnmodify.

Submit suggestions and comments
Submit suggestions (anonymous): http://bit.ly/electromagnetics-suggestion
Email: publishing@vt.edu
Annotate using Hypothes.is http://web.hypothes.is
For more information see the User Feedback Guide: http://bit.ly/userfeedbackguide

Contents

Preface

About This Book

[m0213]

Goals for this book. This book is intended to serve as a primary textbook for the second semester of a two-semester course in undergraduate engineering electromagnetics. The presumed textbook for the first semester is *Electromagnetics Vol. 1*,[1] which addresses the following topics: electric and magnetic fields; electromagnetic properties of materials; electromagnetic waves; and devices that operate according to associated electromagnetic principles including resistors, capacitors, inductors, transformers, generators, and transmission lines. The book you are now reading – *Electromagnetics Vol. 2* – addresses the following topics:

- Chapter 1 ("Preliminary Concepts") provides a brief summary of conventions for units, notation, and coordinate systems, and a synopsis of electromagnetic field theory from *Vol. 1*.
- Chapter 2 ("Magnetostatics Redux") extends the coverage of magnetostatics in *Vol. 1* to include magnetic forces, rudimentary motors, and the Biot-Savart law.
- Chapter 3 ("Wave Propagation in General Media") addresses Poynting's theorem, theory of wave propagation in lossy media, and properties of imperfect conductors.
- Chapter 4 ("Current Flow in Imperfect Conductors") addresses the frequency-dependent distribution of current in wire conductors and subsequently the AC impedance of wires.
- Chapter 5 ("Wave Reflection and Transmission") addresses scattering of plane waves from planar interfaces.
- Chapter 6 ("Waveguides") provides an introduction to waveguide theory via the parallel plate and rectangular waveguides.
- Chapter 7 ("Transmission Lines Redux") extends the coverage of transmission lines in *Vol. 1* to include parallel wire lines, the theory of microstrip lines, attenuation, and power-handling capabilities. The inevitable but hard-to-answer question "What's so special about 50 Ω?" is addressed at the end of this chapter.
- Chapter 8 ("Optical Fiber") provides an introduction to multimode fiber optics, including the concepts of acceptance angle and modal dispersion.
- Chapter 9 ("Radiation") provides a derivation of the electromagnetic fields radiated by a current distribution, emphasizing the analysis of line distributions using the Hertzian dipole as a differential element.
- Chapter 10 ("Antennas") provides an introduction to antennas, emphasizing equivalent circuit models for transmission and reception and characterization in terms of directivity and pattern. This chapter concludes with the Friis transmission equation.

Appendices covering material properties, mathematical formulas, and physical constants are repeated from *Vol. 1*, with a few additional items.

Target audience. This book is intended for electrical engineering students in the third year of a bachelor of science degree program. It is assumed that students have successfully completed one semester of

[1] S.W. Ellingson, *Electromagnetics Vol. 1*, VT Publishing, 2018. CC BY-SA 4.0. ISBN 9780997920185. https://doi.org/10.21061/electromagnetics-vol-1

engineering electromagnetics, nominally using *Vol. 1*. However, the particular topics and sequence of topics in *Vol. 1* are not an essential prerequisite, and in any event this book may be useful as a supplementary reference when a different textbook is used. It is assumed that readers are familiar with the fundamentals of electric circuits and linear systems, which are normally taught in the second year of the degree program. It is also assumed that readers are proficient in basic engineering mathematics, including complex numbers, trigonometry, vectors, partial differential equations, and multivariate calculus.

Notation, examples, and highlights. Section 1.2 summarizes the mathematical notation used in this book. Examples are set apart from the main text as follows:

Example 0.1. This is an example.

"Highlight boxes" are used to identify key ideas as follows:

This is a key idea.

What are those little numbers in square brackets? This book is a product of the *Open Electromagnetics Project*. This project provides a large number of sections ("modules") which are assembled ("remixed") to create new and different versions of the book. The text "[m0213]" that you see at the beginning of this section uniquely identifies the module within the larger set of modules provided by the project. This identification is provided because different remixes of this book may exist, each consisting of a different subset and arrangement of these modules. Prospective authors can use this identification as an aid in creating their own remixes.

Why do some sections of this book seem to repeat material presented in previous sections? In some remixes of this book, authors might choose to eliminate or reorder modules. For this reason, the modules are written to "stand alone" as much as possible. As a result, there may be some redundancy between sections that would not be present in a traditional (non-remixable) textbook. While this may seem awkward to some at first, there are clear benefits: In particular, it never hurts to review relevant past material before tackling a new concept. And, since the electronic version of this book is being offered at no cost, there is not much gained by eliminating this useful redundancy.

Why cite Wikipedia pages as additional reading? Many modules cite Wikipedia entries as sources of additional information. Wikipedia represents both the best and worst that the Internet has to offer. Most educators would agree that citing Wikipedia pages as primary sources is a bad idea, since quality is variable and content is subject to change over time. On the other hand, many Wikipedia pages are excellent, and serve as useful sources of relevant information that is not strictly within the scope of the curriculum. Furthermore, students benefit from seeing the same material presented differently, in a broader context, and with the additional references available as links from Wikipedia pages. We trust instructors and students to realize the potential pitfalls of this type of resource and to be alert for problems.

Acknowledgments. Here's a list of talented and helpful people who contributed to this book:

The staff of Virginia Tech Publishing, University Libraries, Virginia Tech:
Acquisitions/Developmental Editor & Project Manager: Anita Walz
Advisors: Peter Potter, Corinne Guimont
Cover, Print Production: Robert Browder

Other Virginia Tech contributors:
Accessibility: Christa Miller, Corinne Guimont, Sarah Mease
Assessment: Anita Walz

Virginia Tech Students:
Alt text writer: Michel Comer
Figure designers: Kruthika Kikkeri, Sam Lally, Chenhao Wang

Copyediting:
Longleaf Press

External reviewers:
Randy Haupt, Colorado School of Mines
Karl Warnick, Brigham Young University
Anonymous faculty member, research university

Also, thanks are due to the students of the Fall 2019 section of ECE3106 at Virginia Tech who used the beta version of this book and provided useful feedback.

Finally, we acknowledge all those who have contributed their art to Wikimedia Commons (https://commons.wikimedia.org/) under open licenses, allowing their work to appear as figures in this book. These contributors are acknowledged in figures and in the "Image Credits" section at the end of each chapter. Thanks to each of you for your selfless effort.

About the Open Electromagnetics Project

[m0148]

The *Open Electromagnetics Project* (https://www.faculty.ece.vt.edu/swe/oem/) was established at Virginia Tech in 2017 with the goal of creating no-cost openly-licensed textbooks for courses in undergraduate engineering electromagnetics. While a number of very fine traditional textbooks are available on this topic, we feel that it has become unreasonable to insist that students pay hundreds of dollars per book when effective alternatives can be provided using modern media at little or no cost to the student. This project is equally motivated by the desire for the freedom to adopt, modify, and improve educational resources. This work is distributed under a Creative Commons BY SA license which allows – and we hope encourages – others to adopt, modify, improve, and expand the scope of our work.

About the Author

[m0153]

Steven W. Ellingson (ellingson@vt.edu) is an Associate Professor at Virginia Tech in Blacksburg, Virginia, in the United States. He received PhD and MS degrees in Electrical Engineering from the Ohio State University and a BS in Electrical and Computer Engineering from Clarkson University. He was employed by the U.S. Army, Booz-Allen & Hamilton, Raytheon, and the Ohio State University ElectroScience Laboratory before joining the faculty of Virginia Tech, where he teaches courses in electromagnetics, radio frequency electronics, wireless communications, and signal processing. His research includes topics in wireless communications, radio science, and radio frequency instrumentation. Professor Ellingson serves as a consultant to industry and government and is the author of *Radio Systems Engineering* (Cambridge University Press, 2016) and *Electromagnetics Vol. 1* (VT Publishing, 2018).

Chapter 1

Preliminary Concepts

1.1 Units

[m0072]

The term "unit" refers to the measure used to express a physical quantity. For example, the mean radius of the Earth is about 6,371,000 meters; in this case, the unit is the meter.

A number like "6,371,000" becomes a bit cumbersome to write, so it is common to use a prefix to modify the unit. For example, the radius of the Earth is more commonly said to be 6371 kilometers, where one kilometer is understood to mean 1000 meters. It is common practice to use prefixes, such as "kilo-," that yield values in the range of 0.001 to $10,000$. A list of standard prefixes appears in Table 1.1.

Prefix	Abbreviation	Multiply by:
exa	E	10^{18}
peta	P	10^{15}
tera	T	10^{12}
giga	G	10^{9}
mega	M	10^{6}
kilo	k	10^{3}
milli	m	10^{-3}
micro	μ	10^{-6}
nano	n	10^{-9}
pico	p	10^{-12}
femto	f	10^{-15}
atto	a	10^{-18}

Table 1.1: Prefixes used to modify units.

Unit	Abbreviation	Quantifies:
ampere	A	electric current
coulomb	C	electric charge
farad	F	capacitance
henry	H	inductance
hertz	Hz	frequency
joule	J	energy
meter	m	distance
newton	N	force
ohm	Ω	resistance
second	s	time
tesla	T	magnetic flux density
volt	V	electric potential
watt	W	power
weber	Wb	magnetic flux

Table 1.2: Some units that are commonly used in electromagnetics.

Writing out the names of units can also become tedious. For this reason, it is common to use standard abbreviations; e.g., "6731 km" as opposed to "6371 kilometers," where "k" is the standard abbreviation for the prefix "kilo" and "m" is the standard abbreviation for "meter." A list of commonly-used base units and their abbreviations are shown in Table 1.2.

To avoid ambiguity, it is important to always indicate the units of a quantity; e.g., writing "6371 km" as opposed to "6371." Failure to do so is a common source of error and misunderstandings. An example is the expression:

$$l = 3t$$

where l is length and t is time. It could be that l is in meters and t is in seconds, in which case "3" really means "3 m/s." However, if it is intended that l is in kilometers and t is in hours, then "3" really means "3 km/h," and the equation is literally different. To patch this up, one might write "$l = 3t$ m/s"; however, note that this does not resolve the ambiguity we just identified – i.e., we still don't know the units of the constant "3." Alternatively, one might write "$l = 3t$ where l is in meters and t is in seconds," which is unambiguous but becomes quite awkward for more complicated expressions. A better solution is to write instead:

$$l = (3 \text{ m/s})\, t$$

or even better:

$$l = at \quad \text{where } a = 3 \text{ m/s}$$

since this separates the issue of units from the perhaps more-important fact that l is proportional to t and the constant of proportionality (a) is known.

The meter is the fundamental unit of length in the International System of Units, known by its French acronym "SI" and sometimes informally referred to as the "metric system."

In this work, we will use SI units exclusively.

Although SI is probably the most popular for engineering use overall, other systems remain in common use. For example, the English system, where the radius of the Earth might alternatively be said to be about 3959 miles, continues to be used in various applications and to a lesser or greater extent in various regions of the world. An alternative system in common use in physics and material science applications is the CGS ("centimeter-gram-second") system. The CGS system is similar to SI, but with some significant differences. For example, the base unit of energy in the CGS system is not the "joule" but rather the "erg," and the values of some physical constants become unitless. Therefore – once again – it is very important to include units whenever values are stated.

SI defines seven fundamental units from which all other units can be derived. These fundamental units are distance in meters (m), time in seconds (s), current in amperes (A), mass in kilograms (kg), temperature in kelvin (K), particle count in moles (mol), and luminosity in candela (cd). SI units for electromagnetic quantities such as coulombs (C) for charge and volts (V) for electric potential are derived from these fundamental units.

A frequently-overlooked feature of units is their ability to assist in error-checking mathematical expressions. For example, the electric field intensity may be specified in volts per meter (V/m), so an expression for the electric field intensity that yields units of V/m is said to be "dimensionally correct" (but not necessarily correct), whereas an expression that cannot be reduced to units of V/m *cannot* be correct.

Additional Reading:

- "International System of Units" on Wikipedia.
- "Centimetre-gram-second system of units" on Wikipedia.

1.2 Notation

[m0005]

The list below describes notation used in this book.

- *Vectors*: Boldface is used to indicate a vector; e.g., the electric field intensity vector will typically appear as $\mathbf{E}$. Quantities not in boldface are scalars. When writing by hand, it is common to write "$\underline{E}$" or "$\overrightarrow{E}$" in lieu of "$\mathbf{E}$."
- *Unit vectors*: A circumflex is used to indicate a unit vector; i.e., a vector having magnitude equal to one. For example, the unit vector pointing in the $+x$ direction will be indicated as $\hat{\mathbf{x}}$. In discussion, the quantity "$\hat{\mathbf{x}}$" is typically spoken "x hat."
- *Time*: The symbol t is used to indicate time.
- *Position*: The symbols (x, y, z), (ρ, ϕ, z), and (r, θ, ϕ) indicate positions using the Cartesian, cylindrical, and spherical coordinate systems, respectively. It is sometimes convenient to express position in a manner which is independent of a coordinate system; in this case, we typically use the symbol $\mathbf{r}$. For example, $\mathbf{r} = \hat{\mathbf{x}}x + \hat{\mathbf{y}}y + \hat{\mathbf{z}}z$ in the Cartesian coordinate system.
- *Phasors:* A tilde is used to indicate a phasor quantity; e.g., a voltage phasor might be indicated as $\widetilde{V}$, and the phasor representation of $\mathbf{E}$ will be indicated as $\widetilde{\mathbf{E}}$.
- *Curves, surfaces, and volumes:* These geometrical entities will usually be indicated in script; e.g., an open surface might be indicated as $\mathcal{S}$ and the curve bounding this surface might be indicated as $\mathcal{C}$. Similarly, the volume enclosed by a closed surface $\mathcal{S}$ may be indicated as $\mathcal{V}$.
- *Integrations over curves, surfaces, and volumes* will usually be indicated using a single integral sign with the appropriate subscript. For example:

  $\int_{\mathcal{C}} \cdots dl$ is an integral over the curve $\mathcal{C}$

  $\int_{\mathcal{S}} \cdots ds$ is an integral over the surface $\mathcal{S}$

  $\int_{\mathcal{V}} \cdots dv$ is an integral over the volume $\mathcal{V}$.
- *Integrations over <u>closed</u> curves and surfaces* will be indicated using a circle superimposed on the integral sign. For example:

  $\oint_{\mathcal{C}} \cdots dl$ is an integral over the closed curve $\mathcal{C}$

  $\oint_{\mathcal{S}} \cdots ds$ is an integral over the closed surface $\mathcal{S}$

  A "closed curve" is one which forms an unbroken loop; e.g., a circle. A "closed surface" is one which encloses a volume with no openings; e.g., a sphere.
- The symbol "$\cong$" means "approximately equal to." This symbol is used when equality exists, but is not being expressed with exact numerical precision. For example, the ratio of the circumference of a circle to its diameter is π, where $\pi \cong 3.14$.
- The symbol "$\approx$" also indicates "approximately equal to," but in this case the two quantities are unequal even if expressed with exact numerical precision. For example, $e^x = 1 + x + x^2/2 + ...$ as an infinite series, but $e^x \approx 1 + x$ for $x \ll 1$. Using this approximation, $e^{0.1} \approx 1.1$, which is in good agreement with the actual value $e^{0.1} \cong 1.1052$.
- The symbol "$\sim$" indicates "on the order of," which is a relatively weak statement of equality indicating that the indicated quantity is within a factor of 10 or so of the indicated value. For example, $\mu \sim 10^5$ for a class of iron alloys, with exact values being larger or smaller by a factor of 5 or so.
- The symbol "$\triangleq$" means "is defined as" or "is equal as the result of a definition."
- *Complex numbers*: $j \triangleq \sqrt{-1}$.
- See Appendix C for notation used to identify commonly-used physical constants.

1.3 Coordinate Systems

[m0180]

The coordinate systems most commonly used in engineering analysis are the *Cartesian*, *cylindrical*, and *spherical* systems. These systems are illustrated in Figures 1.1, 1.2, and 1.3, respectively. Note that the use of variables is not universal; in particular, it is common to encounter the use of r in lieu of ρ for the radial coordinate in the cylindrical system, and the use of R in lieu of r for the radial coordinate in the spherical system.

Additional Reading:

- "Cylindrical coordinate system" on Wikipedia.
- "Spherical coordinate system" on Wikipedia.

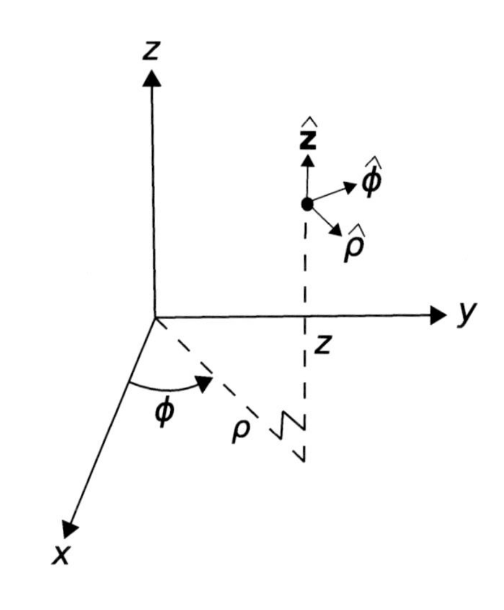

© K. Kikkeri CC BY SA 4.0

Figure 1.2: Cylindrical coordinate system.

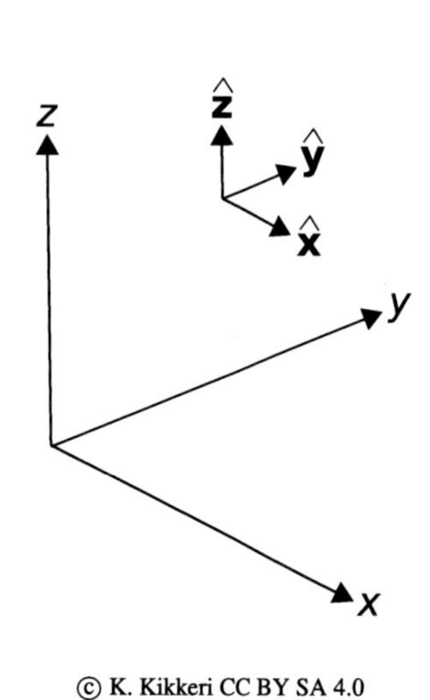

© K. Kikkeri CC BY SA 4.0

Figure 1.1: Cartesian coordinate system.

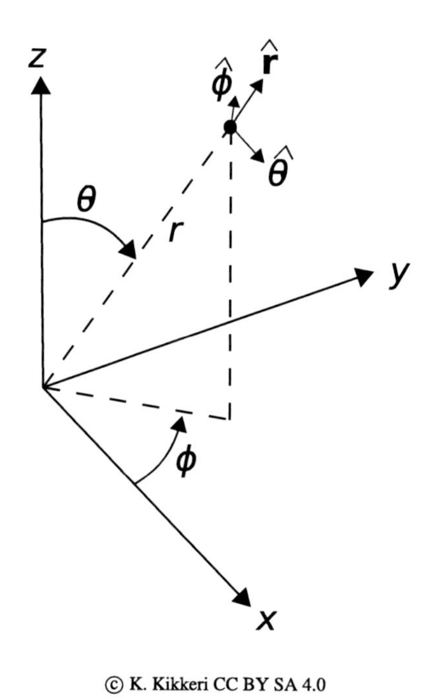

© K. Kikkeri CC BY SA 4.0

Figure 1.3: Spherical coordinate system.

1.4 Electromagnetic Field Theory: A Review

[m0179]

This book is the second in a series of textbooks on electromagnetics. This section presents a summary of electromagnetic field theory concepts presented in the previous volume.

Electric charge and current. Charge is the ultimate source of the electric field and has SI base units of coulomb (C). An important source of charge is the electron, whose charge is defined to be negative. However, the term "charge" generally refers to a large number of charge carriers of various types, and whose relative net charge may be either positive or negative. Distributions of charge may alternatively be expressed in terms of line charge density ρ_l (C/m), surface charge density ρ_s (C/m^2), or volume charge density ρ_v (C/m^3). Electric current describes the net motion of charge. Current is expressed in SI base units of amperes (A) and may alternatively be quantified in terms of surface current density $\mathbf{J}_s$ (A/m) or volume current density $\mathbf{J}$ (A/m^2).

Electrostatics. Electrostatics is the theory of the electric field subject to the constraint that charge does not accelerate. That is, charges may be motionless ("static") or move without acceleration ("steady current").

The electric field may be interpreted in terms of energy or flux. The energy interpretation of the electric field is referred to as *electric field intensity* $\mathbf{E}$ (SI base units of N/C or V/m), and is related to the energy associated with charge and forces between charges. One finds that the electric potential (SI base units of V) over a path $\mathcal{C}$ is given by

$$V = -\int_{\mathcal{C}} \mathbf{E} \cdot d\mathbf{l} \tag{1.1}$$

The principle of *independence of path* means that only the endpoints of $\mathcal{C}$ in Equation 1.1, and no other details of $\mathcal{C}$, matter. This leads to the finding that the electrostatic field is *conservative*; i.e.,

$$\oint_{\mathcal{C}} \mathbf{E} \cdot d\mathbf{l} = 0 \tag{1.2}$$

This is referred to as *Kirchoff's voltage law for electrostatics*. The inverse of Equation 1.1 is

$$\mathbf{E} = -\nabla V \tag{1.3}$$

That is, the electric field intensity points in the direction in which the potential is most rapidly decreasing, and the magnitude is equal to the rate of change in that direction.

The flux interpretation of the electric field is referred to as *electric flux density* $\mathbf{D}$ (SI base units of C/m^2), and quantifies the effect of charge as a flow emanating from the charge. *Gauss' law for electric fields* states that the electric flux through a closed surface is equal to the enclosed charge Q_{encl}; i.e.,

$$\oint_{\mathcal{S}} \mathbf{D} \cdot d\mathbf{s} = Q_{encl} \tag{1.4}$$

Within a material region, we find

$$\mathbf{D} = \epsilon \mathbf{E} \tag{1.5}$$

where ϵ is the *permittivity* (SI base units of F/m) of the material. In free space, ϵ is equal to

$$\epsilon_0 \triangleq 8.854 \times 10^{-12} \text{ F/m} \tag{1.6}$$

It is often convenient to quantify the permittivity of material in terms of the unitless *relative permittivity* $\epsilon_r \triangleq \epsilon/\epsilon_0$.

Both $\mathbf{E}$ and $\mathbf{D}$ are useful as they lead to distinct and independent boundary conditions at the boundary between dissimilar material regions. Let us refer to these regions as Regions 1 and 2, having fields $(\mathbf{E}_1, \mathbf{D}_1)$ and $(\mathbf{E}_2, \mathbf{D}_2)$, respectively. Given a vector $\hat{\mathbf{n}}$ perpendicular to the boundary and pointing into Region 1, we find

$$\hat{\mathbf{n}} \times [\mathbf{E}_1 - \mathbf{E}_2] = 0 \tag{1.7}$$

i.e., the tangential component of the electric field is continuous across a boundary, and

$$\hat{\mathbf{n}} \cdot [\mathbf{D}_1 - \mathbf{D}_2] = \rho_s \tag{1.8}$$

i.e., any discontinuity in the normal component of the electric field must be supported by a surface charge distribution on the boundary.

Magnetostatics. Magnetostatics is the theory of the magnetic field in response to steady current or the intrinsic magnetization of materials. Intrinsic magnetization is a property of some materials, including permanent magnets and magnetizable materials.

Like the electric field, the magnetic field may be quantified in terms of energy or flux. The flux interpretation of the magnetic field is referred to as *magnetic flux density* $\mathbf{B}$ (SI base units of Wb/m^2), and quantifies the field as a flow associated with, but not emanating from, the source of the field. The magnetic flux Φ (SI base units of Wb) is this flow measured through a specified surface. *Gauss' law for magnetic fields* states that

$$\oint_{\mathcal{S}} \mathbf{B} \cdot d\mathbf{s} = 0 \tag{1.9}$$

i.e., the magnetic flux through a closed surface is zero. Comparison to Equation 1.4 leads to the conclusion that the source of the magnetic field cannot be localized; i.e., there is no "magnetic charge" analogous to electric charge. Equation 1.9 also leads to the conclusion that magnetic field lines form closed loops.

The energy interpretation of the magnetic field is referred to as *magnetic field intensity* $\mathbf{H}$ (SI base units of A/m), and is related to the energy associated with sources of the magnetic field. *Ampere's law for magnetostatics* states that

$$\oint_{\mathcal{C}} \mathbf{H} \cdot d\mathbf{l} = I_{encl} \tag{1.10}$$

where I_{encl} is the current flowing past any open surface bounded by $\mathcal{C}$.

Within a homogeneous material region, we find

$$\mathbf{B} = \mu \mathbf{H} \tag{1.11}$$

where μ is the *permeability* (SI base units of H/m) of the material. In free space, μ is equal to

$$\mu_0 \triangleq 4\pi \times 10^{-7} \text{ H/m}. \tag{1.12}$$

It is often convenient to quantify the permeability of material in terms of the unitless *relative permeability* $\mu_r \triangleq \mu/\mu_0$.

Both $\mathbf{B}$ and $\mathbf{H}$ are useful as they lead to distinct and independent boundary conditions at the boundaries between dissimilar material regions. Let us refer to these regions as Regions 1 and 2, having fields $(\mathbf{B}_1, \mathbf{H}_1)$ and $(\mathbf{B}_2, \mathbf{H}_2)$, respectively. Given a vector $\hat{\mathbf{n}}$ perpendicular to the boundary and pointing into Region 1, we find

$$\hat{\mathbf{n}} \cdot [\mathbf{B}_1 - \mathbf{B}_2] = 0 \tag{1.13}$$

i.e., the normal component of the magnetic field is continuous across a boundary, and

$$\hat{\mathbf{n}} \times [\mathbf{H}_1 - \mathbf{H}_2] = \mathbf{J}_s \tag{1.14}$$

i.e., any discontinuity in the tangential component of the magnetic field must be supported by current on the boundary.

Maxwell's equations. Equations 1.2, 1.4, 1.9, and 1.10 are *Maxwell's equations* for static fields in integral form. As indicated in Table 1.3, these equations may alternatively be expressed in differential form. The principal advantage of the differential forms is that they apply at each point in space (as opposed to regions defined by $\mathcal{C}$ or $\mathcal{S}$), and subsequently can be combined with the boundary conditions to solve complex problems using standard methods from the theory of differential equations.

Conductivity. Some materials consist of an abundance of electrons which are loosely-bound to the atoms and molecules comprising the material. The force exerted on these electrons by an electric field may be sufficient to overcome the binding force, resulting in motion of the associated charges and subsequently current. This effect is quantified by *Ohm's law for electromagnetics*:

$$\mathbf{J} = \sigma \mathbf{E} \tag{1.15}$$

where $\mathbf{J}$ in this case is the *conduction current* determined by the conductivity σ (SI base units of S/m). Conductivity is a property of a material that ranges from negligible (i.e., for "insulators") to very large for good conductors, which includes most metals.

A *perfect conductor* is a material within which $\mathbf{E}$ is essentially zero regardless of $\mathbf{J}$. For such material, $\sigma \to \infty$. Perfect conductors are said to be *equipotential regions*; that is, the potential difference

	Electrostatics / Magnetostatics	**Time-Varying (Dynamic)**
Electric & magnetic fields are...	independent	possibly coupled
Maxwell's eqns. (integral)	$\oint_S \mathbf{D}\cdot d\mathbf{s} = Q_{encl}$ $\oint_C \mathbf{E}\cdot d\mathbf{l} = 0$ $\oint_S \mathbf{B}\cdot d\mathbf{s} = 0$ $\oint_C \mathbf{H}\cdot d\mathbf{l} = I_{encl}$	$\oint_S \mathbf{D}\cdot d\mathbf{s} = Q_{encl}$ $\oint_C \mathbf{E}\cdot d\mathbf{l} = -\frac{\partial}{\partial t}\int_S \mathbf{B}\cdot d\mathbf{s}$ $\oint_S \mathbf{B}\cdot d\mathbf{s} = 0$ $\oint_C \mathbf{H}\cdot d\mathbf{l} = I_{encl} + \int_S \frac{\partial}{\partial t}\mathbf{D}\cdot d\mathbf{s}$
Maxwell's eqns. (differential)	$\nabla\cdot\mathbf{D} = \rho_v$ $\nabla\times\mathbf{E} = 0$ $\nabla\cdot\mathbf{B} = 0$ $\nabla\times\mathbf{H} = \mathbf{J}$	$\nabla\cdot\mathbf{D} = \rho_v$ $\nabla\times\mathbf{E} = -\frac{\partial}{\partial t}\mathbf{B}$ $\nabla\cdot\mathbf{B} = 0$ $\nabla\times\mathbf{H} = \mathbf{J} + \frac{\partial}{\partial t}\mathbf{D}$

Table 1.3: Comparison of Maxwell's equations for static and time-varying electromagnetic fields. Differences in the time-varying case relative to the static case are highlighted in blue.

between any two points within a perfect conductor is zero, as can be readily verified using Equation 1.1.

Time-varying fields. *Faraday's law* states that a time-varying magnetic flux induces an electric potential in a closed loop as follows:

$$V = -\frac{\partial}{\partial t}\Phi \tag{1.16}$$

Setting this equal to the left side of Equation 1.2 leads to the *Maxwell-Faraday equation* in integral form:

$$\oint_C \mathbf{E}\cdot d\mathbf{l} = -\frac{\partial}{\partial t}\int_S \mathbf{B}\cdot d\mathbf{s} \tag{1.17}$$

where $\mathcal{C}$ is the closed path defined by the edge of the open surface $\mathcal{S}$. Thus, we see that a time-varying magnetic flux is able to generate an electric field. We also observe that electric and magnetic fields become coupled when the magnetic flux is time-varying.

An analogous finding leads to the general form of Ampere's law:

$$\oint_C \mathbf{H}\cdot d\mathbf{l} = I_{encl} + \int_S \frac{\partial}{\partial t}\mathbf{D}\cdot d\mathbf{s} \tag{1.18}$$

where the new term is referred to as *displacement current*. Through the displacement current, a time-varying electric flux may be a source of the magnetic field. In other words, we see that the electric and magnetic fields are coupled when the electric flux is time-varying.

Gauss' law for electric and magnetic fields, boundary conditions, and constitutive relationships (Equations 1.5, 1.11, and 1.15) are the same in the time-varying case.

As indicated in Table 1.3, the time-varying version of Maxwell's equations may also be expressed in differential form. The differential forms make clear that variations in the electric field with respect to position are associated with variations in the magnetic field with respect to time (the Maxwell-Faraday equation), and vice-versa (Ampere's law).

Time-harmonic waves in source-free and lossless media. The coupling between electric and magnetic fields in the time-varying case leads to wave phenomena. This is most easily analyzed for fields which vary sinusoidally, and may thereby be expressed as phasors.[1] Phasors, indicated in this book by the tilde ("$\sim$"), are complex-valued quantities representing the magnitude and phase of the associated sinusoidal waveform. Maxwell's equations in differential phasor form are:

$$\nabla\cdot\widetilde{\mathbf{D}} = \widetilde{\rho}_v \tag{1.19}$$

$$\nabla\times\widetilde{\mathbf{E}} = -j\omega\widetilde{\mathbf{B}} \tag{1.20}$$

$$\nabla\cdot\widetilde{\mathbf{B}} = 0 \tag{1.21}$$

$$\nabla\times\widetilde{\mathbf{H}} = \widetilde{\mathbf{J}} + j\omega\widetilde{\mathbf{D}} \tag{1.22}$$

where $\omega \triangleq 2\pi f$, and where f is frequency (SI base

[1] Sinusoidally-varying fields are sometimes also said to be *time-harmonic*.

units of Hz). In regions which are free of sources (i.e., charges and currents) and consisting of loss-free media (i.e., $\sigma = 0$), these equations reduce to the following:

$$\nabla \cdot \widetilde{\mathbf{E}} = 0 \tag{1.23}$$

$$\nabla \times \widetilde{\mathbf{E}} = -j\omega\mu\widetilde{\mathbf{H}} \tag{1.24}$$

$$\nabla \cdot \widetilde{\mathbf{H}} = 0 \tag{1.25}$$

$$\nabla \times \widetilde{\mathbf{H}} = +j\omega\epsilon\widetilde{\mathbf{E}} \tag{1.26}$$

where we have used the relationships $\mathbf{D} = \epsilon\mathbf{E}$ and $\mathbf{B} = \mu\mathbf{H}$ to eliminate the flux densities $\mathbf{D}$ and $\mathbf{B}$, which are now redundant. Solving Equations 1.23–1.26 for $\mathbf{E}$ and $\mathbf{H}$, we obtain the vector wave equations:

$$\nabla^2\widetilde{\mathbf{E}} + \beta^2\widetilde{\mathbf{E}} = 0 \tag{1.27}$$

$$\nabla^2\widetilde{\mathbf{H}} + \beta^2\widetilde{\mathbf{H}} = 0 \tag{1.28}$$

where

$$\beta \triangleq \omega\sqrt{\mu\epsilon} \tag{1.29}$$

Waves in source-free and lossless media are solutions to the vector wave equations.

Uniform plane waves in source-free and lossless media. An important subset of solutions to the vector wave equations are uniform plane waves. Uniform plane waves result when solutions are constrained to exhibit constant magnitude and phase in a plane. For example, if this plane is specified to be perpendicular to z (i.e., $\partial/\partial x = \partial/\partial y = 0$) then solutions for $\widetilde{\mathbf{E}}$ have the form:

$$\widetilde{\mathbf{E}} = \hat{\mathbf{x}}\widetilde{E}_x + \hat{\mathbf{y}}\widetilde{E}_y \tag{1.30}$$

where

$$\widetilde{E}_x = E_{x0}^{+}e^{-j\beta z} + E_{x0}^{-}e^{+j\beta z} \tag{1.31}$$

$$\widetilde{E}_y = E_{y0}^{+}e^{-j\beta z} + E_{y0}^{-}e^{+j\beta z} \tag{1.32}$$

and where E_{x0}^{+}, E_{x0}^{-}, E_{y0}^{+}, and E_{y0}^{-} are constant complex-valued coefficients which depend on sources and boundary conditions. The first term and second terms of Equations 1.31 and 1.32 correspond to waves traveling in the $+\hat{\mathbf{z}}$ and $-\hat{\mathbf{z}}$ directions, respectively. Because $\widetilde{\mathbf{H}}$ is a solution to the same vector wave equation, the solution for $\mathbf{H}$ is identical except with different coefficients.

The scalar components of the plane waves described in Equations 1.31 and 1.32 exhibit the same characteristics as other types of waves, including sound waves and voltage and current waves in transmission lines. In particular, the phase velocity of waves propagating in the $+\hat{\mathbf{z}}$ and $-\hat{\mathbf{z}}$ direction is

$$v_p = \frac{\omega}{\beta} = \frac{1}{\sqrt{\mu\epsilon}} \tag{1.33}$$

and the wavelength is

$$\lambda = \frac{2\pi}{\beta} \tag{1.34}$$

By requiring solutions for $\widetilde{\mathbf{E}}$ and $\widetilde{\mathbf{H}}$ to satisfy the Maxwell curl equations (i.e., the Maxwell-Faraday equation and Ampere's law), we find that $\widetilde{\mathbf{E}}$, $\widetilde{\mathbf{H}}$, and the direction of propagation $\hat{\mathbf{k}}$ are mutually perpendicular. In particular, we obtain the *plane wave relationships*:

$$\widetilde{\mathbf{E}} = -\eta\hat{\mathbf{k}} \times \widetilde{\mathbf{H}} \tag{1.35}$$

$$\widetilde{\mathbf{H}} = \frac{1}{\eta}\hat{\mathbf{k}} \times \widetilde{\mathbf{E}} \tag{1.36}$$

where

$$\eta \triangleq \sqrt{\frac{\mu}{\epsilon}} \tag{1.37}$$

is the *wave impedance*, also known as the *intrinsic impedance of the medium*, and $\hat{\mathbf{k}}$ is in the same direction as $\widetilde{\mathbf{E}} \times \widetilde{\mathbf{H}}$.

The power density associated with a plane wave is

$$S = \frac{\left|\widetilde{\mathbf{E}}\right|^2}{2\eta} \tag{1.38}$$

where S has SI base units of W/m^2, and here it is assumed that $\widetilde{\mathbf{E}}$ is in peak (as opposed to rms) units.

Commonly-assumed properties of materials. Finally, a reminder about commonly-assumed properties of the material constitutive parameters ϵ, μ, and σ. We often assume these parameters exhibit the following properties:

- *Homogeneity*. A material that is *homogeneous* is uniform over the space it occupies; that is, the values of its constitutive parameters are constant at all locations within the material.

- *Isotropy*. A material that is *isotropic* behaves in precisely the same way regardless of how it is oriented with respect to sources, fields, and other materials.

- *Linearity*. A material is said to be *linear* if its properties do not depend on the sources and fields applied to the material. Linear media exhibit *superposition*; that is, the response to multiple sources is equal to the sum of the responses to the sources individually.

- *Time-invariance*. A material is said to be *time-invariant* if its properties do not vary as a function of time.

[m0181]

Additional Reading:

- "Maxwell's Equations" on Wikipedia.
- "Wave Equation" on Wikipedia.
- "Electromagnetic Wave Equation" on Wikipedia.
- "Electromagnetic radiation" on Wikipedia.

Image Credits

Fig. 1.1: © K. Kikkeri, https://commons.wikimedia.org/wiki/File:M0006_fCartesianBasis.svg, CC BY SA 4.0 (https://creativecommons.org/licenses/by-sa/4.0/).

Fig. 1.2: © K. Kikkeri, https://commons.wikimedia.org/wiki/File:M0096_fCylindricalCoordinates.svg, CC BY SA 4.0 (https://creativecommons.org/licenses/by-sa/4.0/).

Fig. 1.3: © K. Kikkeri, https://commons.wikimedia.org/wiki/File:Spherical_Coordinate_System.svg, CC BY SA 4.0 (https://creativecommons.org/licenses/by-sa/4.0/).

Chapter 2

Magnetostatics Redux

2.1 Lorentz Force

[m0015]

> The *Lorentz force* is the force experienced by charge in the presence of electric and magnetic fields.

Consider a particle having charge q. The force $\mathbf{F}_e$ experienced by the particle in the presence of electric field intensity $\mathbf{E}$ is

$$\mathbf{F}_e = q\mathbf{E}$$

The force $\mathbf{F}_m$ experienced by the particle in the presence of magnetic flux density $\mathbf{B}$ is

$$\mathbf{F}_m = q\mathbf{v} \times \mathbf{B}$$

where $\mathbf{v}$ is the velocity of the particle. The Lorentz force experienced by the particle is simply the sum of these forces; i.e.,

$$\begin{aligned} \mathbf{F} &= \mathbf{F}_e + \mathbf{F}_m \\ &= q\left(\mathbf{E} + \mathbf{v} \times \mathbf{B}\right) \end{aligned} \tag{2.1}$$

The term "Lorentz force" is simply a concise way to refer to the *combined* contributions of the electric and magnetic fields.

A common application of the Lorentz force concept is in analysis of the motions of charged particles in electromagnetic fields. The Lorentz force causes charged particles to exhibit distinct rotational ("cyclotron") and translational ("drift") motions. This is illustrated in Figures 2.1 and 2.2.

Additional Reading:

- "Lorentz force" on Wikipedia.

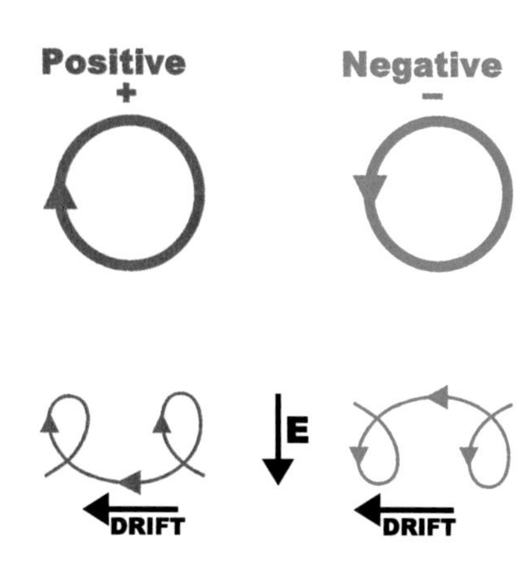

© Stannered CC BY 2.5.

Figure 2.1: Motion of a particle bearing (*left*) positive charge and (*right*) negative charge. *Top*: Magnetic field directed toward the viewer; no electric field. *Bottom*: Magnetic field directed toward the viewer; electric field oriented as shown.

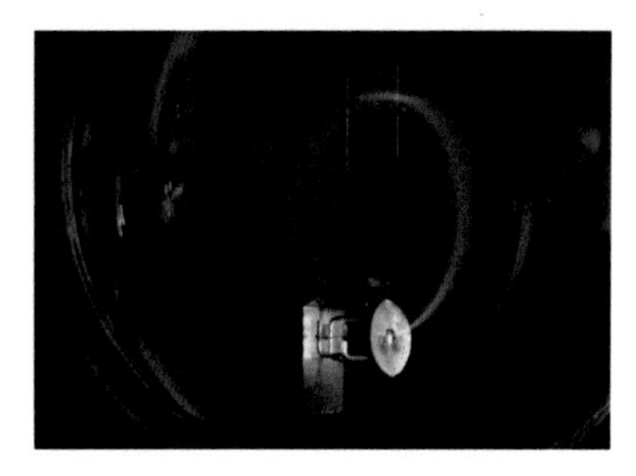

© M. Biaek CC BY-SA 4.0.

Figure 2.2: Electrons moving in a circle in a magnetic field (*cyclotron motion*). The electrons are produced by an electron gun at bottom, consisting of a hot cathode, a metal plate heated by a filament so it emits electrons, and a metal anode at a high voltage with a hole which accelerates the electrons into a beam. The electrons are normally invisible, but enough air has been left in the tube so that the air molecules glow pink when struck by the fast-moving electrons.

2.2 Magnetic Force on a Current-Carrying Wire

[m0017]

Consider an infinitesimally-thin and perfectly-conducting wire bearing a current I (SI base units of A) in free space. Let $\mathbf{B}(\mathbf{r})$ be the impressed magnetic flux density at each point $\mathbf{r}$ in the region of space occupied by the wire. By *impressed*, we mean that the field exists in the absence of the current-carrying wire, as opposed to the field that is induced by this current. Since current consists of charged particles in motion, we expect that $\mathbf{B}(\mathbf{r})$ will exert a force on the current. Since the current is constrained to flow on the wire, we expect this force will also be experienced by the wire. Let us now consider this force.

To begin, recall that the force exerted on a particle bearing charge q having velocity $\mathbf{v}$ is

$$\mathbf{F}_m(\mathbf{r}) = q\mathbf{v}(\mathbf{r}) \times \mathbf{B}(\mathbf{r}) \tag{2.2}$$

Thus, the force exerted on a *differential* amount of charge dq is

$$d\mathbf{F}_m(\mathbf{r}) = dq\, \mathbf{v}(\mathbf{r}) \times \mathbf{B}(\mathbf{r}) \tag{2.3}$$

Let $d\mathbf{l}(\mathbf{r})$ represent a differential-length segment of the wire at $\mathbf{r}$, pointing in the direction of current flow. Then

$$dq\, \mathbf{v}(\mathbf{r}) = I d\mathbf{l}(\mathbf{r}) \tag{2.4}$$

(If this is not clear, it might help to consider the units: On the left, C·m/s = (C/s)·m = A·m, as on the right.) Subsequently,

$$d\mathbf{F}_m(\mathbf{r}) = I d\mathbf{l}(\mathbf{r}) \times \mathbf{B}(\mathbf{r}) \tag{2.5}$$

There are three important cases of practical interest. First, consider a straight segment $\mathbf{l}$ forming part of a closed loop of current in a spatially-uniform impressed magnetic flux density $\mathbf{B}(\mathbf{r}) = \mathbf{B}_0$. In this case, the force exerted by the magnetic field on such a segment is given by Equation 2.5 with $d\mathbf{l}$ replaced by $\mathbf{l}$; i.e.:

$$\boxed{\mathbf{F}_m = I\mathbf{l} \times \mathbf{B}_0} \tag{2.6}$$

Summarizing,

> The force experienced by a straight segment of current-carrying wire in a spatially-uniform magnetic field is given by Equation 2.6.

The second case of practical interest is a rigid closed loop of current in a spatially-uniform magnetic flux density $\mathbf{B}_0$. If the loop consists of straight sides – e.g., a rectangular loop – then the force applied to the loop is the sum of the forces applied to each side separately, as determined by Equation 2.6. However, we wish to consider loops of arbitrary shape. To accommodate arbitrarily-shaped loops, let $\mathcal{C}$ be the path through space occupied by the loop. Then the force experienced by the loop is

$$\begin{aligned} \mathbf{F} &= \int_{\mathcal{C}} d\mathbf{F}_m(\mathbf{r}) \\ &= \int_{\mathcal{C}} I d\mathbf{l}(\mathbf{r}) \times \mathbf{B}_0 \end{aligned} \tag{2.7}$$

Since I and $\mathbf{B}_0$ are constants, they may be extracted from the integral:

$$\mathbf{F} = I\left[\int_{\mathcal{C}} d\mathbf{l}(\mathbf{r})\right] \times \mathbf{B}_0 \tag{2.8}$$

Note the quantity in square brackets is zero. Therefore:

> The net force on a current-carrying loop of wire in a uniform magnetic field is zero.

Note that this does not preclude the possibility that the rigid loop *rotates*; for example, the force on opposite sides of the loop may be equal and opposite. What we have found is merely that the force will not lead to a *translational* net force on the loop; e.g., force that would propel the loop away from its current position in space. The possibility of rotation without translation leads to the most rudimentary concept for an electric motor. Practical electric motors use variations on essentially this same idea; see "Additional Reading" for more information.

The third case of practical interest is the force experienced by two parallel infinitesimally-thin wires in free space, as shown in Figure 2.3. Here the wires are infinite in length (we'll return to that in a moment), lie in the $x = 0$ plane, are separated by distance d, and carry currents I_1 and I_2, respectively. The current in wire 1 gives rise to a magnetic flux density $\mathbf{B}_1$. The force exerted on wire 2 by $\mathbf{B}_1$ is:

$$\mathbf{F}_2 = \int_{\mathcal{C}} \left[I_2 d\mathbf{l}\left(\mathbf{r}\right) \times \mathbf{B}_1\left(\mathbf{r}\right)\right] \tag{2.9}$$

where $\mathcal{C}$ is the path followed by I_2, and $d\mathbf{l}\left(\mathbf{r}\right) = \hat{\mathbf{z}}dz$. A simple way to determine $\mathbf{B}_1$ in this situation is as follows. First, if wire 1 had been aligned along the $x = y = 0$ line, then the magnetic flux density everywhere would be

$$\hat{\phi}\frac{\mu_0 I_1}{2\pi\rho}$$

In the present problem, wire 1 is displaced by $d/2$ in the $-\hat{\mathbf{y}}$ direction. Although this would seem to make the new expression more complicated, note that the only positions where values of $\mathbf{B}_1\left(\mathbf{r}\right)$ are required are those corresponding to $\mathcal{C}$; i.e., points on wire 2. For these points,

$$\mathbf{B}_1\left(\mathbf{r}\right) = -\hat{\mathbf{x}}\frac{\mu_0 I_1}{2\pi d} \quad \text{along } \mathcal{C} \tag{2.10}$$

That is, the relevant distance is d (not ρ), and the direction of $\mathbf{B}_1\left(\mathbf{r}\right)$ for points along $\mathcal{C}$ is $-\hat{\mathbf{x}}$ (not $\hat{\phi}$).

Returning to Equation 2.9, we obtain:

$$\begin{aligned}\mathbf{F}_2 &= \int_{\mathcal{C}} \left[I_2\, \hat{\mathbf{z}}dz \times \left(-\hat{\mathbf{x}}\frac{\mu_0 I_1}{2\pi d}\right)\right] \\ &= -\hat{\mathbf{y}}\frac{\mu_0 I_1 I_2}{2\pi d}\int_{\mathcal{C}} dz\end{aligned} \tag{2.11}$$

The remaining integral is simply the length of wire 2 that we wish to consider. Infinitely-long wires will therefore result in infinite force. This is not a very interesting or useful result. However, the force *per unit length* of wire is finite, and is obtained simply by dropping the integral in the previous equation. We obtain:

$$\frac{\mathbf{F}_2}{\Delta l} = -\hat{\mathbf{y}}\frac{\mu_0 I_1 I_2}{2\pi d} \tag{2.12}$$

where Δl is the length of the section of wire 2 being considered. Note that when the currents I_1 and I_2 flow in the same direction (i.e., have the same sign), the magnetic force exerted by the current on wire 1 pulls wire 2 toward wire 1.

The same process can be used to determine the magnetic force $\mathbf{F}_1$ exerted by the current in wire 1 on wire 2. The result is

$$\frac{\mathbf{F}_1}{\Delta l} = +\hat{\mathbf{y}}\frac{\mu_0 I_1 I_2}{2\pi d} \tag{2.13}$$

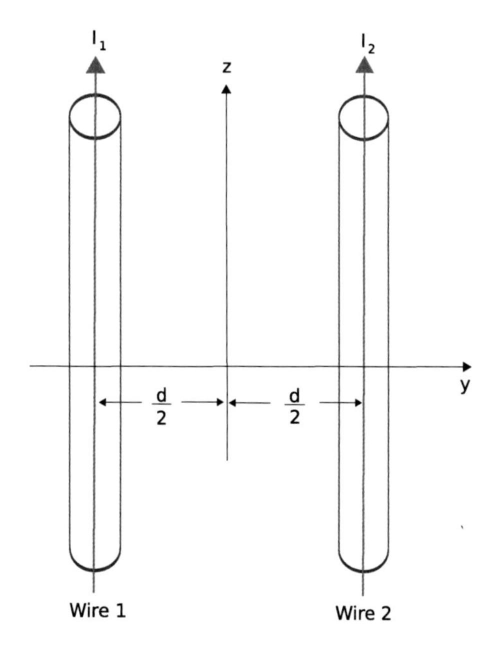

© Y. Zhao CC BY-SA 4.0

Figure 2.3: Parallel current-carrying wires.

When the currents I_1 and I_2 flow in the same direction (i.e., when the product $I_1 I_2$ is positive), then the magnetic force exerted by the current on wire 2 pulls wire 1 toward wire 2.

We are now able to summarize the results as follows:

> If currents in parallel wires flow in the same direction, then the wires attract; whereas if the currents flow in opposite directions, then the wires repel.

Also:

> The magnitude of the associated force is $\mu_0 I_1 I_2 / 2\pi d$ for wires separated by distance d in non-magnetic media.

If the wires are fixed in position and not able to move, these forces represent stored (potential) energy. It is worth noting that this is precisely the energy which is stored by an inductor – for example, the two wire segments here might be interpreted as segments in adjacent windings of a coil-shaped inductor.

Example 2.1. DC power cable.

A power cable connects a 12 V battery to a load exhibiting an impedance of 10 Ω. The conductors are separated by 3 mm by a plastic insulating jacket. Estimate the force between the conductors.

Solution. The current flowing in each conductor is 12 V divided by 10 Ω, which is 1.2 A. In terms of the theory developed in this section, a current $I_1 = +1.2$ A flows from the positive terminal of the battery to the load on one conductor, and a current $I_2 = -1.2$ A returns to the battery on the other conductor. The change in sign indicates that the currents at any given distance from the battery are flowing in opposite directions. Also from the problem statement, $d = 3$ mm and the insulator is presumably non-magnetic. Assuming the conductors are approximately straight, the force between conductors is

$$\approx \frac{\mu_0 I_1 I_2}{2\pi d} \cong -96.0\ \mu\text{N}$$

with the negative sign indicating that the wires repel.

Note in the above example that this force is quite small, which explains why it is not always observed. However, this force becomes significant when the current is large or when many sets of conductors are mechanically bound together (amounting to a larger net current), as in a motor.

Additional Reading:

- "Electric motor" on Wikipedia.

2.3 Torque Induced by a Magnetic Field

[m0024]

A magnetic field exerts a force on current. This force is exerted in a direction perpendicular to the direction of current flow. For this reason, current-carrying structures in a magnetic field tend to rotate. A convenient description of force associated with rotational motion is *torque*. In this section, we define torque and apply this concept to a closed loop of current. These concepts apply to a wide range of practical devices, including electric motors.

Figure 2.4 illustrates the concept of torque. Torque depends on the following:

- A local origin $\mathbf{r}_0$,
- A point $\mathbf{r}$ which is connected to $\mathbf{r}_0$ by a perfectly-rigid mechanical structure, and
- The force $\mathbf{F}$ applied at $\mathbf{r}$.

In terms of these parameters, the torque $\mathbf{T}$ is:

$$\mathbf{T} \triangleq \mathbf{d} \times \mathbf{F} \tag{2.14}$$

where the *lever arm* $\mathbf{d} \triangleq \mathbf{r} - \mathbf{r}_0$ gives the location of $\mathbf{r}$ relative to $\mathbf{r}_0$. Note that $\mathbf{T}$ is a position-free vector

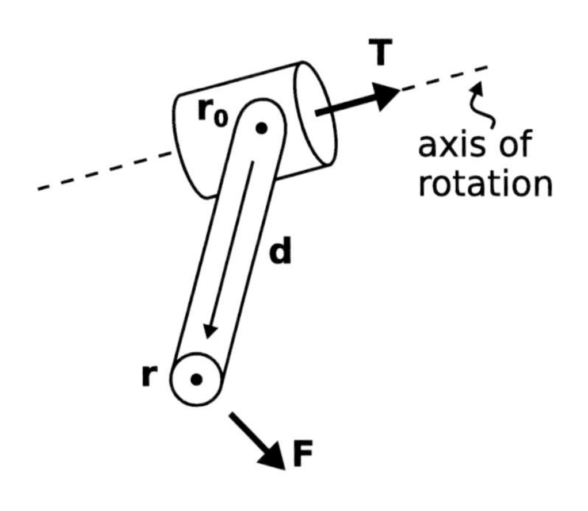

© C. Wang CC BY-SA 4.0

Figure 2.4: Torque associated with a single lever arm.

which points in a direction perpendicular to both $\mathbf{d}$ and $\mathbf{F}$.

Note that $\mathbf{T}$ does not point in the direction of rotation. Nevertheless, $\mathbf{T}$ indicates the direction of rotation through a "right hand rule": If you point the thumb of your right hand in the direction of $\mathbf{T}$, then the curled fingers of your right hand will point in the direction of torque-induced rotation.

Whether rotation actually occurs depends on the geometry of the structure. For example, if $\mathbf{T}$ aligns with the axis of a perfectly-rigid mechanical shaft, then all of the work done by $\mathbf{F}$ will be applied to rotation of the shaft on this axis. Otherwise, torque will tend to rotate the shaft in other directions as well. If the shaft is not free to rotate in these other directions, then the *effective torque* – that is, the torque that contributes to rotation of the shaft – is reduced.

The magnitude of $\mathbf{T}$ has SI base units of N·m and quantifies the energy associated with the rotational force. As you might expect, the magnitude of the torque increases with increasing lever arm magnitude $|\mathbf{d}|$. In other words, the torque resulting from a constant applied force increases with the length of the lever arm.

Torque, like the translational force $\mathbf{F}$, satisfies superposition. That is, the torque resulting from forces applied to multiple rigidly-connected lever arms is the sum of the torques applied to the lever arms individually.

Now consider the current loop shown in Figure 2.5. The loop is perfectly rigid and is rigidly attached to a non-conducting shaft. The assembly consisting of the loop and the shaft may rotate without friction around the axis of the shaft. The loop consists of four straight segments that are perfectly-conducting and infinitesimally-thin. A spatially-uniform and static impressed magnetic flux density $\mathbf{B}_0 = \hat{\mathbf{x}}B_0$ exists throughout the domain of the problem. (Recall that an *impressed* field is one that exists in the absence of any other structure in the problem.) What motion, if any, is expected?

Recall that the net translational force on a current loop in a spatially-uniform and static magnetic field is zero (Section 2.2). However, this does not preclude the possibility of different translational forces acting on each of the loop segments resulting in a rotation of the shaft. Let us first calculate these forces. The force $\mathbf{F}_A$ on segment A is

$$\mathbf{F}_A = I\mathbf{l}_A \times \mathbf{B}_0 \tag{2.15}$$

where $\mathbf{l}_A$ is a vector whose magnitude is equal to the length of the segment and which points in the direction of the current. Thus,

$$\begin{aligned}\mathbf{F}_A &= I\left(\hat{\mathbf{z}}L\right) \times \left(\hat{\mathbf{x}}B_0\right) \\ &= \hat{\mathbf{y}}ILB_0\end{aligned} \tag{2.16}$$

Similarly, the force $\mathbf{F}_C$ on segment C is

$$\begin{aligned}\mathbf{F}_C &= I\left(-\hat{\mathbf{z}}L\right) \times \left(\hat{\mathbf{x}}B_0\right) \\ &= -\hat{\mathbf{y}}ILB_0\end{aligned} \tag{2.17}$$

The forces $\mathbf{F}_B$ and $\mathbf{F}_D$ on segments B and D, respectively, are:

$$\mathbf{F}_B = I\left(-\hat{\mathbf{x}}L\right) \times \left(\hat{\mathbf{x}}B_0\right) = 0 \tag{2.18}$$

and

$$\mathbf{F}_D = I\left(+\hat{\mathbf{x}}L\right) \times \left(\hat{\mathbf{x}}B_0\right) = 0 \tag{2.19}$$

Thus, the force exerted on the current loop by the impressed magnetic field will lead to rotation in the $+\hat{\phi}$ direction.

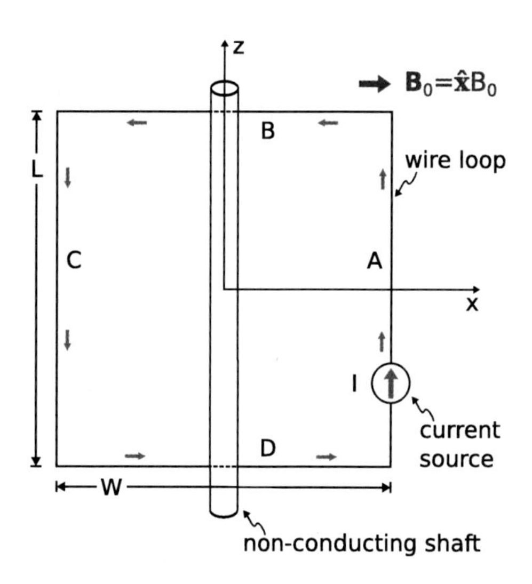

© C. Wang CC BY-SA 4.0

Figure 2.5: A rudimentary electric motor consisting of a single current loop.

We calculate the associated torque $\mathbf{T}$ as

$$\mathbf{T} = \mathbf{T}_A + \mathbf{T}_B + \mathbf{T}_C + \mathbf{T}_D \tag{2.20}$$

where $\mathbf{T}_A$, $\mathbf{T}_B$, $\mathbf{T}_C$, and $\mathbf{T}_D$ are the torques associated with segments A, B, C, and D, respectively. For example, the torque associated with segment A is

$$\begin{aligned}\mathbf{T}_A &= \frac{W}{2}\hat{\mathbf{x}} \times \mathbf{F}_A \\ &= \hat{\mathbf{z}}L\frac{W}{2}IB_0\end{aligned} \tag{2.21}$$

Similarly,

$$\mathbf{T}_B = 0 \text{ since } \mathbf{F}_B = 0 \tag{2.22}$$

$$\mathbf{T}_C = \hat{\mathbf{z}}L\frac{W}{2}IB_0 \tag{2.23}$$

$$\mathbf{T}_D = 0 \text{ since } \mathbf{F}_D = 0 \tag{2.24}$$

Summing these contributions, we find

$$\mathbf{T} = \hat{\mathbf{z}}LWIB_0 \tag{2.25}$$

Note that $\mathbf{T}$ points in the $+\hat{\mathbf{z}}$ direction, indicating rotational force exerted in the $+\hat{\phi}$ direction, as expected. Also note that the torque is proportional to the area LW of the loop, is proportional to the current I, and is proportional to the magnetic field magnitude B_0.

The analysis that we just completed was *static*; that is, it applies only at the instant depicted in Figure 2.5. If the shaft is allowed to turn without friction, then the loop will rotate in the $+\hat{\phi}$ direction. So, what will happen to the forces and torque? First, note that $\mathbf{F}_A$ and $\mathbf{F}_C$ are always in the $+\hat{\mathbf{y}}$ and $-\hat{\mathbf{y}}$ directions, respectively, regardless of the rotation of the loop. Once the loop rotates away from the position shown in Figure 2.5, the forces $\mathbf{F}_B$ and $\mathbf{F}_D$ become non-zero; however, they are always equal and opposite, and so do not affect the rotation. Thus, the loop will rotate one-quarter turn and then come to rest, perhaps with some damped oscillation around the rest position depending on the momentum of the loop. At the rest position, the lever arms for segments A and C are pointing in the same directions as $\mathbf{F}_A$ and $\mathbf{F}_C$, respectively. Therefore, the cross product of the lever arm and translational force for each segment is zero and subsequently $\mathbf{T}_A = \mathbf{T}_C = 0$. Once stopped in this position, both the net translational force and the net torque are zero.

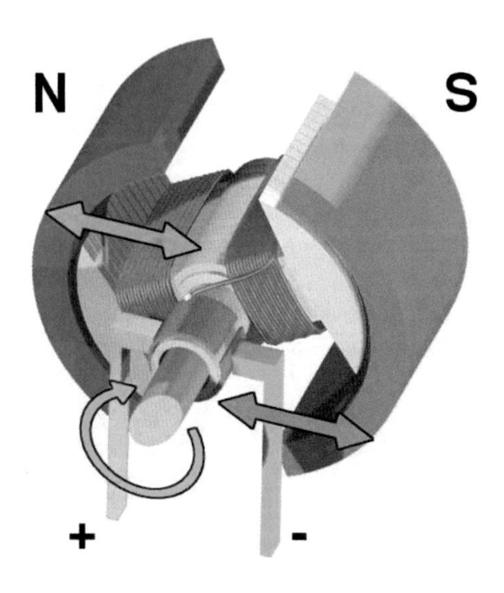

© Abnormaal CC BY-SA 3.0

Figure 2.6: This DC electric motor uses brushes (here, the motionless leads labeled "+" and "−") combined with the motion of the shaft to periodically alternate the direction of current between two coils, thereby creating nearly constant torque.

If such a device is to be used as a motor, it is necessary to find a way to sustain the rotation. There are several ways in which this might be accomplished. First, one might make I variable in time. For example, the direction of I could be reversed as the loop passes the quarter-turn position. This reverses $\mathbf{F}_A$ and $\mathbf{F}_C$, propelling the loop toward the half-turn position. The direction of I can be changed again as the loop passes half-turn position, propelling the loop toward the three-quarter-turn position. Continuing this periodic reversal of the current sustains the rotation. Alternatively, one may periodically reverse the direction of the impressed magnetic field to the same effect. These methods can be combined or augmented using multiple current loops or multiple sets of time-varying impressed magnetic fields. Using an appropriate combination of current loops, magnetic fields, and waveforms for each, it is possible to achieve sustained torque throughout the rotation. An example is shown in Figure 2.6.

Additional Reading:

- "Torque" on Wikipedia.
- "Electric motor" on Wikipedia.

2.4 The Biot-Savart Law

[m0066]

The Biot-Savart law (BSL) provides a method to calculate the magnetic field due to any distribution of steady (DC) current. In magnetostatics, the general solution to this problem employs Ampere's law; i.e.,

$$\int_C \mathbf{H} \cdot d\mathbf{l} = I_{encl} \tag{2.26}$$

in integral form or

$$\nabla \times \mathbf{H} = \mathbf{J} \tag{2.27}$$

in differential form. The integral form is relatively simple when the problem exhibits a high degree of symmetry, facilitating a simple description in a particular coordinate system. An example is the magnetic field due to a straight and infinitely-long current filament, which is easily determined by solving the integral equation in cylindrical coordinates. However, many problems of practical interest do not exhibit the necessary symmetry. A commonly-encountered example is the magnetic field due to a single loop of current, which will be addressed in Example 2.2. For such problems, the differential form of Ampere's law is needed.

BSL is the solution to the differential form of Ampere's law for a differential-length current element, illustrated in Figure 2.7. The current element is $I\ d\mathbf{l}$, where I is the magnitude of the current (SI base units of A) and $d\mathbf{l}$ is a differential-length vector indicating the direction of the current at the "source point" $\mathbf{r}'$. The resulting contribution to the magnetic field intensity at the "field point" $\mathbf{r}$ is

$$\boxed{d\mathbf{H}(\mathbf{r}) = I\ d\mathbf{l}\ \frac{1}{4\pi R^2} \times \hat{\mathbf{R}}} \tag{2.28}$$

where

$$\mathbf{R} = \hat{\mathbf{R}}R \triangleq \mathbf{r} - \mathbf{r}' \tag{2.29}$$

In other words, $\mathbf{R}$ is the vector pointing from the source point to the field point, and $d\mathbf{H}$ at the field point is given by Equation 2.28. The magnetic field due to a current-carrying wire of any shape may be obtained by integrating over the length of the wire:

$$\mathbf{H}(\mathbf{r}) = \int_C d\mathbf{H}(\mathbf{r}) = \frac{I}{4\pi}\int_C \frac{d\mathbf{l} \times \hat{\mathbf{R}}}{R^2} \tag{2.30}$$

In addition to obviating the need to solve a differential equation, BSL provides some useful insight into the behavior of magnetic fields. In particular, Equation 2.28 indicates that magnetic fields follow the *inverse square law* – that is, the magnitude of the magnetic field due to a differential current element decreases in proportion to the inverse square of distance (R^{-2}). Also, Equation 2.28 indicates that the direction of the magnetic field due to a differential current element is perpendicular to both the direction of current flow $\hat{\mathbf{l}}$ and the vector $\hat{\mathbf{R}}$ pointing from the source point to field point. This observation is quite useful in anticipating the direction of magnetic field vectors in complex problems.

It may be helpful to note that BSL is analogous to Coulomb's law for electric fields, which is a solution to the differential form of Gauss' law, $\nabla \cdot \mathbf{D} = \rho_v$. However, BSL applies only under magnetostatic conditions. If the variation in currents or magnetic fields over time is significant, then the problem becomes significantly more complicated. See "Jefimenko's Equations" in "Additional Reading" for more information.

Example 2.2. Magnetic field along the axis of a circular loop of current.

Consider a ring of radius a in the $z = 0$ plane, centered on the origin, as shown in Figure 2.8. As indicated in the figure, the current I flows in

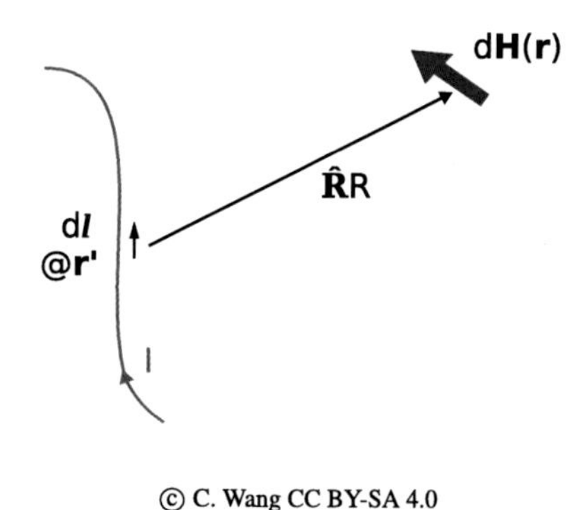

© C. Wang CC BY-SA 4.0

Figure 2.7: Use of the Biot-Savart law to calculate the magnetic field due to a line current.

the $\hat{\phi}$ direction. Find the magnetic field intensity along the z axis.

Solution. The source current position is given in cylindrical coordinates as

$$\mathbf{r}' = \hat{\rho}a \tag{2.31}$$

The position of a field point along the z axis is

$$\mathbf{r} = \hat{\mathbf{z}}z \tag{2.32}$$

Thus,

$$\hat{\mathbf{R}}R \triangleq \mathbf{r} - \mathbf{r}' = -\hat{\rho}a + \hat{\mathbf{z}}z \tag{2.33}$$

and

$$R \triangleq |\mathbf{r} - \mathbf{r}'| = \sqrt{a^2 + z^2} \tag{2.34}$$

Equation 2.28 becomes:

$$\begin{aligned} d\mathbf{H}(\hat{\mathbf{z}}z) &= \frac{I\,\hat{\phi}\,ad\phi}{4\pi\left[a^2+z^2\right]} \times \frac{\hat{\mathbf{z}}z - \hat{\rho}a}{\sqrt{a^2+z^2}} \\ &= \frac{Ia}{4\pi}\,\frac{\hat{\mathbf{z}}a - \hat{\rho}z}{\left[a^2+z^2\right]^{3/2}}\,d\phi \end{aligned} \tag{2.35}$$

Now integrating over the current:

$$\mathbf{H}(\hat{\mathbf{z}}z) = \int_0^{2\pi} \frac{Ia}{4\pi}\,\frac{\hat{\mathbf{z}}a - \hat{\rho}z}{\left[a^2+z^2\right]^{3/2}}\,d\phi \tag{2.36}$$

$$= \frac{Ia}{4\pi\left[a^2+z^2\right]^{3/2}} \int_0^{2\pi} \left(\hat{\mathbf{z}}a - \hat{\rho}z\right)\,d\phi \tag{2.37}$$

$$= \frac{Ia}{4\pi\left[a^2+z^2\right]^{3/2}} \left(\hat{\mathbf{z}}a \int_0^{2\pi} d\phi - z\int_0^{2\pi} \hat{\rho}\,d\phi\right) \tag{2.38}$$

The second integral is equal to zero. To see this, note that the integral is simply summing values of $\hat{\rho}$ for all possible values of ϕ. Since $\hat{\rho}(\phi+\pi) = -\hat{\rho}(\phi)$, the integrand for any given value of ϕ is equal and opposite the integrand π radians later. (This is one example of a *symmetry* argument.)

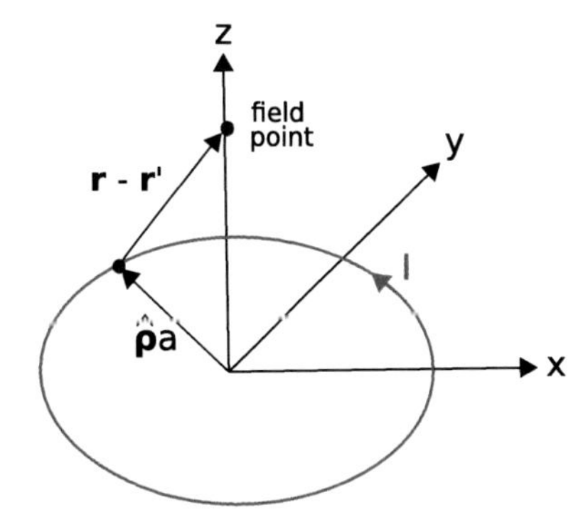

© K. Kikkeri CC BY SA 4.0 (modified)

Figure 2.8: Calculation of the magnetic field along the z axis due to a circular loop of current centered in the $z = 0$ plane.

The first integral in the previous equation is equal to 2π. Thus, we obtain

$$\mathbf{H}(\hat{\mathbf{z}}z) = \hat{\mathbf{z}}\frac{Ia^2}{2\left[a^2+z^2\right]^{3/2}} \tag{2.39}$$

Note that the result is consistent with the associated "right hand rule" of magnetostatics: That is, the direction of the magnetic field is in the direction of the curled fingers of the right hand when the thumb of the right hand is aligned with the location and direction of current. It is a good exercise to confirm that this result is also dimensionally correct.

Equation 2.28 extends straightforwardly to other distributions of current. For example, the magnetic field due to surface current $\mathbf{J}_s$ (SI base units of A/m) can be calculated using Equation 2.28 with $I\ d\mathbf{l}$ replaced by

$$\mathbf{J}_s\ ds$$

where ds is the differential element of surface area. This can be confirmed by dimensional analysis: $I\ d\mathbf{l}$ has SI base units of A·m, as does $\mathbf{J}_S\ ds$. Similarly, the magnetic field due to volume current $\mathbf{J}$ (SI base units of A/m^2) can be calculated using Equation 2.28 with $I\ d\mathbf{l}$ replaced by

$$\mathbf{J}\ dv$$

where dv is the differential element of volume. For a single particle with charge q (SI base units of C) and velocity $\mathbf{v}$ (SI base units of m/s), the relevant quantity is

$$q\mathbf{v}$$

since C·m/s = (C/s)·m = A·m. In all of these cases, Equation 2.28 applies with the appropriate replacement for $I\ d\mathbf{l}$.

Note that the quantities $q\mathbf{v}$, $I\ d\mathbf{l}$, $\mathbf{J}_S\ ds$, and $\mathbf{J}\ dv$, all having the same units of A·m, seem to be referring to the same physical quantity. This physical quantity is known as *current moment*. Thus, the "input" to BSL can be interpreted as current moment, regardless of whether the current of interest is distributed as a line current, a surface current, a volumetric current, or simply as moving charged particles. See "Additional Reading" at the end of this section for additional information on the concept of "moment" in classical physics.

Additional Reading:

- "Biot-Savart Law" on Wikipedia.
- "Jefimenko's Equations" on Wikipedia.
- "Moment (physics)" on Wikipedia.

2.5 Force, Energy, and Potential Difference in a Magnetic Field

[m0059]

The force $\mathbf{F}_m$ experienced by a particle at location $\mathbf{r}$ bearing charge q due to a magnetic field is

$$\mathbf{F}_m = q\mathbf{v} \times \mathbf{B}(\mathbf{r}) \tag{2.40}$$

where $\mathbf{v}$ is the velocity (magnitude and direction) of the particle, and $\mathbf{B}(\mathbf{r})$ is the magnetic flux density at $\mathbf{r}$. Now we must be careful: In this description, the motion of the particle is *not* due to $\mathbf{F}_m$. In fact the cross product in Equation 2.40 clearly indicates that $\mathbf{F}_m$ and $\mathbf{v}$ must be in perpendicular directions. Instead, the reverse is true: i.e., it is the motion of the particle that is giving rise to the force. The motion described by $\mathbf{v}$ may be due to the presence of an electric field, or it may simply be that that charge is contained within a structure that is itself in motion.

Nevertheless, the force $\mathbf{F}_m$ has an associated potential energy. Furthermore, this potential energy may change as the particle moves. This change in potential energy may give rise to an electrical potential difference (i.e., a "voltage"), as we shall now demonstrate.

The change in potential energy can be quantified using the concept of *work*, W. The incremental work ΔW done by moving the particle a short distance Δl, over which we assume the change in $\mathbf{F}_m$ is negligible, is

$$\Delta W \approx \mathbf{F}_m \cdot \hat{\mathbf{l}}\Delta l \tag{2.41}$$

where in this case $\hat{\mathbf{l}}$ is the unit vector in the direction of the motion; i.e., the direction of $\mathbf{v}$. Note that the purpose of the dot product in Equation 2.41 is to ensure that only the component of $\mathbf{F}_m$ parallel to the direction of motion is included in the energy tally. Any component of $\mathbf{v}$ which is due to $\mathbf{F}_m$ (i.e., ultimately due to $\mathbf{B}$) must be perpendicular to $\mathbf{F}_m$, so ΔW for such a contribution must be, from Equation 2.41, equal to zero. In other words: In the absence of a mechanical force or an electric field, the potential energy of a charged particle remains constant regardless of how it is moved by $\mathbf{F}_m$. This surprising result may be summarized as follows:

> The magnetic field does no work.

Instead, the change of potential energy associated with the magnetic field must be completely due to a change in position resulting from other forces, such as a mechanical force or the Coulomb force. The presence of a magnetic field merely increases or decreases this potential difference once the particle has moved, and it is this change in the potential difference that we wish to determine.

We can make the relationship between potential difference and the magnetic field explicit by substituting the right side of Equation 2.40 into Equation 2.41, yielding

$$\Delta W \approx q\,[\mathbf{v} \times \mathbf{B}(\mathbf{r})] \cdot \hat{\mathbf{l}}\Delta l \qquad (2.42)$$

Equation 2.42 gives the work only for a short distance around $\mathbf{r}$. Now let us try to generalize this result. If we wish to know the work done over a larger distance, then we must account for the possibility that $\mathbf{v} \times \mathbf{B}$ varies along the path taken. To do this, we may sum contributions from points along the path traced out by the particle, i.e.,

$$W \approx \sum_{n=1}^{N} \Delta W(\mathbf{r}_n) \qquad (2.43)$$

where $\mathbf{r}_n$ are positions defining the path. Substituting the right side of Equation 2.42, we have

$$W \approx q \sum_{n=1}^{N} [\mathbf{v} \times \mathbf{B}(\mathbf{r}_n)] \cdot \hat{\mathbf{l}}(\mathbf{r}_n)\Delta l \qquad (2.44)$$

Taking the limit as $\Delta l \to 0$, we obtain

$$W = q \int_{\mathcal{C}} [\mathbf{v} \times \mathbf{B}(\mathbf{r})] \cdot \hat{\mathbf{l}}(\mathbf{r})dl \qquad (2.45)$$

where $\mathcal{C}$ is the path (previously, the sequence of $\mathbf{r}_n$'s) followed by the particle. Now omitting the explicit dependence on $\mathbf{r}$ in the integrand for clarity:

$$W = q \int_{\mathcal{C}} [\mathbf{v} \times \mathbf{B}] \cdot d\mathbf{l} \qquad (2.46)$$

where $d\mathbf{l} = \hat{\mathbf{l}}dl$ as usual. Now, we are able to determine the change in potential energy for a charged particle moving along any path in space, given the magnetic field.

At this point, it is convenient to introduce the electric *potential difference* V_{21} between the start point (1) and end point (2) of $\mathcal{C}$. V_{21} is defined as the work done by traversing $\mathcal{C}$, per unit of charge; i.e.,

$$V_{21} \triangleq \frac{W}{q} \qquad (2.47)$$

This has units of J/C, which is volts (V). Substituting Equation 2.46, we obtain:

$$\boxed{V_{21} = \int_{\mathcal{C}} [\mathbf{v} \times \mathbf{B}] \cdot d\mathbf{l}} \qquad (2.48)$$

> Equation 2.48 is electrical potential induced by charge traversing a magnetic field.

Figure 2.9 shows a simple scenario that illustrates this concept. Here, a straight perfectly-conducting wire of length l is parallel to the y axis and moves at speed v in the $+z$ direction through a magnetic field $\mathbf{B} = \hat{\mathbf{x}}B$. Thus,

$$\begin{aligned} \mathbf{v} \times \mathbf{B} &= \hat{\mathbf{z}}v \times \hat{\mathbf{x}}B \\ &= \hat{\mathbf{y}}Bv \end{aligned} \qquad (2.49)$$

Taking endpoints 1 and 2 of the wire to be at $y = y_0$

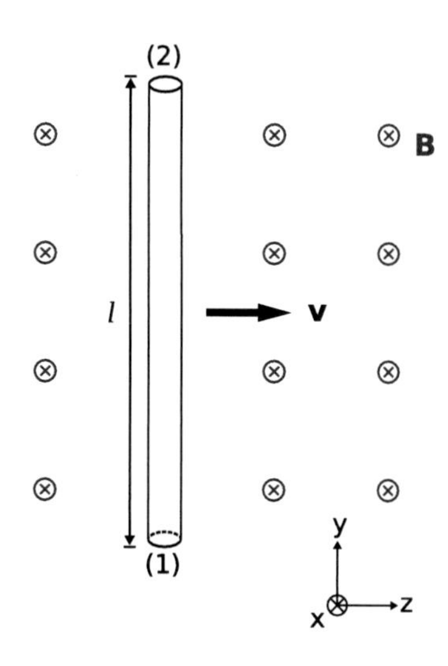

© C. Wang CC BY 4.0

Figure 2.9: A straight wire moving through a magnetic field.

and $y = y_0 + l$, respectively, we obtain

$$V_{21} = \int_{y_0}^{y_0+l} [\hat{\mathbf{y}}Bv] \cdot \hat{\mathbf{y}}dy = Bvl \quad (2.50)$$

Thus, we see that endpoint 2 is at an electrical potential of Bvl greater than that of endpoint 1. This "voltage" exists even though the wire is perfectly-conducting, and therefore cannot be attributed to the electric field. This voltage exists even though the force required for movement must be the same on both endpoints, or could even be zero, and therefore cannot be attributed to mechanical forces. Instead, this change in potential is due entirely to the magnetic field.

Because the wire does not form a closed loop, no current flows in the wire. Therefore, this scenario has limited application in practice. To accomplish something useful with this concept we must at least form a closed loop, so that current may flow. For a closed loop, Equation 2.48 becomes:

$$V = \oint_C [\mathbf{v} \times \mathbf{B}] \cdot d\mathbf{l} \quad (2.51)$$

Examination of this equation indicates one additional requirement: $\mathbf{v} \times \mathbf{B}$ must somehow vary over $\mathcal{C}$. This is because if $\mathbf{v} \times \mathbf{B}$ does not vary over $\mathcal{C}$, the result will be

$$[\mathbf{v} \times \mathbf{B}] \cdot \oint_C d\mathbf{l}$$

which is zero because the integral is zero. The following example demonstrates a practical application of this idea.

Example 2.3. Potential induced in a time-varying loop.

Figure 2.10 shows a modification to the problem originally considered in Figure 2.9. Now, we have created a closed loop using perfectly-conducting and motionless wire to form three sides of a rectangle, and assigned the origin to the lower left corner. An infinitesimally-small gap has been inserted in the left ($z = 0$) side of the loop and closed with an ideal resistor of value R. As before, $\mathbf{B} = \hat{\mathbf{x}}B$ (spatially uniform and time invariant) and $\mathbf{v} = \hat{\mathbf{z}}v$ (constant). What is the voltage V_T across the resistor and what is the current in the loop?

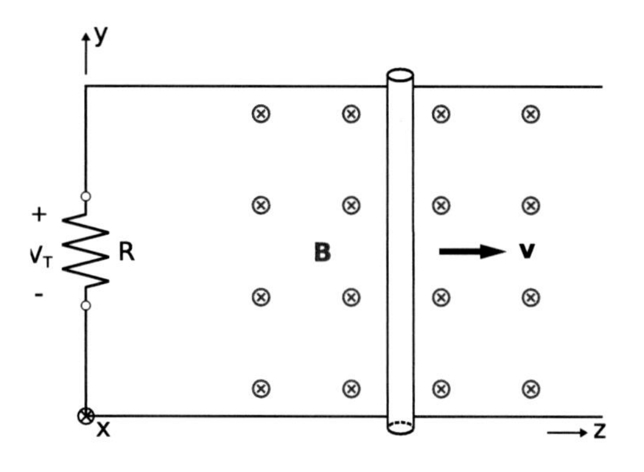

© C. Wang CC BY-SA 4.0

Figure 2.10: A time-varying loop created by moving a "shorting bar" along rails comprising two adjacent sides of the loop.

Solution. Since the gap containing the resistor is infinitesimally small,

$$V_T = \oint_C [\mathbf{v} \times \mathbf{B}] \cdot d\mathbf{l} \quad (2.52)$$

where $\mathcal{C}$ is the perimeter formed by the loop, beginning at the "−" terminal of V_T and returning to the "+" terminal of V_T. Only the shorting bar is in motion, so $\mathbf{v} = 0$ for the other three sides of the loop. Therefore, only the portion of $\mathcal{C}$ traversing the shorting bar contributes to V_T. Thus, we find

$$V_T = \int_{y=0}^{l} [\hat{\mathbf{z}}v \times \hat{\mathbf{x}}B] \cdot \hat{\mathbf{y}}dy = Bvl \quad (2.53)$$

This potential gives rise to a current Bvl/R, which flows in the counter-clockwise direction.

Note in the previous example that the magnetic field has induced V_T, not the current. The current is simply a response to the existence of the potential, regardless of the source. In other words, the same potential V_T would exist even if the gap was not closed by a resistor.

[m0182]

Astute readers will notice that this analysis seems to have a lot in common with Faraday's law,

$$V = -\frac{\partial}{\partial t}\Phi \tag{2.54}$$

which says the potential induced in a single closed loop is proportional to the time rate of change of magnetic flux Φ, where

$$\Phi = \int_S \mathbf{B} \cdot d\mathbf{s} \tag{2.55}$$

and where $\mathcal{S}$ is the surface through which the flux is calculated. From this perspective, we see that Equation 2.51 is simply a special case of Faraday's law, pertaining specifically to "motional emf." Thus, the preceding example can also be solved by Faraday's law, taking $\mathcal{S}$ to be the time-varying surface bounded by $\mathcal{C}$.

Image Credits

Fig. 2.1: © Stannered, https://en.wikipedia.org/wiki/File:Charged-particle-drifts.svg,
CC BY 2.5 (https://creativecommons.org/licenses/by/2.5/deed.en). Modified by Maschen, author.

Fig. 2.2: © M. Biaek, https://en.wikipedia.org/wiki/File:Cyclotron_motion.jpg,
CC BY-SA 4.0 (https://creativecommons.org/licenses/by-sa/4.0/).

Fig. 2.3: © YahuiZ (Y. Zhao), https://commons.wikimedia.org/wiki/File:Figure2.3Yahui.svg,
CC BY SA 4.0 (https://creativecommons.org/licenses/by-sa/4.0/). Modified by author.

Fig. 2.4: © Sevenchw (C. Wang),
https://commons.wikimedia.org/wiki/File:Torque_associated_with_a_single_lever_arm.svg,
CC BY SA 4.0 (https://creativecommons.org/licenses/by-sa/4.0/).

Fig. 2.5: © Sevenchw (C. Wang), https://commons.wikimedia.org/wiki/File:Rudimentary_electric_motor.svg,
CC BY SA 4.0 (https://creativecommons.org/licenses/by-sa/4.0/).

Fig. 2.6: © Abnormaal, https://en.wikipedia.org/wiki/File:Electric_motor.gif,
CC BY SA 3.0 (https://creativecommons.org/licenses/by-sa/3.0/).

Fig. 2.7: © Sevenchw (C. Wang),
https://commons.wikimedia.org/wiki/File:Magnetic_field_due_to_a_line_current.svg,
CC BY SA 4.0 (https://creativecommons.org/licenses/by-sa/4.0/).

Fig. 2.8: © K. Kikkeri, https://commons.wikimedia.org/wiki/File:M0104_fRing.svg,
CC BY SA 4.0 (https://creativecommons.org/licenses/by-sa/4.0/). Modified by author.

Fig. 2.9: © Sevenchw (C. Wang),
https://commons.wikimedia.org/wiki/File:Straight_wire_moving_in_a_magnetic_field.svg,
CC BY SA 4.0 (https://creativecommons.org/licenses/by-sa/4.0/).

Fig. 2.10: © Sevenchw (C. Wang),
https://commons.wikimedia.org/wiki/File:Moving_shorting_bar_of_a_circuit_in_mag_field.svg,
CC BY SA 4.0 (https://creativecommons.org/licenses/by-sa/4.0/).

Chapter 3

Wave Propagation in General Media

3.1 Poynting's Theorem

[m0073]

Despite the apparent complexity of electromagnetic theory, there are in fact merely four ways that electromagnetic energy can be manipulated. Electromagnetic energy can be:

- Transferred; i.e., conveyed by transmission lines or in waves;
- Stored in an electric field (capacitance);
- Stored in a magnetic field (inductance); or
- Dissipated (converted to heat; i.e., resistance).

Poynting's theorem is an expression of conservation of energy that elegantly relates these various possibilities. Once recognized, the theorem has important applications in the analysis and design of electromagnetic systems. Some of these emerge from the derivation of the theorem, as opposed to the unsurprising result. So, let us now derive the theorem.

We begin with a statement of the theorem. Consider a volume $\mathcal{V}$ that may contain materials and structures in any combination. This is crudely depicted in Figure 3.1. Also recall that power is the time rate of change of energy. Then:

$$P_{net,in} = P_E + P_M + P_\Omega \tag{3.1}$$

where $P_{net,in}$ is the net power flow into $\mathcal{V}$, P_E is the power associated with energy storage in electric fields within $\mathcal{V}$, P_M is the power associated with energy storage in magnetic fields within $\mathcal{V}$, and P_Ω is the power dissipated (converted to heat) in $\mathcal{V}$.

Some preliminary mathematical results. We now derive two mathematical relationships that will be useful later. Let $\mathbf{E}$ be the electric field intensity (SI base units of V/m) and let $\mathbf{D}$ be the electric flux density (SI base units of C/m^2). We require that the constituents of $\mathcal{V}$ be linear and time-invariant; therefore, $\mathbf{D} = \epsilon\mathbf{E}$ where the permittivity ϵ is constant with respect to time, but not necessarily with respect to position. Under these conditions, we find

$$\frac{\partial}{\partial t}\left(\mathbf{E}\cdot\mathbf{D}\right) = \frac{1}{\epsilon}\frac{\partial}{\partial t}\left(\mathbf{D}\cdot\mathbf{D}\right) \tag{3.2}$$

Note that $\mathbf{E}$ and $\mathbf{D}$ point in the same direction. Let $\hat{\mathbf{e}}$ be the unit vector describing this direction. Then, $\mathbf{E} = \hat{\mathbf{e}}E$ and $\mathbf{D} = \hat{\mathbf{e}}D$ where E and D are the scalar

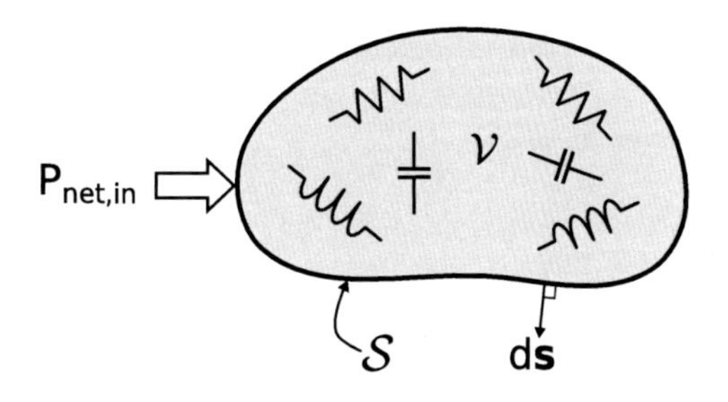

© C. Wang CC BY-SA 4.0

Figure 3.1: Poynting's theorem describes the fate of power entering a region $\mathcal{V}$ consisting of materials and structures capable of storing and dissipating energy.

components of $\mathbf{E}$ and $\mathbf{D}$, respectively. Subsequently,

$$\begin{aligned}\frac{1}{\epsilon}\frac{\partial}{\partial t}(\mathbf{D}\cdot\mathbf{D}) &= \frac{1}{\epsilon}\frac{\partial}{\partial t}D^2 \\ &= \frac{1}{\epsilon}2D\frac{\partial}{\partial t}D \\ &= 2\mathbf{E}\cdot\frac{\partial}{\partial t}\mathbf{D} \end{aligned} \quad (3.3)$$

Summarizing:

$$\frac{\partial}{\partial t}(\mathbf{E}\cdot\mathbf{D}) = 2\mathbf{E}\cdot\frac{\partial}{\partial t}\mathbf{D} \quad (3.4)$$

which is the expression we seek. It is worth noting that the expressions on both sides of the equation have the same units, namely, those of power.

Using the same reasoning, we find:

$$\frac{\partial}{\partial t}(\mathbf{H}\cdot\mathbf{B}) = 2\mathbf{H}\cdot\frac{\partial}{\partial t}\mathbf{B} \quad (3.5)$$

where $\mathbf{H}$ is the magnetic field intensity (SI base units of A/m) and $\mathbf{B}$ is the magnetic flux density (SI base units of T).

Derivation of the theorem. We begin with the differential form of Ampere's law:

$$\nabla\times\mathbf{H} = \mathbf{J} + \frac{\partial}{\partial t}\mathbf{D} \quad (3.6)$$

Taking the dot product with $\mathbf{E}$ on both sides:

$$\mathbf{E}\cdot(\nabla\times\mathbf{H}) = \mathbf{E}\cdot\mathbf{J} + \mathbf{E}\cdot\frac{\partial}{\partial t}\mathbf{D} \quad (3.7)$$

Let's deal with the left side of this equation first. For this, we will employ a vector identity (Equation B.27, Appendix B.3). This identity states that for any two vector fields $\mathbf{F}$ and $\mathbf{G}$,

$$\nabla\cdot(\mathbf{F}\times\mathbf{G}) = \mathbf{G}\cdot(\nabla\times\mathbf{F}) - \mathbf{F}\cdot(\nabla\times\mathbf{G}) \quad (3.8)$$

Substituting $\mathbf{E}$ for $\mathbf{F}$ and $\mathbf{H}$ for $\mathbf{G}$ and rearranging terms, we find

$$\mathbf{E}\cdot(\nabla\times\mathbf{H}) = \mathbf{H}\cdot(\nabla\times\mathbf{E}) - \nabla\cdot(\mathbf{E}\times\mathbf{H}) \quad (3.9)$$

Next, we invoke the Maxwell-Faraday equation:

$$\nabla\times\mathbf{E} = -\frac{\partial}{\partial t}\mathbf{B} \quad (3.10)$$

Using this equation to replace the factor in the parentheses in the second term of Equation 3.9, we obtain:

$$\mathbf{E}\cdot(\nabla\times\mathbf{H}) = \mathbf{H}\cdot\left(-\frac{\partial}{\partial t}\mathbf{B}\right) - \nabla\cdot(\mathbf{E}\times\mathbf{H}) \quad (3.11)$$

Substituting this expression for the left side of Equation 3.7, we have

$$-\mathbf{H}\cdot\frac{\partial}{\partial t}\mathbf{B} - \nabla\cdot(\mathbf{E}\times\mathbf{H}) = \mathbf{E}\cdot\mathbf{J} + \mathbf{E}\cdot\frac{\partial}{\partial t}\mathbf{D} \quad (3.12)$$

Next we invoke the identities of Equations 3.4 and 3.5 to replace the first and last terms:

$$\begin{aligned}-\frac{1}{2}\frac{\partial}{\partial t}(\mathbf{H}\cdot\mathbf{B}) - \nabla\cdot(\mathbf{E}\times\mathbf{H}) \\ = \mathbf{E}\cdot\mathbf{J} + \frac{1}{2}\frac{\partial}{\partial t}(\mathbf{E}\cdot\mathbf{D}) \end{aligned} \quad (3.13)$$

Now we move the first term to the right-hand side and integrate both sides over the volume $\mathcal{V}$:

$$\begin{aligned}-\int_{\mathcal{V}}\nabla\cdot(\mathbf{E}\times\mathbf{H})\,dv \\ &= \int_{\mathcal{V}}\mathbf{E}\cdot\mathbf{J}\,dv \\ &+ \int_{\mathcal{V}}\frac{1}{2}\frac{\partial}{\partial t}(\mathbf{E}\cdot\mathbf{D})\,dv \\ &+ \int_{\mathcal{V}}\frac{1}{2}\frac{\partial}{\partial t}(\mathbf{H}\cdot\mathbf{B})\,dv \end{aligned} \quad (3.14)$$

The left side may be transformed into a surface integral using the divergence theorem:

$$\int_{\mathcal{V}}\nabla\cdot(\mathbf{E}\times\mathbf{H})\,dv = \oint_{\mathcal{S}}(\mathbf{E}\times\mathbf{H})\cdot d\mathbf{s} \quad (3.15)$$

where $\mathcal{S}$ is the closed surface that bounds $\mathcal{V}$ and $d\mathbf{s}$ is the outward-facing normal to this surface, as indicated in Figure 3.1. Finally, we exchange the order of time differentiation and volume integration in the last two terms:

$$\begin{aligned}-\oint_{\mathcal{S}}(\mathbf{E}\times\mathbf{H})\cdot d\mathbf{s} \\ &= \int_{\mathcal{V}}\mathbf{E}\cdot\mathbf{J}\,dv \\ &+ \frac{1}{2}\frac{\partial}{\partial t}\int_{\mathcal{V}}\mathbf{E}\cdot\mathbf{D}\,dv \\ &+ \frac{1}{2}\frac{\partial}{\partial t}\int_{\mathcal{V}}\mathbf{H}\cdot\mathbf{B}\,dv \end{aligned} \quad (3.16)$$

Equation 3.16 is Poynting's theorem. Each of the four terms has the particular physical interpretation identified in Equation 3.1, as we will now demonstrate.

Power dissipated by ohmic loss. The first term of the right side of Equation 3.16 is

$$\boxed{P_\Omega \triangleq \int_\mathcal{V} \mathbf{E}\cdot\mathbf{J}\; dv} \tag{3.17}$$

Equation 3.17 is *Joule's law*. Joule's law gives the power dissipated due to finite conductivity of material. The role of conductivity (σ, SI base units of S/m) can be made explicit using the relationship $\mathbf{J} = \sigma\mathbf{E}$ (Ohm's law) in Equation 3.17, which yields:

$$P_\Omega = \int_\mathcal{V} \mathbf{E}\cdot\sigma\mathbf{E}\; dv = \int_\mathcal{V} \sigma\left|\mathbf{E}\right|^2\; dv \tag{3.18}$$

P_Ω is due to the conversion of the electric field into conduction current, and subsequently into heat. This mechanism is commonly known as *ohmic loss* or *joule heating*. It is worth noting that this expression has the expected units. For example, in Equation 3.17, $\mathbf{E}$ (SI base units of V/m) times $\mathbf{J}$ (SI base units of A/m^2) yields a quantity with units of W/m^3; i.e., power per unit volume, which is power density. Then integration over volume yields units of W; hence, power.

Energy storage in electric and magnetic fields. The second term on the right side of Equation 3.16 is:

$$\boxed{P_E \triangleq \frac{1}{2}\frac{\partial}{\partial t}\int_\mathcal{V} \mathbf{E}\cdot\mathbf{D}\; dv} \tag{3.19}$$

Recall $\mathbf{D} = \epsilon\mathbf{E}$, where ϵ is the permittivity (SI base units of F/m) of the material. Thus, we may rewrite the previous equation as follows:

$$\begin{aligned} P_E &= \frac{1}{2}\frac{\partial}{\partial t}\int_\mathcal{V} \mathbf{E}\cdot\epsilon\mathbf{E}\; dv \\ &= \frac{1}{2}\frac{\partial}{\partial t}\int_\mathcal{V} \epsilon\left|\mathbf{E}\right|^2\; dv \\ &= \frac{\partial}{\partial t}\left(\frac{1}{2}\int_\mathcal{V} \epsilon\left|\mathbf{E}\right|^2\; dv\right) \end{aligned} \tag{3.20}$$

The quantity in parentheses is W_e, the energy stored in the electric field within $\mathcal{V}$.

The third term on the right side of Equation 3.16 is:

$$\boxed{P_M \triangleq \frac{1}{2}\frac{\partial}{\partial t}\int_\mathcal{V} \mathbf{H}\cdot\mathbf{B}\; dv} \tag{3.21}$$

Recall $\mathbf{B} = \mu\mathbf{H}$, where μ is the permeability (SI basc units of H/m) of the material. Thus, we may rewrite the previous equation as follows:

$$\begin{aligned} P_M &= \frac{1}{2}\frac{\partial}{\partial t}\int_\mathcal{V} \mathbf{H}\cdot\mu\mathbf{H}\; dv \\ &= \frac{1}{2}\frac{\partial}{\partial t}\int_\mathcal{V} \mu\left|\mathbf{H}\right|^2\; dv \\ &= \frac{\partial}{\partial t}\left(\frac{1}{2}\int_\mathcal{V} \mu\left|\mathbf{H}\right|^2\; dv\right) \end{aligned} \tag{3.22}$$

The quantity in parentheses is W_m, the energy stored in the magnetic field within $\mathcal{V}$.

Power flux through $\mathcal{S}$. The left side of Equation 3.16 is

$$\boxed{P_{net,in} \triangleq -\oint_\mathcal{S} \left(\mathbf{E}\times\mathbf{H}\right)\cdot d\mathbf{s}} \tag{3.23}$$

The quantity $\mathbf{E}\times\mathbf{H}$ is the *Poynting vector*, which quantifies the spatial power density (SI base units of W/m^2) of an electromagnetic wave and the direction in which it propagates. The reader has likely already encountered this concept. Regardless, we'll confirm this interpretation of the quantity $\mathbf{E}\times\mathbf{H}$ in Section 3.2. For now, observe that integration of the Poynting vector over $\mathcal{S}$ as indicated in Equation 3.23 yields the total power flowing out of $\mathcal{V}$ through $\mathcal{S}$. The negative sign in Equation 3.23 indicates that the combined quantity represents power flow *in* to $\mathcal{V}$ through $\mathcal{S}$. Finally, note the use of a single quantity $P_{net,in}$ does *not* imply that power is entirely inward-directed or outward-directed. Rather, $P_{net,in}$ represents the *net* flux; i.e., the *sum* of the inward- and outward-flowing power.

Summary. Equation 3.16 may now be stated concisely as follows:

$$\boxed{P_{net,in} = P_\Omega + \frac{\partial}{\partial t}W_e + \frac{\partial}{\partial t}W_m} \tag{3.24}$$

Poynting's theorem (Equation 3.24, with Equations 3.23, 3.17, 3.19, and 3.21) states that the net electromagnetic power flowing into a region of space may be either dissipated, or used to change the energy stored in electric and magnetic fields within that region.

Since we derived this result directly from the general form of Maxwell's equations, these three possibilities are *all* the possibilities allowed by classical physics, so this is a statement of conservation of power.

Finally, note the theorem also works in reverse; i.e., the net electromagnetic power flowing *out* of a region of space must have originated from some active source (i.e., the reverse of power dissipation) or released from energy stored in electric or magnetic fields.

Additional Reading:

- "Poynting vector" on Wikipedia.

3.2 Poynting Vector

[m0122]

In this section, we use Poynting's theorem (Section 3.1) to confirm the interpretation of the Poynting vector

$$\boxed{\mathbf{S} \triangleq \mathbf{E} \times \mathbf{H}} \tag{3.25}$$

as the spatial power density (SI base units of W/m^2) and the direction of power flow.

Figure 3.2 shows a uniform plane wave incident on a homogeneous and lossless region $\mathcal{V}$ defined by the closed right cylinder $\mathcal{S}$. The axis of the cylinder is aligned along the direction of propagation $\hat{\mathbf{k}}$ of the plane wave. The ends of the cylinder are planar and perpendicular to $\hat{\mathbf{k}}$.

Now let us apply Poynting's theorem:

$$P_{net,in} = P_{\Omega} + \frac{\partial}{\partial t}W_e + \frac{\partial}{\partial t}W_m \tag{3.26}$$

Since the region is lossless, $P_{\Omega} = 0$. Presuming no other electric or magnetic fields, W_e and W_m must also be zero. Consequently, $P_{net,in} = 0$. However, this does *not* mean that there is no power flowing into $\mathcal{V}$. Instead, $P_{net,in} = 0$ merely indicates that the *net* power flowing into $\mathcal{V}$ is zero. Thus, we might instead express the result for the present scenario as follows:

$$P_{net,in} = P_{in} - P_{out} = 0 \tag{3.27}$$

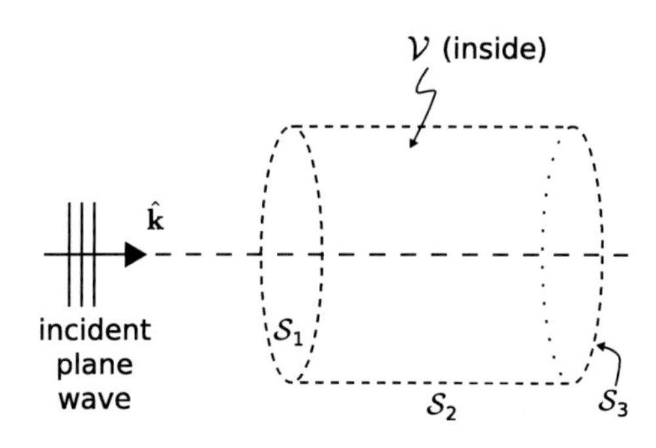

© C. Wang CC BY-SA 4.0

Figure 3.2: A uniform plane wave incident on a region bounded by the cylindrical surface $\mathcal{S}$.

where P_{in} and P_{out} indicate power flow explicitly into and explicitly out of $\mathcal{V}$ as separate quantities.

Proceeding, let's ignore what we know about power flow in plane waves, and instead see where Poynting's theorem takes us. Here,

$$P_{net,in} \triangleq -\oint_{\mathcal{S}} (\mathbf{E} \times \mathbf{H}) \cdot d\mathbf{s} = 0 \tag{3.28}$$

The surface $\mathcal{S}$ consists of three sides: The two flat ends, and the curved surface that connects them. Let us refer to these sides as $\mathcal{S}_1$, $\mathcal{S}_2$, and $\mathcal{S}_3$, from left to right as shown in Figure 3.2. Then,

$$\begin{aligned} &-\int_{\mathcal{S}_1} (\mathbf{E} \times \mathbf{H}) \cdot d\mathbf{s} \\ &-\int_{\mathcal{S}_2} (\mathbf{E} \times \mathbf{H}) \cdot d\mathbf{s} \\ &-\int_{\mathcal{S}_3} (\mathbf{E} \times \mathbf{H}) \cdot d\mathbf{s} = 0 \end{aligned} \tag{3.29}$$

On the curved surface $\mathcal{S}_2$, $d\mathbf{s}$ is everywhere perpendicular to $\mathbf{E} \times \mathbf{H}$ (i.e., perpendicular to $\hat{\mathbf{k}}$). Therefore, the second integral is equal to zero. On the left end $\mathcal{S}_1$, the outward-facing differential surface element $d\mathbf{s} = -\hat{\mathbf{k}}ds$. On the right end $\mathcal{S}_3$, $d\mathbf{s} = +\hat{\mathbf{k}}ds$. We are left with:

$$\begin{aligned} &\int_{\mathcal{S}_1} (\mathbf{E} \times \mathbf{H}) \cdot \hat{\mathbf{k}}ds \\ &-\int_{\mathcal{S}_3} (\mathbf{E} \times \mathbf{H}) \cdot \hat{\mathbf{k}}ds = 0 \end{aligned} \tag{3.30}$$

Compare this to Equation 3.27. Since $\hat{\mathbf{k}}$ is, by definition, the direction in which $\mathbf{E} \times \mathbf{H}$ points, the first integral must be P_{in} and the second integral must be P_{out}. Thus,

$$P_{in} = \int_{\mathcal{S}_1} (\mathbf{E} \times \mathbf{H}) \cdot \hat{\mathbf{k}}ds \tag{3.31}$$

and it follows that the magnitude and direction of $\mathbf{E} \times \mathbf{H}$, which we recognize as the Poynting vector, are spatial power density and direction of power flow, respectively.

The Poynting vector is named after English physicist J.H. Poynting, one of the co-discoverers of the concept. The fact that this vector points in the direction of power flow, and is therefore also a "pointing vector," is simply a remarkable coincidence.

Additional Reading:

- "Poynting vector" on Wikipedia.

3.3 Wave Equations for Lossy Regions

[m0128]

The wave equations for electromagnetic propagation in lossless and source-free media, in differential phasor form, are:

$$\nabla^2\widetilde{\mathbf{E}} + \omega^2\mu\epsilon\widetilde{\mathbf{E}} = 0 \quad (3.32)$$

$$\nabla^2\widetilde{\mathbf{H}} + \omega^2\mu\epsilon\widetilde{\mathbf{H}} = 0 \quad (3.33)$$

The constant $\omega^2\mu\epsilon$ is labeled β^2, and β turns out to be the phase propagation constant.

Now, we wish to upgrade these equations to account for the possibility of loss. First, let's be clear on what we mean by "loss." Specifically, we mean the possibility of conversion of energy from the propagating wave into current, and subsequently to heat. This mechanism is described by Ohm's law:

$$\widetilde{\mathbf{J}} = \sigma\widetilde{\mathbf{E}} \quad (3.34)$$

where σ is conductivity and $\widetilde{\mathbf{J}}$ is conduction current density (SI base units of A/m^2). In the lossless case, σ is presumed to be zero (or at least negligible), so $\mathbf{J}$ is presumed to be zero. To obtain wave equations for media exhibiting significant loss, we cannot assume $\mathbf{J} = 0$.

To obtain equations that account for the possibility of significant conduction current, hence loss, we return to the phasor forms of Maxwell's equations:

$$\nabla \cdot \widetilde{\mathbf{E}} = \frac{\widetilde{\rho}_v}{\epsilon} \quad (3.35)$$

$$\nabla \times \widetilde{\mathbf{E}} = -j\omega\mu\widetilde{\mathbf{H}} \quad (3.36)$$

$$\nabla \cdot \widetilde{\mathbf{H}} = 0 \quad (3.37)$$

$$\nabla \times \widetilde{\mathbf{H}} = \widetilde{\mathbf{J}} + j\omega\epsilon\widetilde{\mathbf{E}} \quad (3.38)$$

where $\widetilde{\rho}_v$ is the charge density. If the region of interest is source-free, then $\widetilde{\rho}_v = 0$. However, we may not similarly suppress $\widetilde{\mathbf{J}}$ since σ may be non-zero. To make progress, let us identify the possible contributions to $\widetilde{\mathbf{J}}$ as follows:

$$\widetilde{\mathbf{J}} = \widetilde{\mathbf{J}}_{imp} + \widetilde{\mathbf{J}}_{ind} \quad (3.39)$$

where $\widetilde{\mathbf{J}}_{imp}$ represents *impressed* sources of current and $\widetilde{\mathbf{J}}_{ind}$ represents current which is *induced* by loss. An impressed current is one whose behavior is independent of other features, analogous to an independent current source in elementary circuit theory. In the absence of such sources, Equation 3.39 becomes:

$$\widetilde{\mathbf{J}} = 0 + \sigma\widetilde{\mathbf{E}} \quad (3.40)$$

Equation 3.38 may now be rewritten as:

$$\nabla \times \widetilde{\mathbf{H}} = \sigma\widetilde{\mathbf{E}} + j\omega\epsilon\widetilde{\mathbf{E}} \quad (3.41)$$

$$= (\sigma + j\omega\epsilon)\,\widetilde{\mathbf{E}} \quad (3.42)$$

$$= j\omega\epsilon_c\widetilde{\mathbf{E}} \quad (3.43)$$

where we defined the new constant ϵ_c as follows:

$$\epsilon_c \triangleq \epsilon - j\frac{\sigma}{\omega} \quad (3.44)$$

This constant is known as *complex permittivity*. In the lossless case, $\epsilon_c = \epsilon$; i.e., the imaginary part of $\epsilon_c \to 0$ so there is no difference between the physical permittivity ϵ and ϵ_c. The effect of the material's loss is represented as a non-zero imaginary component of the permittivity.

It is also common to express ϵ_c as follows:

$$\epsilon_c = \epsilon' - j\epsilon'' \quad (3.45)$$

where the real-valued constants ϵ' and ϵ'' are in this case:

$$\epsilon' = \epsilon \quad (3.46)$$

$$\epsilon'' = \frac{\sigma}{\omega} \quad (3.47)$$

This alternative notation is useful for three reasons. First, some authors use the symbol ϵ to refer to *both* physical permittivity *and* complex permittivity. In this case, the "$\epsilon' - j\epsilon''$" notation is helpful in mitigating confusion. Second, it is often more convenient to specify ϵ'' at a frequency than it is to specify σ, which may also be a function of frequency. In fact, in some applications the loss of a material is most conveniently specified using the ratio ϵ''/ϵ' (known as *loss tangent*, for reasons explained elsewhere). Finally, it turns out that *nonlinearity* of permittivity can *also* be accommodated as an imaginary component of the permittivity. The "ϵ''" notation allows us to accommodate both effects – nonlinearity and conductivity – using common notation. In this section, however, we remain focused exclusively on conductivity.

> Complex permittivity ϵ_c (SI base units of F/m) describes the combined effects of permittivity and conductivity. Conductivity is represented as an imaginary-valued component of the permittivity.

Returning to Equations 3.35–3.38, we obtain:

$$\nabla \cdot \widetilde{\mathbf{E}} = 0 \tag{3.48}$$

$$\nabla \times \widetilde{\mathbf{E}} = -j\omega\mu\widetilde{\mathbf{H}} \tag{3.49}$$

$$\nabla \cdot \widetilde{\mathbf{H}} = 0 \tag{3.50}$$

$$\nabla \times \widetilde{\mathbf{H}} = j\omega\epsilon_c\widetilde{\mathbf{E}} \tag{3.51}$$

These equations are *identical* to the corresponding equations for the lossless case, with the exception that ϵ has been replaced by ϵ_c. Similarly, we may replace the factor $\omega^2\mu\epsilon$ in Equations 3.32 and 3.33, yielding:

$$\nabla^2\widetilde{\mathbf{E}} + \omega^2\mu\epsilon_c\widetilde{\mathbf{E}} = 0 \tag{3.52}$$

$$\nabla^2\widetilde{\mathbf{H}} + \omega^2\mu\epsilon_c\widetilde{\mathbf{H}} = 0 \tag{3.53}$$

In the lossless case, $\omega^2\mu\epsilon_c \to \omega^2\mu\epsilon$, which is β^2 as expected. For the general (i.e., possibly lossy) case, we shall make an analogous definition

$$\gamma^2 \triangleq -\omega^2\mu\epsilon_c \tag{3.54}$$

such that the wave equations may now be written as follows:

$$\boxed{\nabla^2\widetilde{\mathbf{E}} - \gamma^2\widetilde{\mathbf{E}} = 0} \tag{3.55}$$

$$\boxed{\nabla^2\widetilde{\mathbf{H}} - \gamma^2\widetilde{\mathbf{H}} = 0} \tag{3.56}$$

Note the minus sign in Equation 3.54, and the associated changes of signs in Equations 3.55 and 3.56. For the moment, this choice of sign may be viewed as arbitrary – we would have been equally justified in choosing the opposite sign for the definition of γ^2. However, the choice we have made is customary, and yields some notational convenience that will become apparent later.

In the lossless case, β is the phase propagation constant, which determines the rate at which the phase of a wave progresses with increasing distance along the direction of propagation. Given the similarity of Equations 3.55 and 3.56 to Equations 3.32 and 3.33, respectively, the constant γ must play a similar role. So, we are motivated to find an expression for γ. At first glance, this is simple: $\gamma = \sqrt{\gamma^2}$. However, recall that every number has two square roots. When one declares $\beta = \sqrt{\beta^2} = \omega\sqrt{\mu\epsilon}$, there is no concern since β is, by definition, positive; therefore, one knows to take the positive-valued square root. In contrast, γ^2 is complex-valued, and so the two possible values of $\sqrt{\gamma^2}$ are both potentially complex-valued. We are left without clear guidance on which of these values is appropriate and physically-relevant. So we proceed with caution.

First, consider the special case that γ is purely imaginary; e.g., $\gamma = j\gamma''$ where γ'' is a real-valued constant. In this case, $\gamma^2 = -\left(\gamma''\right)^2$ and the wave equations become

$$\nabla^2\widetilde{\mathbf{E}} + \left(\gamma''\right)^2\widetilde{\mathbf{E}} = 0 \tag{3.57}$$

$$\nabla^2\widetilde{\mathbf{H}} + \left(\gamma''\right)^2\widetilde{\mathbf{H}} = 0 \tag{3.58}$$

Comparing to Equations 3.32 and 3.33, we see γ'' plays the exact same role as β; i.e., γ'' is the phase propagation constant for whatever wave we obtain as the solution to the above equations. Therefore, let us make that definition formally:

$$\beta \triangleq \text{Im}\left\{\gamma\right\} \tag{3.59}$$

Be careful: Note that we are *not* claiming that γ'' in the possibly-lossy case is equal to $\omega^2\mu\epsilon$. Instead, we are asserting exactly the opposite; i.e., that there is a phase propagation constant in the general (possibly lossy) case, and we should find that this constant simplifies to $\omega^2\mu\epsilon$ in the lossless case.

Now we make the following definition for the real component of γ:

$$\alpha \triangleq \text{Re}\left\{\gamma\right\} \tag{3.60}$$

Such that

$$\gamma = \alpha + j\beta \tag{3.61}$$

where α and β are real-valued constants.

Now, it is possible to determine γ explicitly in terms of ω and the constitutive properties of the material.

First, note:

$$\begin{aligned}\gamma^2 &= (\alpha + j\beta)^2 \\ &= \alpha^2 - \beta^2 + j2\alpha\beta \end{aligned} \quad (3.62)$$

Expanding Equation 3.54 using Equations 3.45–3.47, we obtain:

$$\begin{aligned}\gamma^2 &= -\omega^2\mu\left(\epsilon - j\frac{\sigma}{\omega}\right) \\ &= -\omega^2\mu\epsilon + j\omega\mu\sigma \end{aligned} \quad (3.63)$$

The real and imaginary parts of Equations 3.62 and 3.63 must be equal. Enforcing this equality yields the following equations:

$$\alpha^2 - \beta^2 = -\omega^2\mu\epsilon \quad (3.64)$$

$$2\alpha\beta = \omega\mu\sigma \quad (3.65)$$

Equations 3.64 and 3.65 are independent simultaneous equations that may be solved for α and β. Sparing the reader the remaining steps, which are purely mathematical, we find:

$$\boxed{\alpha = \omega\left\{\frac{\mu\epsilon'}{2}\left[\sqrt{1+\left(\frac{\epsilon''}{\epsilon'}\right)^2} - 1\right]\right\}^{1/2}} \quad (3.66)$$

$$\boxed{\beta = \omega\left\{\frac{\mu\epsilon'}{2}\left[\sqrt{1+\left(\frac{\epsilon''}{\epsilon'}\right)^2} + 1\right]\right\}^{1/2}} \quad (3.67)$$

Equations 3.66 and 3.67 can be verified by confirming that Equations 3.64 and 3.65 are satisfied. It is also useful to confirm that the expected results are obtained in the lossless case. In the lossless case, $\sigma = 0$, so $\epsilon'' = 0$. Subsequently, Equation 3.66 yields $\alpha = 0$ and Equation 3.67 yields $\beta = \omega\sqrt{\mu\epsilon}$, as expected.

> The electromagnetic wave equations accounting for the possibility of lossy media are Equations 3.55 and 3.56 with $\gamma = \alpha + j\beta$, where α and β are the positive real-valued constants determined by Equations 3.66 and 3.67, respectively.

We conclude this section by pointing out a very useful analogy to transmission line theory. In the section "Wave Propagation on a TEM Transmission Line,"[1] we found that the potential and current along a transverse electromagnetic (TEM) transmission line satisfy the same wave equations that we have developed in this section, having a complex-valued propagation constant $\gamma = \alpha + j\beta$, and the same physical interpretation of β as the phase propagation constant. As is explained in another section, α too has the same interpretation in both applications – that is, as the *attenuation constant*.

Additional Reading:

- "Electromagnetic Wave Equation" on Wikipedia.

[1]This section may appear in a different volume, depending on the version of this book.

3.4 Complex Permittivity

[m0134]

The relationship between electric field intensity $\mathbf{E}$ (SI base units of V/m) and electric flux density $\mathbf{D}$ (SI base units of C/m^2) is:

$$\mathbf{D} = \epsilon\mathbf{E} \tag{3.68}$$

where ϵ is the permittivity (SI base units of F/m). In simple media, ϵ is a real positive value which does not depend on the time variation of $\mathbf{E}$. That is, the response ($\mathbf{D}$) to a change in $\mathbf{E}$ is observed instantaneously and without delay.

In practical materials, however, the change in $\mathbf{D}$ in response to a change in $\mathbf{E}$ may depend on the manner in which $\mathbf{E}$ changes. The response may not be instantaneous, but rather might take some time to fully manifest. This behavior can be modeled using the following generalization of Equation 3.68:

$$\mathbf{D} = a_0\mathbf{E} + a_1\frac{\partial}{\partial t}\mathbf{E} + a_2\frac{\partial^2}{\partial t^2}\mathbf{E} + a_3\frac{\partial^3}{\partial t^3}\mathbf{E} + ... \tag{3.69}$$

where a_0, a_1, a_2, and so on are real-valued constants, and the number of terms is infinite. In practical materials, the importance of the terms tends to diminish with increasing order. Thus, it is common that only the first few terms are significant. In many applications involving common materials, only the first term is significant; i.e., $a_0 \approx \epsilon$ and $a_n \approx 0$ for $n \geq 1$. As we shall see in a moment, this distinction commonly depends on frequency.

In the phasor domain, differentiation with respect to time becomes multiplication by $j\omega$. Thus, Equation 3.69 becomes

$$\begin{aligned}\widetilde{\mathbf{D}} &= a_0\widetilde{\mathbf{E}} + a_1\left(j\omega\right)\widetilde{\mathbf{E}} + a_2\left(j\omega\right)^2\widetilde{\mathbf{E}} + a_3\left(j\omega\right)^3\widetilde{\mathbf{E}} + ... \\ &= a_0\widetilde{\mathbf{E}} + j\omega a_1\widetilde{\mathbf{E}} - \omega^2 a_2\widetilde{\mathbf{E}} - j\omega^3 a_3\widetilde{\mathbf{E}} + ... \\ &= \left(a_0 + j\omega a_1 - \omega^2 a_2 - j\omega^3 a_3 + ...\right)\widetilde{\mathbf{E}} \end{aligned} \tag{3.70}$$

Note that the factor in parentheses is a complex-valued number which depends on frequency ω and materials parameters a_0, a_1, ... We may summarize this as follows:

$$\widetilde{\mathbf{D}} = \epsilon_c\widetilde{\mathbf{E}} \tag{3.71}$$

where ϵ_c is a complex-valued constant that depends on frequency.

The notation "ϵ_c" is used elsewhere in this book (e.g., Section 3.3) to represent a generalization of simple permittivity that accommodates loss associated with non-zero conductivity σ. In Section 3.3, we defined

$$\epsilon_c \triangleq \epsilon' - j\epsilon'' \tag{3.72}$$

where $\epsilon' \triangleq \epsilon$ (i.e., real-valued, simple permittivity) and $\epsilon'' \triangleq \sigma/\omega$ (i.e., the effect of non-zero conductivity). Similarly, ϵ_c in Equation 3.71 can be expressed as

$$\epsilon_c \triangleq \epsilon' - j\epsilon'' \tag{3.73}$$

but in this case

$$\epsilon' \triangleq a_0 - \omega^2 a_2 + ... \tag{3.74}$$

and

$$\epsilon'' \triangleq -\omega a_1 + \omega^3 a_3 - ... \tag{3.75}$$

> When expressed as phasors, the temporal relationship between electric flux density and electric field intensity can be expressed as a complex-valued permittivity.

Thus, we now see two possible applications for the concept of complex permittivity: Modeling the delayed response of $\mathbf{D}$ to changing $\mathbf{E}$, as described above; and modeling loss associated with non-zero conductivity. In practical work, it may not always be clear precisely what combination of effects the complex permittivity $\epsilon_c = \epsilon' - j\epsilon''$ is taking into account. For example, if ϵ_c is obtained by measurement, both delayed response and conduction loss may be represented. Therefore, it is not reasonable to assume a value of ϵ'' obtained by measurement represents only conduction loss (i.e., is equal to σ/ω); in fact, the measurement also may include a significant frequency-dependent contribution associated with the delayed response behavior identified in this section.

An example of the complex permittivity of a typical dielectric material is shown in Figure 3.3. Note the frequency dependence is quite simple and slowly-varying at frequencies below 1 GHz or so, but becomes relatively complex at higher frequencies.

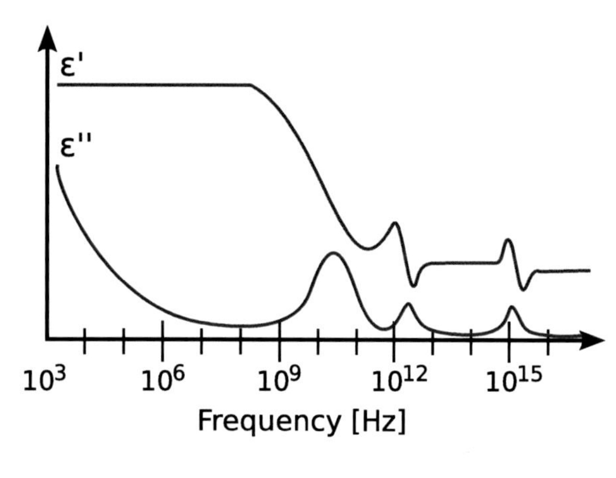

© K.A. Mauritz (modified)

Figure 3.3: The relative contributions of the real and imaginary components of permittivity for a typical dielectric material (in this case, a polymer).

Additional Reading:

- "Permittivity" on Wikipedia.

3.5 Loss Tangent

[m0132]

In Section 3.3, we found that the effect of loss due to non-zero conductivity σ could be concisely quantified using the ratio

$$\frac{\epsilon''}{\epsilon'} = \frac{\sigma}{\omega\epsilon} \tag{3.76}$$

where ϵ' and ϵ'' are the real and imaginary components of the complex permittivity ϵ_c, and $\epsilon' \triangleq \epsilon$. In this section, we explore this relationship in greater detail.

Recall Ampere's law in differential (but otherwise general) form:

$$\nabla \times \mathbf{H} = \mathbf{J} + \frac{\partial}{\partial t}\mathbf{D} \tag{3.77}$$

The first term on the right is conduction current, whereas the second term on the right is displacement current. In the phasor domain, differentiation with respect to time ($\partial/\partial t$) becomes multiplication by $j\omega$. Therefore, the phasor form of Equation 3.77 is

$$\nabla \times \widetilde{\mathbf{H}} = \widetilde{\mathbf{J}} + j\omega\widetilde{\mathbf{D}} \tag{3.78}$$

Also recall that $\widetilde{\mathbf{J}} = \sigma\widetilde{\mathbf{E}}$ and that $\widetilde{\mathbf{D}} = \epsilon\widetilde{\mathbf{E}}$. Thus,

$$\nabla \times \widetilde{\mathbf{H}} = \sigma\widetilde{\mathbf{E}} + j\omega\epsilon\widetilde{\mathbf{E}} \tag{3.79}$$

Interestingly, the total current is the sum of a real-valued conduction current and an imaginary-valued displacement current. This is shown graphically in Figure 3.4.

Note that the angle δ indicated in Figure 3.4 is given by

$$\boxed{\tan\delta \triangleq \frac{\sigma}{\omega\epsilon}} \tag{3.80}$$

The quantity $\tan\delta$ is referred to as the *loss tangent*. Note that loss tangent is zero for a lossless ($\sigma \equiv 0$) material, and increases with increasing loss. Thus, loss tangent provides an alternative way to quantify the effect of loss on the electromagnetic field within a material.

> Loss tangent presuming only ohmic (conduction) loss is given by Equation 3.80.

Comparing Equation 3.80 to Equation 3.76, we see loss tangent can equivalently be calculated as

$$\tan\delta = \frac{\epsilon''}{\epsilon} \tag{3.81}$$

and subsequently interpreted as shown in Figure 3.5.

The discussion in this section has assumed that ϵ_c is complex-valued solely due to ohmic loss. However, it is explained in Section 3.4 that permittivity may also be complex-valued as a way to model delay in the response of **D** to changing **E**. Does the concept of loss tangent apply also in this case? Since the math does not distinguish between permittivity which is complex due to loss and permittivity which is complex due to delay, subsequent mathematically-derived results apply in either case. On the other hand, there may be potentially significant differences in the physical manifestation of these effects. For example, a material having large loss tangent due to ohmic loss might become hot when a large electric field is applied, whereas a material having large loss tangent due to delayed response might not. Summarizing:

> The expression for loss tangent given by Equation 3.81 and Figure 3.5 does not distinguish between ohmic loss and delayed response.

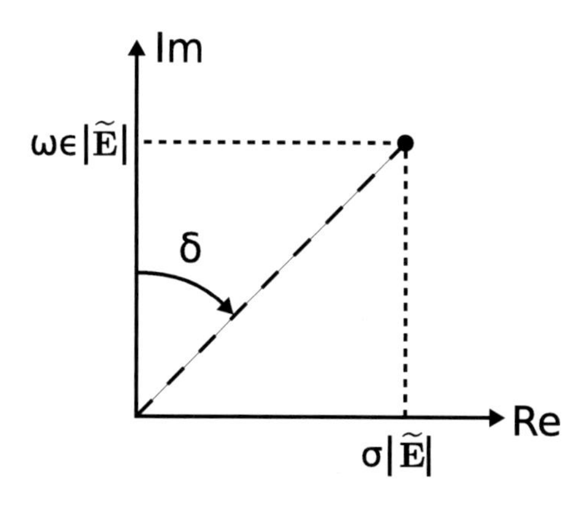

© C. Wang CC BY-SA 4.0

Figure 3.4: In the phasor domain, the total current is the sum of a real-valued conduction current and an imaginary-valued displacement current.

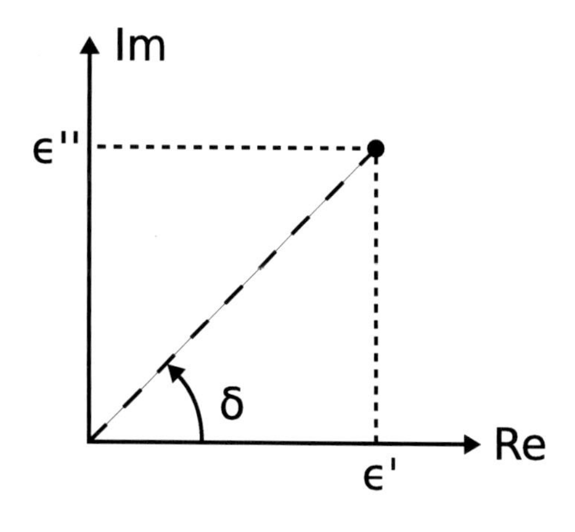

© C. Wang CC BY-SA 4.0

Figure 3.5: Loss tangent defined in terms of the real and imaginary components of the complex permittivity ϵ_c.

Additional Reading:

- "Dielectric loss" on Wikipedia.

3.6 Plane Waves in Lossy Regions

[m0130]

The electromagnetic wave equations for source-free regions consisting of possibly-lossy material are (see Section 3.3):

$$\nabla^2\widetilde{\mathbf{E}} - \gamma^2\widetilde{\mathbf{E}} = 0 \tag{3.82}$$

$$\nabla^2\widetilde{\mathbf{H}} - \gamma^2\widetilde{\mathbf{H}} = 0 \tag{3.83}$$

where

$$\gamma^2 \triangleq -\omega^2\mu\epsilon_c \tag{3.84}$$

We now turn our attention to the question, what are the characteristics of waves that propagate in these conditions? As in the lossless case, these equations permit waves having a variety of geometries including plane waves, cylindrical waves, and spherical waves. In this section, we will consider the important special case of uniform plane waves.

To obtain the general expression for the uniform plane wave solution, we follow precisely the same procedure described in the section "Uniform Plane Waves: Derivation."[2] Although that section presumed lossless media, the only difference in the present situation is that the real-valued constant $+\beta^2$ is replaced with the complex-valued constant $-\gamma^2$. Thus, we obtain the desired solution through a simple modification of the solution for the lossless case. For a wave exhibiting uniform magnitude and phase in planes of constant z, we find that the electric field is:

$$\widetilde{\mathbf{E}} = \hat{\mathbf{x}}\widetilde{E}_x + \hat{\mathbf{y}}\widetilde{E}_y \tag{3.85}$$

where

$$\widetilde{E}_x = E_{x0}^{+}e^{-\gamma z} + E_{x0}^{-}e^{+\gamma z} \tag{3.86}$$

$$\widetilde{E}_y = E_{y0}^{+}e^{-\gamma z} + E_{y0}^{-}e^{+\gamma z} \tag{3.87}$$

where the complex-valued coefficients E_{x0}^{+}, E_{x0}^{-}, E_{y0}^{+}, and E_{y0}^{-} are determined by boundary conditions (possibly including sources) outside the region of interest. This result can be confirmed by verifying that Equations 3.86 and 3.87 each satisfy Equation 3.82. Also, it may be helpful to note that these expressions are identical to those obtained for the voltage and current in lossy transmission lines, as described in the section "Wave Equation for a TEM Transmission Line."[3]

Let's consider the special case of an $\hat{\mathbf{x}}$-polarized plane wave propagating in the $+\hat{\mathbf{z}}$ direction:

$$\widetilde{\mathbf{E}} = \hat{\mathbf{x}}E_{x0}^{+}e^{-\gamma z} \tag{3.88}$$

We established in Section 3.3 that γ may be written explicitly in terms of its real and imaginary components as follows:

$$\gamma = \alpha + j\beta \tag{3.89}$$

where α and β are positive real-valued constants depending on frequency (ω) and constitutive properties of the medium; i.e., permittivity, permeability, and conductivity. Thus:

$$\begin{aligned}\widetilde{\mathbf{E}} &= \hat{\mathbf{x}}E_{x0}^{+}e^{-(\alpha+j\beta)z} \\ &= \hat{\mathbf{x}}E_{x0}^{+}e^{-\alpha z}e^{-j\beta z}\end{aligned} \tag{3.90}$$

Observe that the variation of phase with distance is determined by β through the factor $e^{-j\beta z}$; thus, β is the phase propagation constant and plays precisely the same role as in the lossless case. Observe also that the variation in magnitude is determined by α through the real-valued factor $e^{-\alpha z}$. Specifically, magnitude is reduced inverse-exponentially with increasing distance along the direction of propagation. Thus, α is the attenuation constant and plays precisely the same role as the attenuation constant for a lossy transmission line.

> The presence of loss in material gives rise to a real-valued factor $e^{-\alpha z}$ which describes the attenuation of the wave with propagation (in this case, along z) in the material.

We may continue to exploit the similarity of the potentially-lossy and lossless plane wave results to quickly ascertain the characteristics of the magnetic field. In particular, the plane wave relationships apply exactly as they do in the lossless case. These relationships are:

$$\widetilde{\mathbf{H}} = \frac{1}{\eta}\hat{\mathbf{k}} \times \widetilde{\mathbf{E}} \tag{3.91}$$

[2] Depending on the version of this book, this section may appear in a different volume.

[3] Depending on the version of this book, this section may appear in a different volume.

$$\widetilde{\mathbf{E}} = -\eta\hat{\mathbf{k}} \times \widetilde{\mathbf{H}} \tag{3.92}$$

where $\hat{\mathbf{k}}$ is the direction of propagation and η is the wave impedance. In the lossless case, $\eta = \sqrt{\mu/\epsilon}$; however, in the possibly-lossy case we must replace $\epsilon = \epsilon'$ with $\epsilon_c = \epsilon' - j\epsilon''$. Thus:

$$\eta \rightarrow \eta_c = \sqrt{\frac{\mu}{\epsilon_c}} = \sqrt{\frac{\mu}{\epsilon' - j\epsilon''}}$$
$$= \sqrt{\frac{\mu}{\epsilon'}}\sqrt{\frac{1}{1 - j\left(\epsilon''/\epsilon'\right)}} \tag{3.93}$$

Thus:

$$\boxed{\eta_c = \sqrt{\frac{\mu}{\epsilon'}} \cdot \left[1 - j\frac{\epsilon''}{\epsilon'}\right]^{-1/2}} \tag{3.94}$$

Remarkably, we find that the wave impedance for a lossy material is equal to $\sqrt{\mu/\epsilon}$ – the wave impedance we would calculate if we neglected loss (i.e., assumed $\sigma = 0$) – times a correction factor that accounts for the loss. This correction factor is complex-valued; therefore, $\mathbf{E}$ and $\mathbf{H}$ are not in phase when propagating through lossy material. We now see that in the phasor domain:

$$\widetilde{\mathbf{H}} = \frac{1}{\eta_c}\hat{\mathbf{k}} \times \widetilde{\mathbf{E}} \tag{3.95}$$

$$\widetilde{\mathbf{E}} = -\eta_c\hat{\mathbf{k}} \times \widetilde{\mathbf{H}} \tag{3.96}$$

The plane wave relationships in media which are possibly lossy are given by Equations 3.95 and 3.96, with the complex-valued wave impedance given by Equation 3.94.

3.7 Wave Power in a Lossy Medium

[m0133]

In this section, we consider the power associated with waves propagating in materials which are potentially lossy; i.e., having conductivity σ significantly greater than zero. This topic has previously been considered in the section "Wave Power in a Lossless Medium" for the case in loss is not significant.[4] A review of that section may be useful before reading this section.

Recall that the Poynting vector

$$\mathbf{S} \triangleq \mathbf{E} \times \mathbf{H} \tag{3.97}$$

indicates the power density (i.e., W/m^2) of a wave and the direction of power flow. This is "instantaneous" power, applicable to waves regardless of the way they vary with time. Often we are interested specifically in waves which vary sinusoidally, and which subsequently may be represented as phasors. In this case, the *time-average* Poynting vector is

$$\mathbf{S}_{ave} \triangleq \frac{1}{2}\text{Re}\left\{\widetilde{\mathbf{E}} \times \widetilde{\mathbf{H}}^*\right\} \tag{3.98}$$

Further, we have already used this expression to find that the time-average power density for a sinusoidally-varying uniform plane wave in a lossless medium is simply

$$S_{ave} = \frac{|E_0|^2}{2\eta} \quad \text{(lossless case)} \tag{3.99}$$

where $|E_0|$ is the peak (as opposed to RMS) magnitude of the electric field intensity phasor, and η is the wave impedance.

Let us now use Equation 3.98 to determine the expression corresponding to Equation 3.99 in the case of possibly-lossy media. We may express the electric and magnetic field intensities of a uniform plane wave as

$$\widetilde{\mathbf{E}} = \hat{\mathbf{x}}E_0 e^{-\alpha z}e^{-j\beta z} \tag{3.100}$$

and

$$\widetilde{\mathbf{H}} = \hat{\mathbf{y}}\frac{E_0}{\eta_c}e^{-\alpha z}e^{-j\beta z} \tag{3.101}$$

[4]Depending on the version of this book, this section may appear in another volume.

where α and β are the attenuation constant and phase propagation constant, respectively, and η_c is the complex-valued wave impedance. As written, these expressions describe a wave which is $+\hat{\mathbf{x}}$-polarized and propagates in the $+\hat{\mathbf{z}}$ direction. We make these choices for convenience only – as long as the medium is homogeneous and isotropic, we expect our findings to apply regardless of polarization and direction of propagation. Applying Equation 3.98:

$$\begin{aligned}\mathbf{S}_{ave} &= \frac{1}{2}\text{Re}\left\{\widetilde{\mathbf{E}} \times \widetilde{\mathbf{H}}^*\right\} \\ &= \frac{1}{2}\,\hat{\mathbf{z}}\,\text{Re}\left\{\frac{|E_0|^2}{\eta_c^*}e^{-2\alpha z}\right\} \\ &= \hat{\mathbf{z}}\frac{|E_0|^2}{2}\,\text{Re}\left\{\frac{1}{\eta_c^*}\right\}e^{-2\alpha z} \qquad (3.102)\end{aligned}$$

Because η_c is complex-valued when the material is lossy, we must proceed with caution. First, let us write η_c explicitly in terms of its magnitude $|\eta_c|$ and phase ψ_η:

$$\eta \triangleq |\eta|\, e^{j\psi_\eta} \qquad (3.103)$$

Then:

$$\eta_c^* = |\eta_c|\, e^{-j\psi_\eta} \qquad (3.104)$$

$$(\eta_c^*)^{-1} = |\eta_c|^{-1}\, e^{+j\psi_\eta} \qquad (3.105)$$

$$\text{Re}\left\{(\eta_c^*)^{-1}\right\} = |\eta_c|^{-1}\cos\psi_\eta \qquad (3.106)$$

Then Equation 3.102 may be written:

$$\boxed{\mathbf{S}_{ave} = \hat{\mathbf{z}}\frac{|E_0|^2}{2\,|\eta_c|}\, e^{-2\alpha z}\, \cos\psi_\eta} \qquad (3.107)$$

> The time-average power density of the plane wave described by Equation 3.100 in a possibly-lossy material is given by Equation 3.107.

As a check, note that this expression gives the expected result for lossless media; i.e., $\alpha = 0$, $|\eta_c| = \eta$, and $\psi_\eta = 0$. We now see that the effect of loss is that power density is now proportional to $(e^{-\alpha z})^2$, so, as expected, power density is proportional to the square of either $|\mathbf{E}|$ or $|\mathbf{H}|$. The result further indicates a one-time scaling of the power density by a factor of

$$\frac{|\eta|}{|\eta_c|}\cos\psi_\eta < 1 \qquad (3.108)$$

relative to a medium without loss.

> The reduction in power density due to non-zero conductivity is proportional to a distance-dependent factor $e^{-2\alpha z}$ and an additional factor that depends on the magnitude and phase of η_c.

3.8 Decibel Scale for Power Ratio

[m0154]

In many disciplines within electrical engineering, it is common to evaluate the ratios of powers and power densities that differ by many orders of magnitude. These ratios could be expressed in scientific notation, but it is more common to use the logarithmic *decibel* (dB) scale in such applications.

In the conventional (linear) scale, the ratio of power P_1 to power P_0 is simply

$$G = \frac{P_1}{P_0} \quad \text{(linear units)} \tag{3.109}$$

Here, "G" might be interpreted as "power gain." Note that $G < 1$ if $P_1 < P_0$ and $G > 1$ if $P_1 > P_0$.

In the decibel scale, the ratio of power P_1 to power P_0 is

$$\boxed{G \triangleq 10\log_{10}\frac{P_1}{P_0} \quad \text{(dB)}} \tag{3.110}$$

where "dB" denotes a unitless quantity which is expressed in the decibel scale. Note that $G < 0$ dB (i.e., is "negative in dB") if $P_1 < P_0$ and $G > 0$ dB if $P_1 > P_0$.

> The power gain P_1/P_0 in dB is given by Equation 3.110.

Alternatively, one might choose to interpret a power ratio as a loss L with $L \triangleq 1/G$ in linear units, which is $L = -G$ when expressed in dB. Most often, but not always, engineers interpret a power ratio as "gain" if the output power is expected to be greater than input power (e.g., as expected for an amplifier) and as "loss" if output power is expected to be less than input power (e.g., as expected for a lossy transmission line).

> Power loss L is the reciprocal of power gain G. Therefore, $L = -G$ when these quantities are expressed in dB.

Example 3.1. Power loss from a long cable.

A 2 W signal is injected into a long cable. The power arriving at the other end of the cable is 10 μW. What is the power loss in dB?

In linear units:

$$G = \frac{10\ \mu\text{W}}{2\ \text{W}} = 5 \times 10^{-6} \quad \text{(linear units)}$$

In dB:

$$G = 10\log_{10}\left(5 \times 10^{-6}\right) \cong -53.0\ \text{dB}$$
$$L = -G \cong \underline{+53.0\ \text{dB}}$$

The decibel scale is used in precisely the same way to relate ratios of spatial power densities for waves. For example, the loss incurred when the spatial power density is reduced from S_0 (SI base units of W/m^2) to S_1 is

$$L = 10\log_{10}\frac{S_0}{S_1} \quad \text{(dB)} \tag{3.111}$$

This works because the common units of m^{-2} in the numerator and denominator cancel, leaving a power ratio.

A common point of confusion is the proper use of the decibel scale to represent voltage or current ratios. To avoid confusion, simply refer to the definition expressed in Equation 3.110. For example, let's say $P_1 = V_1^2/R_1$ where V_1 is potential and R_1 is the impedance across which V_1 is defined. Similarly, let us define $P_0 = V_0^2/R_0$ where V_0 is potential and R_0 is the impedance across which V_0 is defined. Applying Equation 3.110:

$$\begin{aligned} G &\triangleq 10\log_{10}\frac{P_1}{P_0} \quad \text{(dB)} \\ &= 10\log_{10}\frac{V_1^2/R_1}{V_0^2/R_0} \quad \text{(dB)} \end{aligned} \tag{3.112}$$

Now, if $R_1 = R_0$, then

$$\begin{aligned} G &= 10\log_{10}\frac{V_1^2}{V_0^2} \quad \text{(dB)} \\ &= 10\log_{10}\left(\frac{V_1}{V_0}\right)^2 \quad \text{(dB)} \\ &= 20\log_{10}\frac{V_1}{V_0} \quad \text{(dB)} \end{aligned} \tag{3.113}$$

However, note that this is *not* true if $R_1 \neq R_0$.

> A power ratio in dB is equal to $20\log_{10}$ of the voltage ratio only if the associated impedances are equal.

Adding to the potential for confusion on this point is the concept of *voltage gain* G_v:

$$G_v \triangleq 20\log_{10}\frac{V_1}{V_0} \text{ (dB)} \quad (3.114)$$

which applies regardless of the associated impedances. Note that $G_v = G$ only if the associated impedances are equal, and that these ratios are different otherwise. Be careful!

The decibel scale simplifies common calculations. Here's an example. Let's say a signal having power P_0 is injected into a transmission line having loss L. Then the output power $P_1 = P_0/L$ in linear units. However, in dB, we find:

$$\begin{aligned} 10\log_{10} P_1 &= 10\log_{10}\frac{P_0}{L} \\ &= 10\log_{10} P_0 - 10\log_{10} L \end{aligned}$$

Division has been transformed into subtraction; i.e.,

$$P_1 = P_0 - L \text{ (dB)} \quad (3.115)$$

This form facilitates easier calculation and visualization, and so is typically preferred.

Finally, note that the units of P_1 and P_0 in Equation 3.115 are not dB *per se*, but rather dB with respect to the original power units. For example, if P_1 is in mW, then taking $10\log_{10}$ of this quantity results in a quantity having units of dB relative to 1 mW. A power expressed in dB relative to 1 mW is said to have units of "dBm." For example, "0 dBm" means 0 dB relative to 1 mW, which is simply 1 mW. Similarly $+10$ dBm is 10 mW, -10 dBm is 0.1 mW, and so on.

Additional Reading:

- "Decibel" on Wikipedia.
- "Scientific notation" on Wikipedia.

3.9 Attenuation Rate

[m0155]

Attenuation rate is a convenient way to quantify loss in general media, including transmission lines, using the decibel scale.

Consider a transmission line carrying a wave in the $+z$ direction. Let P_0 be the power at $z = 0$. Let P_1 be the power at $z = l$. Then the power at $z = 0$ relative to the power at $z = l$ is:

$$\frac{P_0}{P_1} = \frac{e^{-2\alpha\cdot 0}}{e^{-2\alpha\cdot l}} = e^{2\alpha l} \text{ (linear units)} \quad (3.116)$$

where α is the attenuation constant; that is, the real part of the propagation constant $\gamma = \alpha + j\beta$. Expressed in this manner, the power ratio is a loss; that is, a number greater than 1 represents attenuation. In the decibel scale, the loss is

$$\begin{aligned} 10\log_{10}\frac{P_0}{P_1} &= 10\log_{10} e^{2\alpha l} \\ &= 20\alpha l \log_{10} e \\ &\cong 8.69\alpha l \text{ dB} \end{aligned} \quad (3.117)$$

Attenuation rate is defined as this quantity per unit length. Dividing by l, we obtain:

$$\text{attenuation rate} \cong 8.69\alpha \quad (3.118)$$

This has units of dB/length, where the units of length are the same length units in which α is expressed. For example, if α is expressed in units of m^{-1}, then attenuation rate has units of dB/m.

> Attenuation rate $\cong 8.69\alpha$ is the loss in dB, per unit length.

The utility of the attenuation rate concept is that it allows us to quickly calculate loss for any distance of wave travel: This loss is simply attenuation rate (dB/m) times length (m), which yields loss in dB.

Example 3.2. Attenuation rate in a long cable.

A particular coaxial cable has an attenuation constant $\alpha \cong 8.5 \times 10^{-3}\ \text{m}^{-1}$. What is the attenuation rate and the loss in dB for 100 m of this cable?

The attenuation rate is

$$\cong 8.69\alpha \cong \underline{0.0738 \text{ dB/m}}$$

The loss in 100 m of this cable is

$$\cong (0.0738 \text{ dB/m})\,(100 \text{ m}) \cong \underline{7.4 \text{ dB}}$$

Note that it would be entirely appropriate, and equivalent, to state that the attenuation rate for this cable is 7.4 dB/(100 m).

The concept of attenuation rate is used in precisely the same way to relate ratios of spatial power densities for unguided waves. This works because spatial power density has SI base units of W/m^2, so the common units of m^{-2} in the numerator and denominator cancel in the power density ratio, leaving a simple power ratio.

3.10 Poor Conductors

[m0156]

A *poor conductor* is a material for which conductivity is low, yet sufficient to exhibit significant loss. To be clear, the loss we refer to here is the conversion of the electric field to current through Ohm's law.

The threshold of significance depends on the application. For example, the dielectric spacer separating the conductors in a coaxial cable might be treated as lossless ($\sigma = 0$) for short lengths at low frequencies; whereas the loss of the cable for long lengths and higher frequencies is typically significant, and must be taken into account. In the latter case, the material is said to be a poor conductor because the loss is significant yet the material can still be treated in most other respects as an ideal dielectric.

A quantitative but approximate criterion for identification of a poor conductor can be obtained from the concept of complex permittivity ϵ_c, which has the form:

$$\epsilon_c = \epsilon' - j\epsilon'' \tag{3.119}$$

Recall that ϵ'' quantifies loss, whereas ϵ' exists independently of loss. In fact, $\epsilon_c = \epsilon' = \epsilon$ for a perfectly lossless material. Therefore, we may quantify the lossiness of a material using the ratio ϵ''/ϵ', which is sometimes referred to as *loss tangent* (see Section 3.5). Using this quantity, we define a poor conductor as a material for which ϵ'' is very small relative to ϵ'. Thus,

$$\frac{\epsilon''}{\epsilon'} \ll 1 \quad \text{(poor conductor)} \tag{3.120}$$

A poor conductor is a material having loss tangent much less than 1, such that it behaves in most respects as an ideal dielectric except that ohmic loss may not be negligible.

An example of a poor conductor commonly encountered in electrical engineering includes the popular printed circuit board substrate material FR4 (fiberglass epoxy), which has $\epsilon''/\epsilon' \sim 0.008$ over the frequency range it is most commonly used. Another example, already mentioned, is the dielectric spacer material (for example, polyethylene) typically used in coaxial cables. The loss of these materials may or may not be significant, depending on the particulars of the application.

The imprecise definition of Equation 3.120 is sufficient to derive some characteristics exhibited by all poor conductors. To do so, first recall that the propagation constant γ is given in general as follows:

$$\gamma^2 = -\omega^2 \mu \epsilon_c \tag{3.121}$$

Therefore:

$$\gamma = \sqrt{-\omega^2 \mu \epsilon_c} \tag{3.122}$$

In general a number has two square roots, so some caution is required here. In this case, we may proceed as follows:

$$\begin{aligned}\gamma &= j\omega\sqrt{\mu}\sqrt{\epsilon' - j\epsilon''} \\ &= j\omega\sqrt{\mu\epsilon'}\sqrt{1 - j\frac{\epsilon''}{\epsilon'}}\end{aligned} \tag{3.123}$$

The requirement that $\epsilon''/\epsilon' \ll 1$ for a poor conductor allows this expression to be "linearized." For this, we invoke the *binomial series* representation:

$$(1+x)^n = 1 + nx + \frac{n(n-1)}{2!}x^2 + \ldots \tag{3.124}$$

where x and n are, for our purposes, any constants; and "..." indicates the remaining terms in this infinite series, with each term containing the factor x^n with $n > 2$. If $x \ll 1$, then all terms containing x^n with $n \geq 2$ will be very small relative to the first two terms of the series. Thus,

$$(1+x)^n \approx 1 + nx \quad \text{for } x \ll 1 \tag{3.125}$$

Applying this to the present problem:

$$\left(1 - j\frac{\epsilon''}{\epsilon'}\right)^{1/2} \approx 1 - j\frac{\epsilon''}{2\epsilon'} \tag{3.126}$$

where we have used $n = 1/2$ and $x = -j\epsilon''/\epsilon'$. Applying this approximation to Equation 3.123, we obtain:

$$\begin{aligned}\gamma &\approx j\omega\sqrt{\mu\epsilon'}\left(1 - j\frac{\epsilon''}{2\epsilon'}\right) \\ &\approx j\omega\sqrt{\mu\epsilon'} + \omega\sqrt{\mu\epsilon'}\frac{\epsilon''}{2\epsilon'}\end{aligned} \tag{3.127}$$

At this point, we are able to identify an expression for the phase propagation constant:

$$\boxed{\beta \triangleq \text{Im}\{\gamma\} \approx \omega\sqrt{\mu\epsilon'} \quad \text{(poor conductor)}} \tag{3.128}$$

Remarkably, we find that β for a poor conductor is approximately equal to β for an ideal dielectric.

For the attenuation constant, we find

$$\boxed{\alpha \triangleq \text{Re}\{\gamma\} \approx \omega\sqrt{\mu\epsilon'}\frac{\epsilon''}{2\epsilon'} \quad \text{(poor conductor)}} \tag{3.129}$$

Alternatively, this expression may be written in the following form:

$$\alpha \approx \frac{1}{2}\beta\frac{\epsilon''}{\epsilon'} \quad \text{(poor conductor)} \tag{3.130}$$

Presuming that ϵ_c is determined entirely by ohmic loss, then

$$\frac{\epsilon''}{\epsilon'} = \frac{\sigma}{\omega\epsilon} \tag{3.131}$$

Under this condition, Equation 3.129 may be rewritten:

$$\alpha \approx \omega\sqrt{\mu\epsilon'}\frac{\sigma}{2\omega\epsilon} \quad \text{(poor conductor)} \tag{3.132}$$

Since $\epsilon' = \epsilon$ under these assumptions, the expression simplifies to

$$\alpha \approx \frac{\sigma}{2}\sqrt{\frac{\mu}{\epsilon}} = \frac{1}{2}\sigma\eta \quad \text{(poor conductor)} \tag{3.133}$$

where $\eta \triangleq \sqrt{\mu/\epsilon'}$ is the wave impedance presuming lossless material. This result is remarkable for two reasons: First, factors of ω have been eliminated, so there is no dependence on frequency separate from the frequency dependence of the constitutive parameters σ, μ, and ϵ. These parameters vary slowly with frequency, so the value of α for a poor conductor also varies slowly with frequency. Second, we see α is proportional to σ and η. This makes it quite easy to anticipate how the attenuation constant is affected by changes in conductivity and wave impedance in poor conductors.

Finally, what is the wave impedance in a poor conductor? In contrast to η, η_c is potentially complex-valued and may depend on σ. First, recall:

$$\eta_c = \sqrt{\frac{\mu}{\epsilon'}} \cdot \left[1 - j\frac{\epsilon''}{\epsilon'}\right]^{-1/2} \tag{3.134}$$

Applying the same approximation applied to γ earlier, this may be written

$$\eta_c \approx \sqrt{\frac{\mu}{\epsilon'}} \cdot \left[1 - j\frac{\epsilon''}{2\epsilon'}\right] \quad \text{(poor conductor)} \quad (3.135)$$

We see that for a poor conductor, $\text{Re}\{\eta_c\} \approx \eta$ and that $\text{Im}\{\eta_c\} \ll \text{Re}\{\eta_c\}$. The usual approximation in this case is simply

$$\boxed{\eta_c \approx \eta \quad \text{(poor conductor)}} \quad (3.136)$$

Additional Reading:

- "Binomial series" on Wikipedia.

3.11 Good Conductors

[m0157]

A *good conductor* is a material which behaves in most respects as a perfect conductor, yet exhibits significant loss. Now, we have to be very careful: The term "loss" applied to the concept of a "conductor" means something quite different from the term "loss" applied to other types of materials. Let us take a moment to disambiguate this term.

Conductors are materials which are intended to efficiently sustain current, which requires high conductivity σ. In contrast, non-conductors are materials which are intended to efficiently sustain the electric field, which requires low σ. "Loss" for a non-conductor (see in particular "poor conductors," Section 3.10) means the conversion of energy in the electric field into current. In contrast, "loss" for a conductor refers to energy *already* associated with current, which is subsequently dissipated in resistance. Summarizing: A good ("low-loss") conductor is a material with *high* conductivity, such that power dissipated in the resistance of the material is low.

A quantitative criterion for a good conductor can be obtained from the concept of complex permittivity ϵ_c, which has the form:

$$\epsilon_c = \epsilon' - j\epsilon'' \quad (3.137)$$

Recall that ϵ'' is proportional to conductivity (σ) and so ϵ'' is very large for a good conductor. Therefore, we may identify a good conductor using the ratio ϵ''/ϵ', which is sometimes referred to as "loss tangent" (see Section 3.5). Using this quantity we define a good conductor as a material for which:

$$\frac{\epsilon''}{\epsilon'} \gg 1 \quad \text{(good conductor)} \quad (3.138)$$

This condition is met for most materials classified as "metals," and especially for metals exhibiting very high conductivity such as gold, copper, and aluminum.

A good conductor is a material having loss tangent much greater than 1.

The imprecise definition of Equation 3.138 is sufficient to derive some characteristics that are common to materials over a wide range of conductivity. To derive these characteristics, first recall that the propagation constant γ is given in general as follows:

$$\gamma^2 = -\omega^2\mu\epsilon_c \tag{3.139}$$

Therefore:

$$\gamma = \sqrt{-\omega^2\mu\epsilon_c} \tag{3.140}$$

In general, a number has two square roots, so some caution is required here. In this case, we may proceed as follows:

$$\begin{aligned}\gamma &= j\omega\sqrt{\mu}\sqrt{\epsilon' - j\epsilon''} \\ &= j\omega\sqrt{\mu\epsilon'}\sqrt{1 - j\frac{\epsilon''}{\epsilon'}}\end{aligned} \tag{3.141}$$

Since $\epsilon''/\epsilon' \gg 1$ for a good conductor,

$$\begin{aligned}\gamma &\approx j\omega\sqrt{\mu\epsilon'}\sqrt{-j\frac{\epsilon''}{\epsilon'}} \\ &\approx j\omega\sqrt{\mu\epsilon''}\sqrt{-j}\end{aligned} \tag{3.142}$$

To proceed, we must determine the principal value of $\sqrt{-j}$. The answer is that $\sqrt{-j} = (1-j)/\sqrt{2}$.[5] Continuing:

$$\gamma \approx j\omega\sqrt{\frac{\mu\epsilon''}{2}} + \omega\sqrt{\frac{\mu\epsilon''}{2}} \tag{3.143}$$

We are now able to identify expressions for the attenuation and phase propagation constants:

$$\boxed{\alpha \triangleq \text{Re}\{\gamma\} \approx \omega\sqrt{\frac{\mu\epsilon''}{2}} \quad \text{(good conductor)}} \tag{3.144}$$

$$\boxed{\beta \triangleq \text{Im}\{\gamma\} \approx \alpha \quad \text{(good conductor)}} \tag{3.145}$$

Remarkably, we find that $\alpha \approx \beta$ for a good conductor, and neither α nor β depend on ϵ'.

In the special case that ϵ_c is determined entirely by conductivity loss (i.e., $\sigma > 0$) and is not accounting for delayed polarization response (as described in Section 3.4), then

$$\epsilon'' = \frac{\sigma}{\omega} \tag{3.146}$$

Under this condition, Equation 3.144 may be rewritten:

$$\alpha \approx \omega\sqrt{\frac{\mu\sigma}{2\omega}} = \sqrt{\frac{\omega\mu\sigma}{2}} \quad \text{(good conductor)} \tag{3.147}$$

Since $\omega = 2\pi f$, another possible form for this expression is

$$\boxed{\alpha \approx \sqrt{\pi f\mu\sigma} \quad \text{(good conductor)}} \tag{3.148}$$

The conductivity of most materials changes very slowly with frequency, so this expression indicates that α (and β) increases approximately in proportion to the square root of frequency for good conductors. This is commonly observed in electrical engineering applications. For example, the attenuation rate of transmission lines increases approximately as $\sqrt{f}$. This is so because the principal contribution to the attenuation is resistance in the conductors comprising the line.

> The attenuation rate for signals conveyed by transmission lines is approximately proportional to the square root of frequency.

Let us now consider the wave impedance η_c in a good conductor. Recall:

$$\eta_c = \sqrt{\frac{\mu}{\epsilon'}} \cdot \left[1 - j\frac{\epsilon''}{\epsilon'}\right]^{-1/2} \tag{3.149}$$

Applying the same approximation applied to γ earlier in this section, the previous expression may be written

$$\begin{aligned}\eta_c &\approx \sqrt{\frac{\mu}{\epsilon'}} \cdot \left[-j\frac{\epsilon''}{\epsilon'}\right]^{-1/2} \quad \text{(good conductor)} \\ &\approx \sqrt{\frac{\mu}{\epsilon''}} \cdot \frac{1}{\sqrt{-j}}\end{aligned} \tag{3.150}$$

We've already established that $\sqrt{-j} = (1-j)/\sqrt{2}$. Applying that result here:

$$\eta_c \approx \sqrt{\frac{\mu}{\epsilon''}} \cdot \frac{\sqrt{2}}{1-j} \tag{3.151}$$

[5] You can confirm this simply by squaring this result. The easiest way to derive this result is to work in polar form, in which $-j$ is 1 at an angle of $-\pi/2$, and the square root operation consists of taking the square root of the magnitude and dividing the phase by 2.

Now multiplying numerator and denominator by $1 + j$, we obtain

$$\eta_c \approx \sqrt{\frac{\mu}{2\epsilon''}} \cdot (1 + j) \qquad (3.152)$$

In the special case that ϵ_c is determined entirely by conductivity loss and is not accounting for delayed polarization response, then $\epsilon'' = \sigma/\omega$, and we find:

$$\boxed{\eta_c \approx \sqrt{\frac{\mu\omega}{2\sigma}} \cdot (1 + j)} \qquad (3.153)$$

There are at least two other ways in which this expression is commonly written. First, we can use $\omega = 2\pi f$ to obtain:

$$\eta_c \approx \sqrt{\frac{\pi f \mu}{\sigma}} \cdot (1 + j) \qquad (3.154)$$

Second, we can use the fact that $\alpha \approx \sqrt{\pi f \mu \sigma}$ for good conductors to obtain:

$$\eta_c \approx \frac{\alpha}{\sigma} \cdot (1 + j) \qquad (3.155)$$

In any event, we see that the magnitude of the wave impedance bears little resemblance to the wave impedance for a poor conductor. In particular, there is no dependence on the physical permittivity $\epsilon' = \epsilon$, as we saw also for α and β. In this sense, the concept of permittivity does not apply to good conductors, and especially so for perfect conductors.

Note also that ψ_η, the phase of η_c, is always $\approx \pi/4$ for a good conductor, in contrast to ≈ 0 for a poor conductor. This has two implications that are useful to know. First, since η_c is the ratio of the magnitude of the electric field intensity to the magnitude of the magnetic field intensity, the phase of the magnetic field will be shifted by $\approx \pi/4$ relative to the phase of the electric field in a good conductor. Second, recall from Section 3.7 that the power density for a wave is proportional to $\cos \psi_\eta$. Therefore, the extent to which a good conductor is able to "extinguish" a wave propagating through it is determined entirely by α, and specifically is proportional to $e^{-\alpha l}$ where l is distance traveled through the material. In other words, only a perfect conductor ($\sigma \to \infty$) is able to completely suppress wave propagation, whereas waves are always able to penetrate some distance into any conductor which is merely "good." A measure of this distance is the *skin depth* of the material. The concept of skin depth is presented in Section 3.12.

The dependence of β on conductivity leads to a particularly surprising result for the phase velocity of the beleaguered waves that do manage to propagate within a good conductor. Recall that for both lossless and low-loss ("poor conductor") materials, the phase velocity v_p is either exactly or approximately $c/\sqrt{\epsilon_r}$, where $\epsilon_r \triangleq \epsilon'/\epsilon_0$, resulting in typical phase velocities within one order of magnitude of c. For a good conductor, we find instead:

$$v_p = \frac{\omega}{\beta} \approx \frac{\omega}{\sqrt{\pi f \mu \sigma}} \quad \text{(good conductor)} \qquad (3.156)$$

and since $\omega = 2\pi f$:

$$v_p \approx \sqrt{\frac{4\pi f}{\mu \sigma}} \quad \text{(good conductor)} \qquad (3.157)$$

Note that the phase velocity in a good conductor increases with frequency and decreases with conductivity. In contrast to poor conductors and non-conductors, the phase velocity in good conductors is usually a tiny fraction of c. For example, for a non-magnetic ($\mu \approx \mu_0$) good conductor with typical $\sigma \sim 10^6$ S/m, we find $v_p \sim 100$ km/s at 1 GHz – just $\sim 0.03\%$ of the speed of light in free space.

This result also tells us something profound about the nature of signals that are conveyed by transmission lines. Regardless of whether we analyze such signals as voltage and current waves associated with the conductors or in terms of guided waves between the conductors, we find that the phase velocity is within an order of magnitude or so of c. Thus, *the information conveyed by signals propagating along transmission lines travels primarily within the space between the conductors, and not within the conductors*. Information cannot travel primarily in the conductors, as this would then result in apparent phase velocity which is orders of magnitude less than c, as noted previously. Remarkably, classical transmission line theory employing the R', G', C', L' equivalent circuit model[6] gets this right, even though that approach does not explicitly consider the possibility of guided waves traveling between the conductors.

[6] Depending on the version of this book, this topic may appear in another volume.

3.12 Skin Depth

[m0158]

The electric and magnetic fields of a wave are diminished as the wave propagates through lossy media. The magnitude of these fields is proportional to

$$e^{-\alpha l}$$

where $\alpha \triangleq \text{Re}\{\gamma\}$ is the attenuation constant (SI base units of m^{-1}), γ is the propagation constant, and l is the distance traveled. Although the rate at which magnitude is reduced is completely described by α, particular values of α typically do not necessarily provide an intuitive sense of this rate.

An alternative way to characterize attenuation is in terms of *skin depth* δ_s, which is defined as the distance at which the magnitude of the electric and magnetic fields is reduced by a factor of $1/e$. In other words:

$$e^{-\alpha\delta_s} = e^{-1} \cong 0.368 \tag{3.158}$$

Skin depth δ_s is the distance over which the magnitude of the electric or magnetic field is reduced by a factor of $1/e \cong 0.368$.

Since power is proportional to the square of the field magnitude, δ_s may also be interpreted as the distance at which the power in the wave is reduced by a factor of $(1/e)^2 \cong 0.135$. In yet other words: δ_s is the distance at which $\cong 86.5\%$ of the power in the wave is lost.

This definition for skin depth makes δ_s easy to compute: From Equation 3.158, it is simply

$$\boxed{\delta_s = \frac{1}{\alpha}} \tag{3.159}$$

The concept of skin depth is most commonly applied to good conductors. For a good conductor, $\alpha \approx \sqrt{\pi f \mu \sigma}$ (Section 3.11), so

$$\delta_s \approx \frac{1}{\sqrt{\pi f \mu \sigma}} \quad \text{(good conductors)} \tag{3.160}$$

Example 3.3. Skin depth of aluminum.

Aluminum, a good conductor, exhibits $\sigma \approx 3.7 \times 10^7$ S/m and $\mu \approx \mu_0$ over a broad range of radio frequencies. Using Equation 3.160, we find $\delta_s \sim 26~\mu$m at 10 MHz. Aluminum sheet which is 1/16-in ($\cong 1.59$ mm) thick can also be said to have a thickness of $\sim 61\delta_s$ at 10 MHz. The reduction in the power density of an electromagnetic wave after traveling through this sheet will be

$$\sim \left(e^{-\alpha(61\delta_s)}\right)^2 = \left(e^{-\alpha(61/\alpha)}\right)^2 = e^{-122}$$

which is effectively zero from a practical engineering perspective. Therefore, 1/16-in aluminum sheet provides excellent shielding from electromagnetic waves at 10 MHz.

At 1 kHz, the situation is significantly different. At this frequency, $\delta_s \sim 2.6$ mm, so 1/16-in aluminum is only $\sim 0.6\delta_s$ thick. In this case the power density is reduced by only

$$\sim \left(e^{-\alpha(0.6\delta_s)}\right)^2 = \left(e^{-\alpha(0.6/\alpha)}\right)^2 = e^{-1.2} \approx 0.3$$

This is a reduction of only $\sim 70\%$ in power density. Therefore, 1/16-in aluminum sheet provides very little shielding at 1 kHz.

[m0183]

Image Credits

Fig. 3.1: © Sevenchw (C. Wang),
https://commons.wikimedia.org/wiki/File:Poynting%E2%80%99s_theorem_illustration.svg,
CC BY SA 4.0 (https://creativecommons.org/licenses/by-sa/4.0/).

Fig. 3.2: © Sevenchw (C. Wang),
https://commons.wikimedia.org/wiki/File:Uniform_plane_wave_incident_cylindrical_surface.svg,
CC BY SA 4.0 (https://creativecommons.org/licenses/by-sa/4.0/).

Fig. 3.3: © K.A. Mauritz, https://commons.wikimedia.org/wiki/File:Dielectric_responses.svg,
Used with permission (see URL) and modified by author.

Fig. 3.4: © Sevenchw (C. Wang),
https://commons.wikimedia.org/wiki/File:Total_current_in_phasor_domain.svg,
CC BY SA 4.0 (https://creativecommons.org/licenses/by-sa/4.0/).

Fig. 3.5: © Sevenchw (C. Wang), https://commons.wikimedia.org/wiki/File:Loss_tangent_definition.svg,
CC BY SA 4.0 (https://creativecommons.org/licenses/by-sa/4.0/).

Chapter 4

Current Flow in Imperfect Conductors

4.1 AC Current Flow in a Good Conductor

[m0069]

In this section, we consider the distribution of current in a conductor which is imperfect (i.e., a "good conductor") and at frequencies greater than DC.

To establish context, consider the simple DC circuit shown in Figure 4.1. In this circuit, the current source provides a steady current which flows through a cylinder-shaped wire. As long as the conductivity σ (SI base units of S/m) of the wire is uniform throughout the wire, the current density $\mathbf{J}$ (SI base units of A/m^2) is uniform throughout the wire.

Now let us consider the AC case. Whereas the electric field intensity $\mathbf{E}$ is constant in the DC case, $\mathbf{E}$ exists as a wave in the AC case. In a good conductor, the magnitude of $\mathbf{E}$ decreases in proportion to $e^{-\alpha d}$ where α is the attenuation constant and d is distance traversed by the wave. The attenuation constant increases with increasing σ, so the rate of decrease of the magnitude of $\mathbf{E}$ increases with increasing σ.

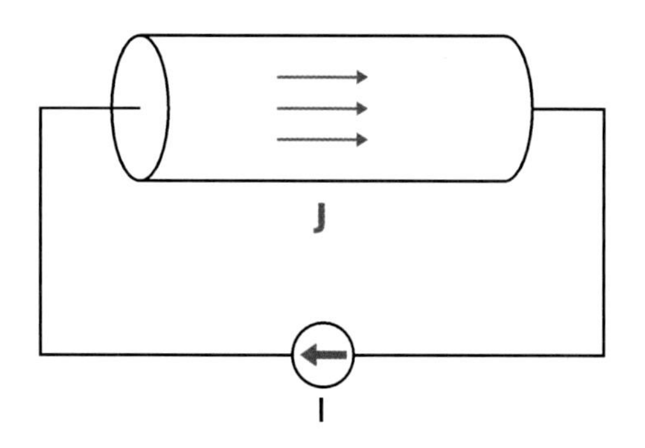

© C. Wang CC BY-SA 4.0

Figure 4.1: Current flow in cylinder at DC.

In the limiting case of a perfect conductor, $\alpha \to \infty$ and so $\mathbf{E} \to 0$ everywhere inside the material. Any current within the wire must be the result of either an impressed source or it must be a response to $\mathbf{E}$. Without either of these, we conclude that in the AC case, $\mathbf{J} \to 0$ everywhere inside a perfect conductor.[1] But if $\mathbf{J} = 0$ in the material, then how does current pass through the wire? We are forced to conclude that the current must exist as a *surface current*; i.e., entirely outside the wire, yet bound to the surface of the wire. Thus:

> In the AC case, the current passed by a perfectly-conducting material lies entirely on the surface of the material.

The perfectly-conducting case is unobtainable in practice, but the result gives us a foothold from which we may determine what happens when σ is not infinite. If σ is merely finite, then α is also finite and subsequently wave magnitude may be non-zero over finite distances.

Let us now consider the direction in which this putative wave propagates. The two principal directions in the present problem are parallel to the

[1] You might be tempted to invoke Ohm's law ($\mathbf{J} = \sigma\mathbf{E}$) to argue against this conclusion. However, Ohm's law provides no useful information about the current in this case, since $\sigma \to \infty$ at the same time $\mathbf{E} \to 0$. What Ohm's law is really saying in this case is that $\mathbf{E} = \mathbf{J}/\sigma \to 0$ because $\mathbf{J}$ must be finite and $\sigma \to \infty$.

axis of the wire and perpendicular to the axis of the wire. Waves propagating in any other direction may be expressed as a linear combination of waves traveling in the principal directions, so we need only consider the principal directions to obtain a complete picture.

Consider waves propagating in the perpendicular direction first. In this case, we presume a boundary condition in the form of non-zero surface current, which we infer from the perfectly-conducting case considered previously. We also note that $\mathbf{E}$ deep inside the wire must be weaker than $\mathbf{E}$ closer to the surface, since a wave deep inside the wire must have traversed a larger quantity of material than a wave measured closer to the surface. Applying Ohm's law ($\mathbf{J} = \sigma\mathbf{E}$), the current deep inside the wire must similarly diminish for a good conductor. We conclude that a wave traveling in the perpendicular direction exists and propagates toward the center of the wire, decreasing in magnitude with increasing distance from the surface.

We are unable to infer the presence of a wave traveling in the other principal direction – i.e., along the axis of the wire – since there is no apparent boundary condition to be satisfied on either end of the wire. Furthermore, the presence of such a wave would mean that different cross-sections of the wire exhibit different radial distributions of current. This is not consistent with physical observations.

We conclude that the only relevant wave is one which travels from the surface of the wire inward. Since the current density is proportional to the electric field magnitude, we conclude:

> In the AC case, the current passed by a wire comprised of a good conductor is distributed with maximum current density on the surface of the wire, and the current density decays exponentially with increasing distance from the surface.

This phenomenon is known as the *skin effect*, referring to the notion of current forming a skin-like layer below the surface of the wire. The effect is illustrated in Figure 4.2.

Since α increases with increasing frequency, we see that the specific distribution of current within the wire depends on frequency. In particular, the current will be concentrated close to the surface at high frequencies, uniformly distributed throughout the wire at DC, and in an intermediate state for intermediate frequencies.

by Biezl (modified) (public domain)

Figure 4.2: Distribution of AC current in a wire of circular cross-section. Shading indicates current density.

Additional Reading:

- "Skin effect" on Wikipedia.

4.2 Impedance of a Wire

[m0159]

The goal of this section is to determine the impedance – the ratio of potential to current – of a wire. The answer to this question is relatively simple in the DC ("steady current") case: The impedance is found to be equal to the resistance of the wire, which is given by

$$R = \frac{l}{\sigma A} \quad \text{(DC)} \tag{4.1}$$

where l is the length of the wire and A is the cross-sectional area of the wire. Also, the impedance of a wire comprised of a perfect conductor at *any* frequency is simply zero, since there is no mechanism in the wire that can dissipate or store energy in this case.

However, all practical wires are comprised of good – not perfect – conductors, and of course many practical signals are time-varying, so the two cases above do not address a broad category of practical interest. The more general case of non-steady currents in imperfect conductors is complicated by the fact that the current in an imperfect conductor is not uniformly distributed in the wire, but rather is concentrated near the surface and decays exponentially with increasing distance from the surface (this is determined in Section 4.1).

We are now ready to consider the AC case for a wire comprised of a good but imperfect conductor. What is the impedance of the wire if the current source is sinusoidally-varying? Equation 4.1 for the DC case was determined by first obtaining expressions for the potential (V) and net current (I) for a length-l section of wire in terms of the electric field intensity $\mathbf{E}$ in the wire. To follow that same approach here, we require an expression for I in terms of $\mathbf{E}$ that accounts for the non-uniform distribution of current. This is quite difficult to determine in the case of a cylindrical wire. However, we may develop an approximate solution by considering a surface which is not cylindrical, but rather planar. Here we go:

Consider the experiment described in Figure 4.3. Here, a semi-infinite region filled with a homogeneous good conductor meets a semi-infinite region of free space along a planar interface at $z = 0$, with increasing z corresponding to increasing depth into the material. A plane wave propagates in the $+\hat{\mathbf{z}}$ direction, beginning from just inside the structure's surface. The justification for presuming the existence of this wave was presented in Section 4.1. The electric field intensity is given by

$$\widetilde{\mathbf{E}} = \hat{\mathbf{x}} E_0 e^{-\alpha z} e^{-j\beta z} \tag{4.2}$$

where E_0 is an arbitrary complex-valued constant. The current density is given by Ohm's law of electromagnetics:[2]

$$\widetilde{\mathbf{J}} = \sigma \widetilde{\mathbf{E}} = \hat{\mathbf{x}} \sigma E_0 e^{-\alpha z} e^{-j\beta z} \tag{4.3}$$

Recall that $\alpha = \delta_s^{-1}$ where δ_s is skin depth (see Section 3.12). Also, for a good conductor, we know that $\beta \approx \alpha$ (Section 3.11). Using these relationships, we may rewrite Equation 4.3 as follows:

$$\begin{aligned} \widetilde{\mathbf{J}} &\approx \hat{\mathbf{x}} \sigma E_0 e^{-z/\delta_s} e^{-jz/\delta_s} \\ &= \hat{\mathbf{x}} \sigma E_0 e^{-(1+j)z/\delta_s} \end{aligned} \tag{4.4}$$

The net current $\widetilde{I}$ is obtained by integrating $\widetilde{\mathbf{J}}$ over any cross-section S through which all the current flows; i.e.,

$$\widetilde{I} = \int_S \widetilde{\mathbf{J}} \cdot d\mathbf{s} \tag{4.5}$$

Here, the simplest solution is obtained by choosing S to be a rectangular surface that is perpendicular to the direction of $\widetilde{\mathbf{J}}$ at $x = 0$. This is shown in Figure 4.4.

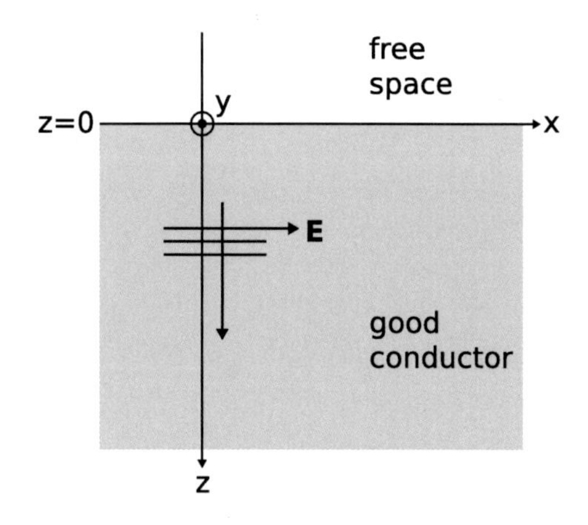

© C. Wang CC BY-SA 4.0

Figure 4.3: Experiment used to determine current density and resistance in the AC case.

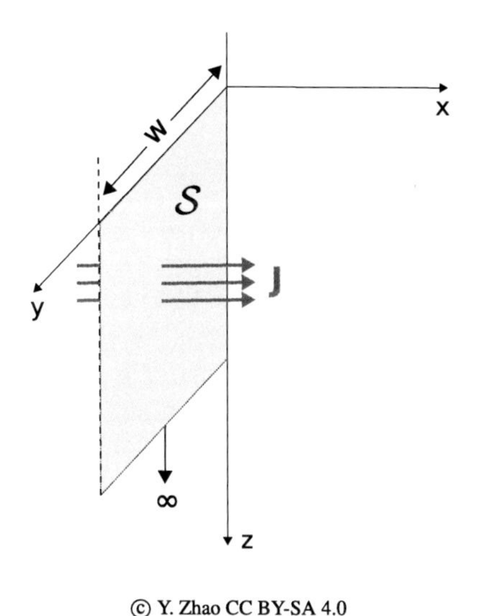

© Y. Zhao CC BY-SA 4.0

Figure 4.4: Choice of $\mathcal{S}$ for calculating net current I.

The dimensions of $\mathcal{S}$ are width W in the y dimension and extending to infinity in the z direction. Then we have

$$\begin{aligned}\widetilde{I} &\approx \int_{y=0}^{W}\int_{z=0}^{\infty}\left(\hat{\mathbf{x}}\sigma E_0 e^{-(1+j)z/\delta_s}\right)\cdot(\hat{\mathbf{x}}\,dy\,dz)\\ &= \sigma E_0 W\int_{z=0}^{\infty} e^{-(1+j)z/\delta_s}dz \end{aligned}\tag{4.6}$$

For convenience, let us define the constant $K \triangleq (1+j)/\delta_s$. Since K is constant with respect to z, the remaining integral is straightforward to evaluate:

$$\begin{aligned}\int_0^{\infty} e^{-Kz}dz &= -\frac{1}{K}e^{-Kz}\Big|_0^{\infty}\\ &= +\frac{1}{K}\end{aligned}\tag{4.7}$$

Incorporating this result into Equation 4.6, we obtain:

$$\widetilde{I} \approx \sigma E_0 W\frac{\delta_s}{1+j}\tag{4.8}$$

We calculate $\widetilde{V}$ for a length l of the wire as follows:

$$\widetilde{V} = -\int_{x=l}^{0}\widetilde{\mathbf{E}}\cdot d\mathbf{l}\tag{4.9}$$

where we have determined that $x=0$ corresponds to the "+" terminal and $x=l$ corresponds to the "−" terminal.[3] The path of integration can be *any* path that begins and ends at the proscribed terminals. The simplest path to use is one along the surface, parallel to the x axis. Along this path, $z=0$ and thus $\widetilde{\mathbf{E}} = \hat{\mathbf{x}}E_0$. For this path:

$$\widetilde{V} = -\int_{x=l}^{0}(\hat{\mathbf{x}}E_0)\cdot(\hat{\mathbf{x}}dx) = E_0 l\tag{4.10}$$

The impedance Z measured across terminals at $x=0$ and $x=l$ is now determined to be:

$$Z \triangleq \frac{\widetilde{V}}{\widetilde{I}} \approx \frac{1+j}{\sigma\delta_s}\cdot\frac{l}{W}\tag{4.11}$$

The resistance is simply the real part, so we obtain

$$R \approx \frac{l}{\sigma(\delta_s W)} \quad \text{(AC case)}\tag{4.12}$$

The quantity R in this case is referred to specifically as the *ohmic resistance*, since it is due entirely to the limited conductivity of the material as quantified by Ohm's law.[4]

Note the resemblance to Equation 4.1 (the solution for the DC case): In the AC case, the product $\delta_s W$, having units of area, plays the role of the physical cross-section S. Thus, we see an interesting new interpretation of the skin depth δ_s: It is the depth to which a uniform (DC) current would need to flow in order to produce a resistance equal to the observed (AC) resistance.

Equations 4.11 and 4.12 were obtained for a good conductor filling an infinite half-space, having a flat surface. How well do these results describe a cylindrical wire? The answer depends on the radius of the wire, a. For $\delta_s \ll a$, Equations 4.11 and 4.12 are excellent approximations, since $\delta_s \ll a$ implies that most of the current lies in a thin shell close to the surface of the wire. In this case, the model used to develop the equations is a good approximation for any given radial slice through the wire, and we are

[2] To be clear, this is the "point form" of Ohm's law, as opposed to the circuit theory form ($V = IR$).

[3] If this is not clear, recall that the electric field vector must point away from positive charge (thus, the + terminal).

[4] This is in contrast to other ways that voltage and current can be related; for example, the non-linear V-I characteristic of a diode, which is not governed by Ohm's law.

justified in replacing W with the circumference $2\pi a$. Thus, we obtain the following expressions:

$$Z \approx \frac{1+j}{\sigma\delta_s} \cdot \frac{l}{2\pi a} \quad (\delta_s \ll a) \tag{4.13}$$

and so

$$R \approx \frac{l}{\sigma(\delta_s 2\pi a)} \quad (\delta_s \ll a) \tag{4.14}$$

The impedance of a wire of length l and radius $a \gg \delta_s$ is given by Equation 4.13. The resistance of such a wire is given by Equation 4.14.

If, on the other hand, $a < \delta_s$ or merely $\sim \delta_s$, then current density is significant throughout the wire, including along the axis of the wire. In this case, we cannot assume that the current density decays smoothly to zero with increasing distance from the surface, and so the model leading to Equation 4.13 is a poor approximation. The frequency required for validity of Equation 4.13 can be determined by noting that $\delta_s \approx 1/\sqrt{\pi f \mu \sigma}$ for a good conductor; therefore, we require

$$\frac{1}{\sqrt{\pi f \mu \sigma}} \ll a \tag{4.15}$$

for the derived expressions to be valid. Solving for f, we find:

$$f \gg \frac{1}{\pi \mu \sigma a^2} \tag{4.16}$$

For commonly-encountered wires comprised of typical good conductors, this condition applies at frequencies in the MHz regime and above.

These results lead us to one additional interesting finding about the AC resistance of wires. Since $\delta_s \approx 1/\sqrt{\pi f \mu \sigma}$ for a good conductor, Equation 4.14 may be rewritten in the following form:

$$R \approx \frac{1}{2}\sqrt{\frac{\mu f}{\pi \sigma}} \cdot \frac{l}{a} \tag{4.17}$$

We have found that R is approximately proportional to $\sqrt{f}$. For example, increasing frequency by a factor of 4 increases resistance by a factor of 2. This frequency dependence is evident in all kinds of practical wires and transmission lines. Summarizing:

The resistance of a wire comprised of a good but imperfect conductor is proportional to the square root of frequency.

At this point, we have determined that resistance is given approximately by Equation 4.17 for $\delta_s \ll a$, corresponding to frequencies in the MHz regime and above, and by Equation 4.1 for $\delta_s \gg a$, typically corresponding to frequencies in the kHz regime and below. We have also found that resistance changes slowly with frequency; i.e., in proportion to $\sqrt{f}$. Thus, it is often possible to roughly estimate resistance at frequencies between these two frequency regimes by comparing the DC resistance from Equation 4.1 to the AC resistance from Equation 4.17. An example follows.

Example 4.1. Resistance of the inner conductor of RG-59.

Elsewhere we have considered RG-59 coaxial cable (see the section "Coaxial Line," which may appear in another volume depending on the version of this book). We noted that it was not possible to determine the AC resistance per unit length R' for RG-59 from purely electrostatic and magnetostatic considerations. We are now able to consider the resistance per unit length of the inner conductor, which is a solid wire of the type considered in this section. Let us refer to this quantity as R'_{ic}. Note that

$$R' = R'_{ic} + R'_{oc} \tag{4.18}$$

where R'_{oc} is the resistance per unit length of the outer conductor. R'_{oc} remains a bit too complicated to address here. However, R'_{ic} is typically much greater than R'_{oc}, so $R' \sim R'_{ic}$. That is, we get a pretty good idea of R' for RG-59 by considering the inner conductor alone.

The relevant parameters of the inner conductor are $\mu \approx \mu_0$, $\sigma \cong 2.28 \times 10^7$ S/m, and

$a \cong 0.292$ mm. Using Equation 4.17, we find:

$$R'_{ic} \triangleq \frac{R_{ic}}{l} = \frac{1}{2}\sqrt{\frac{\mu f}{\pi\sigma}} \cdot \frac{1}{a} \cong \left(227\ \mu\Omega \cdot \text{m}^{-1} \cdot \text{Hz}^{-1/2}\right)\sqrt{f} \quad (4.19)$$

Using Expression 4.16, we find this is valid only for $f \gg 130$ kHz. So, for example, we may be confident that $R'_{ic} \approx 0.82$ Ω/m at 13 MHz.

At the other extreme ($f \ll 130$ kHz), Equation 4.1 (the DC resistance) is a better estimate. In this low frequency case, we estimate that $R'_{ic} \approx 0.16$ Ω/m and is approximately constant with frequency.

We now have a complete picture: As frequency is increased from DC to 13 MHz, we expect that R'_{ic} will increase monotonically from ≈ 0.16 Ω/m to ≈ 0.82 Ω/m, and will continue to increase in proportion to $\sqrt{f}$ from that value.

Returning to Equation 4.11, we see that resistance is not the whole story here. The impedance $Z = R + jX$ also has a reactive component X equal to the resistance R; i.e.,

$$X \approx R \approx \frac{l}{\sigma(\delta_s 2\pi a)} \quad (4.20)$$

This is unique to good conductors at AC; that is, we see no such reactance at DC. Because this reactance is positive, it is often referred to as an inductance. However, this is misleading since inductance refers to the ability of a structure to store energy in a magnetic field, and energy storage is decidedly *not* what is happening here. The similarity to inductance is simply that this reactance is positive, as is the reactance associated with inductance. As long as we keep this in mind, it is reasonable to model the reactance of the wire as an *equivalent* inductance:

$$L_{eq} \approx \frac{1}{2\pi f} \cdot \frac{l}{\sigma(\delta_s 2\pi a)} \quad (4.21)$$

Now substituting an expression for skin depth:

$$L_{eq} \approx \frac{1}{2\pi f} \cdot \sqrt{\frac{\pi f \mu}{\sigma}} \cdot \frac{l}{2\pi a} = \frac{1}{4\pi^{3/2}}\sqrt{\frac{\mu}{\sigma f}} \cdot \frac{l}{a} \quad (4.22)$$

for a wire having a circular cross-section with $\delta_s \ll a$. The utility of this description is that it facilitates the modeling of wire reactance as an inductance in an equivalent circuit. Summarizing:

> A practical wire may be modeled using an equivalent circuit consisting of an ideal resistor (Equation 4.17) in series with an ideal inductor (Equation 4.22). Whereas resistance increases with the square root of frequency, inductance *decreases* with the square root of frequency.

If the positive reactance of a wire is not due to physical inductance, then to what physical mechanism shall we attribute this effect? A wire has reactance because there is a phase shift between potential and current. This is apparent by comparing Equation 4.6 to Equation 4.10. This is the same phase shift that was found to exist between the electric and magnetic fields propagating in a good conductor, as explained in Section 3.11.

Example 4.2. Equivalent inductance of the inner conductor of RG-59.

Elsewhere in the book we worked out that the inductance per unit length L' of RG-59 coaxial cable was about 370 nH/m. We calculated this from magnetostatic considerations, so the reactance associated with skin effect is not included in this estimate. Let's see how L' is affected by skin effect for the inner conductor. Using Equation 4.22 with $\mu = \mu_0$, $\sigma \cong 2.28 \times 10^7$ S/m, and $a \cong 0.292$ mm, we find

$$L_{eq} \approx \left(3.61 \times 10^{-5}\ \text{H}\cdot\text{m}^{-1}\cdot\text{Hz}^{1/2}\right)\frac{l}{\sqrt{f}} \quad (4.23)$$

Per unit length:

$$L'_{eq} \triangleq \frac{L_{eq}}{l} \approx \frac{3.61 \times 10^{-5}\ \text{H}\cdot\text{Hz}^{1/2}}{\sqrt{f}} \quad (4.24)$$

This equals the magnetostatic inductance per unit length (≈ 370 nH/m) at $f \approx 9.52$ kHz, and decreases with increasing frequency.

Summarizing: The equivalent inductance

associated with skin effect is as important as the magnetostatic inductance in the kHz regime, and becomes gradually less important with increasing frequency.

Recall that the phase velocity in a low-loss transmission line is approximately $1/\sqrt{L'C'}$. This means that skin effect causes the phase velocity in such lines to decrease with decreasing frequency. In other words:

Skin effect in the conductors comprising common transmission lines leads to a form of dispersion in which higher frequencies travel faster than lower frequencies.

This phenomenon is known as *chromatic dispersion*, or simply "dispersion," and leads to significant distortion for signals having large bandwidths.

Additional Reading:

- "Skin effect" on Wikipedia.

4.3 Surface Impedance

[m0160]

In Section 4.2, we derived the following expression for the impedance Z of a good conductor having width W, length l, and which is infinitely deep:

$$Z \approx \frac{1+j}{\sigma\delta_s} \cdot \frac{l}{W} \quad \text{(AC case)} \tag{4.25}$$

where σ is conductivity (SI base units of S/m) and δ_s is skin depth. Note that δ_s and σ are constitutive parameters of material, and do not depend on geometry; whereas l and W describe geometry. With this in mind, we define the *surface impedance* Z_S as follows:

$$\boxed{Z_S \triangleq \frac{1+j}{\sigma\delta_s}} \tag{4.26}$$

so that

$$Z \approx Z_S \frac{l}{W} \tag{4.27}$$

Unlike the terminal impedance Z, Z_S is strictly a materials property. In this way, it is like the intrinsic or "wave" impedance η, which is also a materials property. Although the units of Z_S are those of impedance (i.e., ohms), surface impedance is usually indicated as having units of "$\Omega/\Box$" ("ohms per square") to prevent confusion with the terminal impedance. Summarizing:

Surface impedance Z_S (Equation 4.26) is a materials property having units of $\Omega/\Box$, and which characterizes the AC impedance of a material independently of the length and width of the material.

Surface impedance is often used to specify sheet materials used in the manufacture of electronic and semiconductor devices, where the real part of the surface impedance is more commonly known as the *surface resistance* or *sheet resistance*.

Additional Reading:

- "Sheet resistance" on Wikipedia.

[m0184]

Image Credits

Fig. 4.1: © Sevenchw (C. Wang),
https://commons.wikimedia.org/wiki/File:Current_flow_in_cylinder_new.svg,
CC BY SA 4.0 (https://creativecommons.org/licenses/by-sa/4.0/).

Fig. 4.2: Biezl, https://commons.wikimedia.org/wiki/File:Skin_depth.svg, public domain. Modified from original.

Fig. 4.3: © Sevenchw (C. Wang),
https://commons.wikimedia.org/wiki/File:Experiment_for_current_density_and_resistance.svg,
CC BY SA 4.0 (https://creativecommons.org/licenses/by-sa/4.0/).

Fig. 4.4: © YahuiZ (Y. Zhao), https://commons.wikimedia.org/wiki/File:Figure4.4.svg,
CC BY SA 4.0 (https://creativecommons.org/licenses/by-sa/4.0/). Modified by author.

Chapter 5

Wave Reflection and Transmission

5.1 Plane Waves at Normal Incidence on a Planar Boundary

[m0161]

When a plane wave encounters a discontinuity in media, reflection from the discontinuity and transmission into the second medium is possible. In this section, we consider the scenario illustrated in Figure 5.1: a uniform plane wave which is normally incident on the planar boundary between two semi-infinite material regions. By "normally-incident" we mean the direction of propagation $\hat{\mathbf{k}}$ is perpendicular to the boundary. We shall assume that the media are "simple" and lossless (i.e., the imaginary component of permittivity ϵ'' is equal to zero) and therefore the media are completely defined by a real-valued permittivity and a real-valued permeability.

Figure 5.1 shows the wave incident on the boundary, which is located at the $z = 0$ plane. The electric field intensity $\widetilde{\mathbf{E}}^i$ of this wave is given by

$$\widetilde{\mathbf{E}}^i(z) = \hat{\mathbf{x}}E_0^i e^{-j\beta_1 z} \ , \ z \leq 0 \tag{5.1}$$

where $\beta_1 = \omega\sqrt{\mu_1\epsilon_1}$ is the phase propagation constant in Region 1 and E_0^i is a complex-valued constant. $\widetilde{\mathbf{E}}^i$ serves as the "stimulus" in this problem. That is, all other contributions to the total field may be expressed in terms of $\widetilde{\mathbf{E}}^i$. In fact, all other contributions to the total field may be expressed in terms of E_0^i.

From the plane wave relationships, we determine that the associated magnetic field intensity is

$$\widetilde{\mathbf{H}}^i(z) = \hat{\mathbf{y}}\frac{E_0^i}{\eta_1} e^{-j\beta_1 z} \ , \ z \leq 0 \tag{5.2}$$

where $\eta_1 = \sqrt{\mu_1/\epsilon_1}$ is the wave impedance in Region 1.

The possibility of a reflected plane wave propagating in exactly the opposite direction is inferred from two pieces of evidence: The general solution to the wave equation, which includes terms corresponding to waves traveling in both $+\hat{\mathbf{z}}$ or $-\hat{\mathbf{z}}$; and the geometrical symmetry of the problem, which precludes waves traveling in any other directions. The symmetry of the problem also precludes a change of polarization, so the reflected wave should have no $\hat{\mathbf{y}}$ component. Therefore, we may be confident that the reflected electric field has the form

$$\widetilde{\mathbf{E}}^r(z) = \hat{\mathbf{x}}Be^{+j\beta_1 z} \ , \ z \leq 0 \tag{5.3}$$

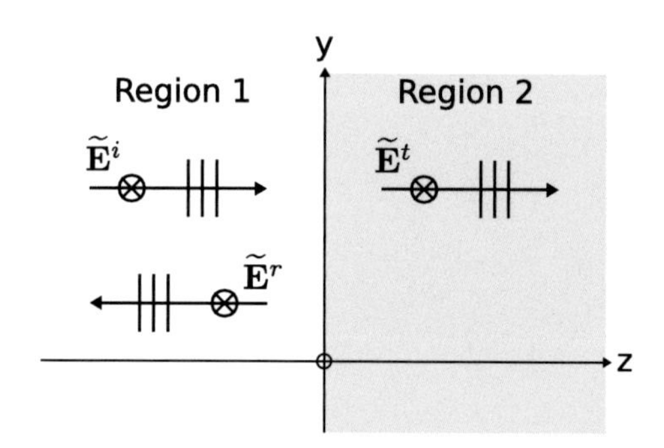

© C. Wang CC BY-SA 4.0

Figure 5.1: A uniform plane wave normally incident on the planar boundary between two semi-infinite material regions.

where B is a complex-valued constant that remains to be determined. Since the direction of propagation for the reflected wave is $-\hat{\mathbf{z}}$, we have from the plane wave relationships that

$$\widetilde{\mathbf{H}}^r(z) = -\hat{\mathbf{y}}\frac{B}{\eta_1}e^{+j\beta_1 z}\ ,\ z \leq 0 \tag{5.4}$$

Similarly, we infer the existence of a "transmitted" plane wave propagating on the $z > 0$ side of the boundary. The symmetry of the problem precludes any direction of propagation other than $+\mathbf{z}$, and with no possibility of a wave traveling in the $-\hat{\mathbf{z}}$ direction for $z > 0$. Therefore, we may be confident that the transmitted electric field has the form:

$$\widetilde{\mathbf{E}}^t(z) = \hat{\mathbf{x}}Ce^{-j\beta_2 z}\ ,\ z \geq 0 \tag{5.5}$$

and an associated magnetic field having the form

$$\widetilde{\mathbf{H}}^t(z) = \hat{\mathbf{y}}\frac{C}{\eta_2}e^{-j\beta_2 z}\ ,\ z \geq 0 \tag{5.6}$$

where $\beta_2 = \omega\sqrt{\mu_2\epsilon_2}$ and $\eta_2 = \sqrt{\mu_2/\epsilon_2}$ are the phase propagation constant and wave impedance, respectively, in Region 2. The constant C, like B, is a complex-valued constant that remains to be determined.

At this point, the only unknowns in this problem are the complex-valued constants B and C. Once these values are known, the problem is completely solved. These values can be determined by the application of boundary conditions at $z = 0$. First, recall that the tangential component of the total electric field intensity must be continuous across a material boundary. To apply this boundary condition, let us define $\widetilde{\mathbf{E}}_1$ and $\widetilde{\mathbf{E}}_2$ to be the total electric field intensities in Regions 1 and 2, respectively. The total field in Region 1 is the sum of incident and reflected fields, so

$$\widetilde{\mathbf{E}}_1(z) = \widetilde{\mathbf{E}}^i(z) + \widetilde{\mathbf{E}}^r(z) \tag{5.7}$$

The field in Region 2 is simply

$$\widetilde{\mathbf{E}}_2(z) = \widetilde{\mathbf{E}}^t(z) \tag{5.8}$$

Also, we note that all field components are already tangent to the boundary. Thus, continuity of the tangential component of the electric field across the boundary requires $\widetilde{\mathbf{E}}_1(0) = \widetilde{\mathbf{E}}_2(0)$, and therefore

$$\widetilde{\mathbf{E}}^i(0) + \widetilde{\mathbf{E}}^r(0) = \widetilde{\mathbf{E}}^t(0) \tag{5.9}$$

Now employing Equations 5.1, 5.3, and 5.5, we obtain:

$$E_0^i + B = C \tag{5.10}$$

Clearly a second equation is required to determine both B and C. This equation can be obtained by enforcing the boundary condition on the magnetic field. Recall that any discontinuity in the tangential component of the total magnetic field intensity must be supported by a current flowing on the surface. There is no impressed current in this problem, and there is no reason to suspect a current will arise in response to the fields present in the problem. Therefore, the tangential components of the magnetic field must be continuous across the boundary. This becomes the same boundary condition that we applied to the total electric field intensity, so the remaining steps are the same. We define $\widetilde{\mathbf{H}}_1$ and $\widetilde{\mathbf{H}}_2$ to be the total magnetic field intensities in Regions 1 and 2, respectively. The total field in Region 1 is

$$\widetilde{\mathbf{H}}_1(z) = \widetilde{\mathbf{H}}^i(z) + \widetilde{\mathbf{H}}^r(z) \tag{5.11}$$

The field in Region 2 is simply

$$\widetilde{\mathbf{H}}_2(z) = \widetilde{\mathbf{H}}^t(z) \tag{5.12}$$

The boundary condition requires $\widetilde{\mathbf{H}}_1(0) = \widetilde{\mathbf{H}}_2(0)$, and therefore

$$\widetilde{\mathbf{H}}^i(0) + \widetilde{\mathbf{H}}^r(0) = \widetilde{\mathbf{H}}^t(0) \tag{5.13}$$

Now employing Equations 5.2, 5.4, and 5.6, we obtain:

$$\frac{E_0^i}{\eta_1} - \frac{B}{\eta_1} = \frac{C}{\eta_2} \tag{5.14}$$

Equations 5.10 and 5.14 constitute a linear system of two simultaneous equations with two unknowns. A straightforward method of solution is to first eliminate C by substituting the left side of Equation 5.10 into Equation 5.14, and then to solve for B. One obtains:

$$B = \Gamma_{12}E_0^i \tag{5.15}$$

where

$$\boxed{\Gamma_{12} \triangleq \frac{\eta_2 - \eta_1}{\eta_2 + \eta_1}} \tag{5.16}$$

Γ_{12} is known as a *reflection coefficient*. The subscript "12" indicates that this coefficient applies for incidence from Region 1 toward Region 2. We may now solve for C by substituting Equation 5.15 into Equation 5.10. We find:

$$C = (1 + \Gamma_{12})\, E_0^i \tag{5.17}$$

Now summarizing the solution:

$$\boxed{\widetilde{\mathbf{E}}^r(z) = \hat{\mathbf{x}}\Gamma_{12}E_0^i e^{+j\beta_1 z} \quad ,\ z \leq 0} \tag{5.18}$$

$$\boxed{\widetilde{\mathbf{E}}^t(z) = \hat{\mathbf{x}}\,(1 + \Gamma_{12})\, E_0^i e^{-j\beta_2 z} \quad ,\ z \geq 0} \tag{5.19}$$

> Equations 5.18 and 5.19 are the reflected and transmitted fields, respectively, in response to the incident field given in Equation 5.1 in the normal incidence scenario shown in Figure 5.1.

Expressions for $\widetilde{\mathbf{H}}^r$ and $\widetilde{\mathbf{H}}^t$ may be obtained by applying the plane wave relationships to the preceding expressions.

It is useful to check this solution by examining some special cases. First: If the material in Region 2 is identical to the material in Region 1, then there should be no reflection and $\widetilde{\mathbf{E}}^t = \widetilde{\mathbf{E}}^i$. In this case, $\eta_2 = \eta_1$, so $\Gamma_{12} = 0$, and we obtain the expected result.

A second case of practical interest is when Region 2 is a perfect conductor. First, note that this may seem at first glance to be a violation of the "lossless" assumption made at the beginning of this section. While it is true that we did not explicitly account for the possibility of a perfect conductor in Region 2, let's see what the present analysis has to say about this case. If the material in Region 2 is a perfect conductor, then there should be no transmission since the electric field is zero in a perfect conductor. In this case, $\eta_2 = 0$ since the ratio of electric field intensity to magnetic field intensity is zero in Region 2, and subsequently $\Gamma_{12} = -1$ and $1 + \Gamma_{12} = 0$. As expected, $\widetilde{\mathbf{E}}^t$ is found to be zero, and the reflected electric field experiences a sign change as required to enforce the boundary condition $\widetilde{\mathbf{E}}^i(0) + \widetilde{\mathbf{E}}^r(0) = 0$. Thus, we obtained the correct answer because we were able to independently determine that $\eta_2 = 0$ in a perfect conductor.

> When Region 2 is a perfect conductor, the reflection coefficient $\Gamma_{12} = -1$ and the solution described in Equations 5.18 and 5.19 applies.

It may be helpful to note the very strong analogy between reflection of the electric field component of a plane wave from a planar boundary and the reflection of a voltage wave in a transmission line from a terminating impedance. In a transmission line, the voltage reflection coefficient Γ is given by

$$\Gamma = \frac{Z_L - Z_0}{Z_L + Z_0} \tag{5.20}$$

where Z_L is the load impedance and Z_0 is the characteristic impedance of the transmission line. Comparing this to Equation 5.16, we see η_1 is analogous to Z_0 and η_2 is analogous to Z_L. Furthermore, we see the special case $\eta_2 = \eta_1$, considered previously, is analogous to a matched load, and the special case $\eta_2 = 0$, also considered previously, is analogous to a short-circuit load.

In the case of transmission lines, we were concerned about what fraction of the power was delivered into a load and what fraction of the power was reflected from a load. A similar question applies in the case of plane wave reflection. In this case, we are concerned about what fraction of the power *density* is transmitted into Region 2 and what fraction of the power *density* is reflected from the boundary. The time-average power density S_{ave}^i associated with the incident wave is:

$$S_{ave}^i = \frac{|E_0^i|^2}{2\eta_1} \tag{5.21}$$

presuming that E_0^i is expressed in peak (as opposed to rms) units. Similarly, the time-average power density S_{ave}^r associated with the reflected wave is:

$$\begin{aligned} S_{ave}^r &= \frac{\left|\Gamma_{12}E_0^i\right|^2}{2\eta_1} \\ &= \left|\Gamma_{12}\right|^2 \frac{\left|E_0^i\right|^2}{2\eta_1} \\ &= \left|\Gamma_{12}\right|^2 S_{ave}^i \end{aligned} \tag{5.22}$$

From the principle of conservation of power, the power density S_{ave}^t transmitted into Region 2 must be equal to the incident power density minus the reflected power density. Thus:

$$\begin{aligned} S^t_{ave} &= S^i_{ave} - S^r_{ave} \\ &= \left(1 - |\Gamma_{12}|^2\right) S^i_{ave} \end{aligned} \quad (5.23)$$

In other words, the ratio of power density transmitted into Region 2 to power density incident from Region 1 is

$$\boxed{\frac{S^t_{ave}}{S^i_{ave}} = 1 - |\Gamma_{12}|^2} \quad (5.24)$$

Again, the analogy to transmission line theory is evident.

> The fractions of power density reflected and transmitted relative to power density incident are given in terms of the reflection coefficient Γ_{12} by Equations 5.22 and 5.24, respectively.

Finally, note that a variety of alternative expressions exist for the reflection coefficient Γ_{12}. Since the wave impedance $\eta = \sqrt{\mu/\epsilon}$ in lossless media, and since most lossless materials are non-magnetic (i.e., exhibit $\mu \approx \mu_0$), it is possible to express Γ_{12} purely in terms of permittivity for these media. Assuming $\mu = \mu_0$, we find:

$$\begin{aligned} \Gamma_{12} &= \frac{\eta_2 - \eta_1}{\eta_2 + \eta_1} \\ &= \frac{\sqrt{\mu_0/\epsilon_2} - \sqrt{\mu_0/\epsilon_1}}{\sqrt{\mu_0/\epsilon_2} + \sqrt{\mu_0/\epsilon_1}} \\ &= \frac{\sqrt{\epsilon_1} - \sqrt{\epsilon_2}}{\sqrt{\epsilon_1} + \sqrt{\epsilon_2}} \end{aligned} \quad (5.25)$$

Moreover, recall that permittivity can be expressed in terms of relative permittivity; that is, $\epsilon = \epsilon_r \epsilon_0$. Making the substitution above and eliminating all extraneous factors of ϵ_0, we find:

$$\Gamma_{12} = \frac{\sqrt{\epsilon_{r1}} - \sqrt{\epsilon_{r2}}}{\sqrt{\epsilon_{r1}} + \sqrt{\epsilon_{r2}}} \quad (5.26)$$

where ϵ_{r1} and ϵ_{r2} are the relative permittivities in Regions 1 and 2, respectively.

Example 5.1. Radio reflection from the surface of the Moon.

At radio frequencies, the Moon can be modeled as a low-loss dielectric with relative permittivity of about 3. Characterize the efficiency of reflection of a radio wave from the Moon.

Solution. At radio frequencies, a wavelength is many orders of magnitude less than the diameter of the Moon, so we are justified in treating the Moon's surface as a planar boundary between free space and a semi-infinite region of lossy dielectric material. The reflection coefficient is given approximately by Equation 5.26 with $\epsilon_{r1} \approx 1$ and $\epsilon_{r2} \sim 3$. Thus, $\Gamma_{12} \sim -0.27$. Subsequently, the fraction of power reflected from the Moon relative to power incident is $|\Gamma_{12}|^2 \sim 0.07$; i.e., about 7%.

In optics, it is common to make the definition $n \triangleq \sqrt{\epsilon_r}$ where n is known as the *index of refraction* or *refractive index*.[1] In terms of the indices of refraction n_1 and n_2 for Regions 1 and 2, respectively:

$$\Gamma_{12} = \frac{n_1 - n_2}{n_1 + n_2} \quad (5.27)$$

Additional Reading:

- "Refractive index" on Wikipedia.

[1] A bit of a misnomer, since the definition applies even when there is no refraction, as in the scenario considered in this section.

5.2 Plane Waves at Normal Incidence on a Material Slab

[m0162]

In Section 5.1, we considered what happens when a uniform plane wave is normally incident on the planar boundary between two semi-infinite media. In this section, we consider the problem shown in Figure 5.2: a uniform plane wave normally incident on a "slab" sandwiched between two semi-infinite media. This scenario arises in many practical engineering problems, including the design and analysis of filters and impedance-matching devices at RF and optical frequencies, the analysis of RF propagation through walls, and the design and analysis of radomes. The findings of Section 5.1 are an important stepping stone to the solution of this problem, so a review of Section 5.1 is recommended before reading this section.

For consistency of terminology, let us refer to the problem considered in Section 5.1 as the "single-boundary" problem and the present (slab) problem as the "double-boundary" problem. Whereas there are only two regions ("Region 1" and "Region 2") in the single-boundary problem, in the double-boundary problem there is a third region that we shall refer to as "Region 3." We assume that the media comprising each slab are "simple" and lossless (i.e., the imaginary component of permittivity ϵ'' is equal to zero) and therefore the media are completely defined by a real-valued permittivity and a real-valued permeability. The boundary between Regions 1 and 2 is at $z = -d$, and the boundary between Regions 2 and 3 is at $z = 0$. Thus, the thickness of the slab is d. In both problems, we presume an incident wave in Region 1 incident on the boundary with Region 2 having electric field intensity

$$\widetilde{\mathbf{E}}^i(z) = \hat{\mathbf{x}} E_0^i e^{-j\beta_1 z} \quad \text{(Region 1)} \tag{5.28}$$

where $\beta_1 = \omega\sqrt{\mu_1\epsilon_1}$ is the phase propagation constant in Region 1. $\widetilde{\mathbf{E}}^i$ serves as the "stimulus" in this problem. That is, all other contributions to the total field may be expressed in terms of $\widetilde{\mathbf{E}}^i$.

From the plane wave relationships, we determine that the associated magnetic field intensity is

$$\widetilde{\mathbf{H}}^i(z) = \hat{\mathbf{y}} \frac{E_0^i}{\eta_1} e^{-j\beta_1 z} \quad \text{(Region 1)} \tag{5.29}$$

where $\eta_1 = \sqrt{\mu_1/\epsilon_1}$ is the wave impedance in Region 1.

The symmetry arguments of the single-boundary problem apply in precisely the same way to the double-boundary problem. Therefore, we presume that the reflected electric field intensity is:

$$\widetilde{\mathbf{E}}^r(z) = \hat{\mathbf{x}} B e^{+j\beta_1 z} \quad \text{(Region 1)} \tag{5.30}$$

where B is a complex-valued constant that remains to be determined; and subsequently the reflected magnetic field intensity is:

$$\widetilde{\mathbf{H}}^r(z) = -\hat{\mathbf{y}} \frac{B}{\eta_1} e^{+j\beta_1 z} \quad \text{(Region 1)} \tag{5.31}$$

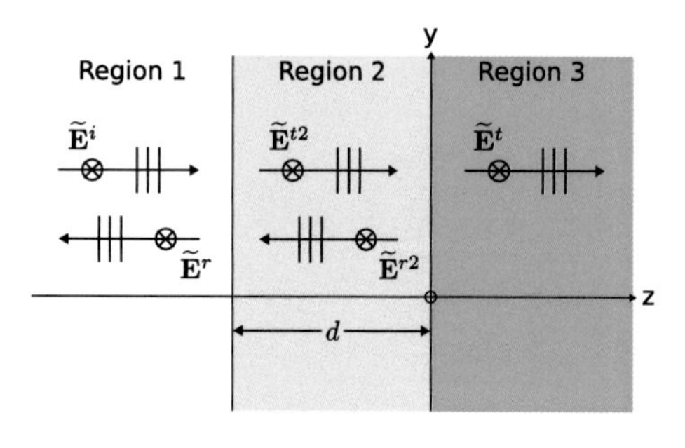

© C. Wang CC BY-SA 4.0

Figure 5.2: A uniform plane wave normally incident on a slab.

Similarly, we infer the existence of a transmitted plane wave propagating in the $+\hat{\mathbf{z}}$ direction in Region 2. The electric and magnetic field intensities of this wave are given by:

$$\widetilde{\mathbf{E}}^{t2}(z) = \hat{\mathbf{x}} C e^{-j\beta_2 z} \quad \text{(Region 2)} \tag{5.32}$$

and an associated magnetic field having the form:

$$\widetilde{\mathbf{H}}^{t2}(z) = \hat{\mathbf{y}} \frac{C}{\eta_2} e^{-j\beta_2 z} \quad \text{(Region 2)} \tag{5.33}$$

where $\beta_2 = \omega\sqrt{\mu_2\epsilon_2}$ and $\eta_2 = \sqrt{\mu_2/\epsilon_2}$ are the phase propagation constant and wave impedance, respectively, in Region 2. The constant C, like B, is a complex-valued constant that remains to be determined.

Now let us consider the boundary between Regions 2 and 3. Note that $\widetilde{\mathbf{E}}^{t2}$ is incident on this boundary in precisely the same manner as $\widetilde{\mathbf{E}}^{i}$ is incident on the boundary between Regions 1 and 2. Therefore, we infer a reflected electric field intensity in Region 2 as follows:

$$\widetilde{\mathbf{E}}^{r2}(z) = \hat{\mathbf{x}} D e^{+j\beta_2 z} \quad \text{(Region 2)} \tag{5.34}$$

where D is a complex-valued constant that remains to be determined; and an associated magnetic field

$$\widetilde{\mathbf{H}}^{r2}(z) = -\hat{\mathbf{y}} \frac{D}{\eta_2} e^{+j\beta_2 z} \quad \text{(Region 2)} \tag{5.35}$$

Subsequently, we infer a transmitted electric field intensity in Region 3 as follows:

$$\widetilde{\mathbf{E}}^{t}(z) = \hat{\mathbf{x}} F e^{-j\beta_3 z} \quad \text{(Region 3)} \tag{5.36}$$

and an associated magnetic field having the form

$$\widetilde{\mathbf{H}}^{t}(z) = \hat{\mathbf{y}} \frac{F}{\eta_3} e^{-j\beta_3 z} \quad \text{(Region 3)} \tag{5.37}$$

where $\beta_3 = \omega\sqrt{\mu_3 \epsilon_3}$ and $\eta_3 = \sqrt{\mu_3/\epsilon_3}$ are the phase propagation constant and wave impedance, respectively, in Region 3. The constant F, like D, is a complex-valued constant that remains to be determined. We infer no wave traveling in the $(-\hat{\mathbf{z}})$ in Region 3, just as we inferred no such wave in Region 2 of the single-boundary problem.

For convenience, Table 5.1 shows a complete summary of the field components we have just identified. Note that the *total* field intensity in each region is the *sum* of the field components in that region. For example, the total electric field intensity in Region 2 is $\widetilde{\mathbf{E}}^{t2} + \widetilde{\mathbf{E}}^{r2}$.

Now observe that there are four unknown constants remaining; namely B, C, D, and F. The double-boundary problem is completely solved once we have expressions for these constants in terms of the "given" quantities in the problem statement. Solutions for the unknown constants can be obtained by enforcing boundary conditions on the electric and magnetic fields at each of the two boundaries. As in the single-boundary case, the relevant boundary condition is that the total field should be continuous across each boundary. Applying this condition to the boundary at $z = 0$, we obtain:

$$\widetilde{\mathbf{E}}^{t2}(0) + \widetilde{\mathbf{E}}^{r2}(0) = \widetilde{\mathbf{E}}^{t}(0) \tag{5.38}$$

$$\widetilde{\mathbf{H}}^{t2}(0) + \widetilde{\mathbf{H}}^{r2}(0) = \widetilde{\mathbf{H}}^{t}(0) \tag{5.39}$$

Applying this condition to the boundary at $z = -d$, we obtain:

$$\widetilde{\mathbf{E}}^{i}(-d) + \widetilde{\mathbf{E}}^{r}(-d) = \widetilde{\mathbf{E}}^{t2}(-d) + \widetilde{\mathbf{E}}^{r2}(-d) \tag{5.40}$$

$$\widetilde{\mathbf{H}}^{i}(-d) + \widetilde{\mathbf{H}}^{r}(-d) = \widetilde{\mathbf{E}}^{t2}(-d) + \widetilde{\mathbf{E}}^{r2}(-d) \tag{5.41}$$

Making substitutions from Table 5.1 and dividing out common factors, Equation 5.38 becomes:

$$C + D = F \tag{5.42}$$

Equation 5.39 becomes:

$$\frac{C}{\eta_2} - \frac{D}{\eta_2} = \frac{F}{\eta_3} \tag{5.43}$$

Equation 5.40 becomes:

$$E_0^i e^{+j\beta_1 d} + B e^{-j\beta_1 d} = C e^{+j\beta_2 d} + D e^{-j\beta_2 d} \tag{5.44}$$

Equation 5.41 becomes:

$$\frac{E_0^i}{\eta_1} e^{+j\beta_1 d} - \frac{B}{\eta_1} e^{-j\beta_1 d} = \frac{C}{\eta_2} e^{+j\beta_2 d} - \frac{D}{\eta_2} e^{-j\beta_2 d} \tag{5.45}$$

Equations 5.42–5.45 are recognizable as a system of 4 simultaneous linear equations with the number of unknowns equal to the number of equations. We could simply leave it at that, however, some very useful insights are gained by solving this system of equations in a particular manner. First, note the resemblance between the situation at the $z = 0$ boundary in this problem and the situation at $z = 0$ boundary in the single-boundary problem. In fact, the two are the *same* problem, with the following transformation of variables (single-boundary $\rightarrow$ double-boundary):

$$E_0^i \rightarrow C \quad \text{i.e., the independent variable} \tag{5.46}$$

$$B \rightarrow D \quad \text{i.e., reflection} \tag{5.47}$$

$$C \rightarrow F \quad \text{i.e., transmission} \tag{5.48}$$

	Electric Field Intensity	Magnetic Field Intensity	Region of Validity
Region 1	$\widetilde{\mathbf{E}}^i(z) = \hat{\mathbf{x}}E_0^i e^{-j\beta_1 z}$	$\widetilde{\mathbf{H}}^i(z) = +\hat{\mathbf{y}}\left(E_0^i/\eta_1\right)e^{-j\beta_1 z}$	$z \leq -d$
	$\widetilde{\mathbf{E}}^r(z) = \hat{\mathbf{x}}Be^{+j\beta_1 z}$	$\widetilde{\mathbf{H}}^r(z) = -\hat{\mathbf{y}}\left(B/\eta_1\right)e^{+j\beta_1 z}$	
Region 2	$\widetilde{\mathbf{E}}^{t2}(z) = \hat{\mathbf{x}}Ce^{-j\beta_2 z}$	$\widetilde{\mathbf{H}}^{t2}(z) = +\hat{\mathbf{y}}\left(C/\eta_2\right)e^{-j\beta_2 z}$	$-d \leq z \leq 0$
	$\widetilde{\mathbf{E}}^{r2}(z) = \hat{\mathbf{x}}De^{+j\beta_2 z}$	$\widetilde{\mathbf{H}}^{r2}(z) = -\hat{\mathbf{y}}\left(D/\eta_2\right)e^{+j\beta_2 z}$	
Region 3	$\widetilde{\mathbf{E}}^t(z) = \hat{\mathbf{x}}Fe^{-j\beta_3 z}$	$\widetilde{\mathbf{H}}^t(z) = +\hat{\mathbf{y}}\left(F/\eta_3\right)e^{-j\beta_3 z}$	$z \geq 0$

Table 5.1: Field components in the double-boundary (slab) problem of Figure 5.2.

It immediately follows that

$$D = \Gamma_{23}C \tag{5.49}$$

and

$$F = (1 + \Gamma_{23})\, C \tag{5.50}$$

where

$$\boxed{\Gamma_{23} \triangleq \frac{\eta_3 - \eta_2}{\eta_3 + \eta_2}} \tag{5.51}$$

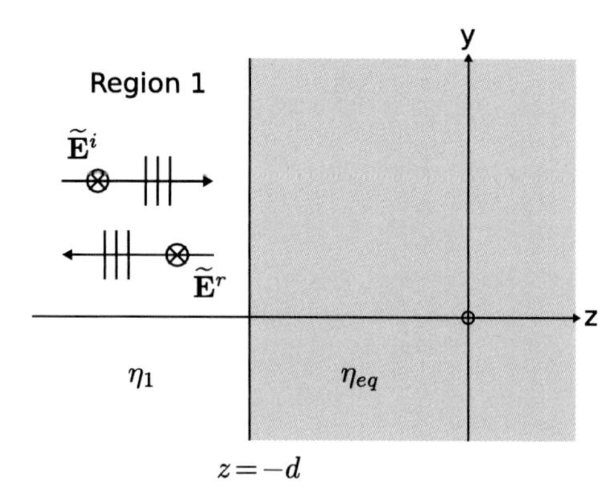

© C. Wang CC BY-SA 4.0

Figure 5.3: Representing the double-boundary problem as an equivalent single-boundary problem.

At this point, we could use the expressions we have just derived to eliminate D and F in the system of four simultaneous equations identified earlier. This would reduce the problem to that of two equations in two unknowns – a dramatic simplification!

However, even this is more work than is necessary, and a little cleverness at this point pays big dividends later. The key idea is that we usually have no interest in the fields internal to the slab; in most problems, we are interested merely in reflection into Region 1 from the $z = -d$ boundary and transmission into Region 3 through the $z = 0$ interface. With this in mind, let us simply replace the two-interface problem in Figure 5.2 with an "equivalent" single-boundary problem shown in Figure 5.3. This problem is "equivalent" in the following sense only: Fields in Region 1 are identical to those in Region 1 of the original problem. The material properties in the region to the right of the $z = -d$ boundary in the equivalent problem seem unlikely to be equal to those in Regions 2 or 3 of the original problem, so we define a new wave impedance η_{eq} to represent this new condition. If we can find an expression for η_{eq}, then we can develop a solution to the original (two-boundary) problem that looks like a solution to the equivalent (simpler, single-boundary) problem.

To obtain an expression for η_{eq}, we invoke the definition of wave impedance: It is simply the ratio of electric field intensity to magnetic field intensity in the medium. Thus:

$$\eta_{eq} \triangleq \frac{\hat{\mathbf{x}} \cdot \widetilde{\mathbf{E}}_2(z_2)}{\hat{\mathbf{y}} \cdot \widetilde{\mathbf{H}}_2(z_2)} = \frac{\hat{\mathbf{x}} \cdot \left[\widetilde{\mathbf{E}}^{t2}(z_2) + \widetilde{\mathbf{E}}^{r2}(z_2)\right]}{\hat{\mathbf{y}} \cdot \left[\widetilde{\mathbf{H}}^{t2}(z_2) + \widetilde{\mathbf{H}}^{r2}(z_2)\right]} \tag{5.52}$$

where z_2 is any point in Region 2. For simplicity, let us choose $z_2 = -d$. Making substitutions, we obtain:

$$\eta_{eq} = \frac{Ce^{+j\beta_2 d} + De^{-j\beta_2 d}}{\left(C/\eta_2\right)e^{+j\beta_2 d} - \left(D/\eta_2\right)e^{-j\beta_2 d}} \tag{5.53}$$

Bringing the factor of η_2 to the front and substituting $D = \Gamma_{23}C$:

$$\eta_{eq} = \eta_2 \frac{Ce^{+j\beta_2 d} + \Gamma_{23}Ce^{-j\beta_2 d}}{Ce^{+j\beta_2 d} - \Gamma_{23}Ce^{-j\beta_2 d}} \tag{5.54}$$

Finally, we divide out the common factor of C and multiply numerator and denominator by $e^{-j\beta_2 d}$, yielding:

$$\eta_{eq} = \eta_2 \frac{1 + \Gamma_{23}e^{-j2\beta_2 d}}{1 - \Gamma_{23}e^{-j2\beta_2 d}} \tag{5.55}$$

Equation 5.55 is the wave impedance in the region to the right of the boundary in the equivalent scenario shown in Figure 5.3. "Equivalent" in this case means that the incident and reflected fields in Region 1 are identical to those in the original (slab) problem.

Two comments on this expression before proceeding. First: Note that if the materials in Regions 2 and 3 are identical, then $\eta_2 = \eta_3$, so $\Gamma_{23} = 0$, and thus $\eta_{eq} = \eta_2$, as expected. Second: Note that η_{eq} is, in general, complex-valued. This may initially seem troubling, since the imaginary component of the wave impedance is normally associated with general (e.g., possibly lossy) material. We specifically precluded this possibility in the problem statement, so clearly the complex value of the wave impedance is not indicating loss. Instead, the non-zero phase of η_{eq} represents the ability of the standing wave inside the slab to impart a phase shift between the electric and magnetic fields. This is *precisely* the same effect that one observes at the input of a transmission line: The input impedance Z_{in} is, in general, complex-valued even if the line is lossless and the characteristic impedance and load impedance are real-valued.[2] In fact, the impedance looking into a transmission line is given by an expression of precisely the same form as Equation 5.55. This striking analogy between plane waves at planar boundaries and voltage and current waves in transmission lines applies broadly.

We can now identify an "equivalent reflection coefficient" $\Gamma_{1,eq}$ for the scenario shown in Figure 5.3:

$$\Gamma_{1,eq} \triangleq \frac{\eta_{eq} - \eta_1}{\eta_{eq} + \eta_1} \tag{5.56}$$

The quantity $\Gamma_{1,eq}$ may now be used precisely in the same way as Γ_{12} was used in the single-boundary problem to find the reflected fields and reflected power density in Region 1.

[2]See the section "Input Impedance of a Terminated Lossless Transmission Line" for a reminder. This section may appear in a different volume depending on the version of this book.

Example 5.2. Reflection of WiFi from a glass pane.

A WiFi (wireless LAN) signal at a center frequency of 2.45 GHz is normally incident on a glass pane which is 1 cm thick and is well-characterized in this application as a lossless dielectric with $\epsilon_r = 4$. The source of the signal is sufficiently distant from the window that the incident signal is well-approximated as a plane wave. Determine the fraction of power reflected from the pane.

Solution. In this case, we identify Regions 1 and 3 as approximately free space, and Region 2 as the pane. Thus

$$\eta_1 = \eta_3 = \eta_0 \cong 376.7\ \Omega \tag{5.57}$$

and

$$\eta_2 = \frac{\eta_0}{\sqrt{\epsilon_r}} \cong 188.4\ \Omega \tag{5.58}$$

The reflection coefficient from Region 2 to Region 3 is

$$\begin{aligned}\Gamma_{23} &= \frac{\eta_3 - \eta_2}{\eta_3 + \eta_2} \\ &= \frac{\eta_0 - \eta_2}{\eta_0 + \eta_2} \\ &\cong 0.3333\end{aligned} \tag{5.59}$$

Given $f = 2.45$ GHz, the phase propagation constant in the glass is

$$\beta_2 = \frac{2\pi}{\lambda} = \frac{2\pi f\sqrt{\epsilon_r}}{c} \cong 102.6\ \text{rad/m} \tag{5.60}$$

Given $d = 1$ cm, the equivalent wave impedance is

$$\begin{aligned}\eta_{eq} &= \eta_2 \frac{1 + \Gamma_{23}e^{-j2\beta_2 d}}{1 - \Gamma_{23}e^{-j2\beta_2 d}} \\ &\cong 117.9 - j78.4\ \Omega\end{aligned} \tag{5.61}$$

Next we calculate

$$\begin{aligned}\Gamma_{1,eq} &= \frac{\eta_{eq} - \eta_1}{\eta_{eq} + \eta_1} \\ &\cong -0.4859 - j0.2354\end{aligned} \tag{5.62}$$

The ratio of reflected power density to incident power density is simply the squared magnitude of this reflection coefficient, i.e.:

$$\frac{S^r_{ave}}{S^i_{ave}} = \left|\Gamma_{1,eq}\right|^2 = 0.292 \cong \boxed{29.2\%} \quad (5.63)$$

where S^r_{ave} and S^i_{ave} are the reflected and incident power densities, respectively.

Since $B = \Gamma_{1,eq}E^i_0$, we have:

$$\widetilde{\mathbf{E}}^r(z) = \hat{\mathbf{x}}\Gamma_{1,eq}E^i_0 e^{+j\beta_1 z} \ , \ z \leq -d \quad (5.64)$$

and $\widetilde{\mathbf{H}}^r(z)$ can be obtained from the plane wave relationships. If desired, it is now quite simple to obtain solutions for the electric and magnetic fields in Regions 2 and 3. However, it is the usually the power density transmitted into Region 3 that is of greatest interest. This power density is easily determined from the principle of conservation of power. If the loss in Region 2 is negligible, then no power can be dissipated there. In this case, all power not reflected from the $z = -d$ interface must be transmitted into Region 3. In other words:

$$\boxed{\frac{S^t_{ave}}{S^i_{ave}} = 1 - \left|\Gamma_{1,eq}\right|^2} \quad (5.65)$$

where S^t_{ave} is the transmitted power density.

Example 5.3. Transmission of WiFi through a glass pane.

Continuing Example 5.2: What fraction of incident power passes completely through the glass pane?

Solution.

$$\frac{S^t_{ave}}{S^i_{ave}} = 1 - \left|\Gamma_{1,eq}\right|^2 \cong \boxed{70.8\%} \quad (5.66)$$

Additional Reading:

- "Radome" on Wikipedia.

5.3 Total Transmission Through a Slab

[m0163]

Section 5.2 details the solution of the "single-slab" problem. This problem is comprised of three material regions: A semi-infinite Region 1, from which a uniform plane wave is normally incident; Region 2, the slab, defined by parallel planar boundaries separated by distance d; and a semi-infinite Region 3, through which the plane wave exits. The solution that was developed assumes simple media with negligible loss, so that the media in each region is characterized entirely by permittivity and permeability.

We now focus on a particular class of applications involving this structure. In this class of applications, we seek total transmission through the slab. By "total transmission" we mean 100% of power incident on the slab is transmitted through the slab into Region 3, and 0% of the power is reflected back into Region 1. There are many applications for such a structure. One application is the *radome*, a protective covering which partially or completely surrounds an antenna, but nominally does not interfere with waves being received by or transmitted from the antenna. Another application is RF and optical wave filtering; that is, passing or rejecting waves falling within a narrow range of frequencies. In this section, we will first describe the conditions for total transmission, and then shall provide some examples of these applications.

We begin with characterization of the media. Region 1 is characterized by its permittivity ϵ_1 and permeability μ_1, such that the wave impedance in Region 1 is $\eta_1 = \sqrt{\mu_1/\epsilon_1}$. Similarly, Region 2 is characterized by its permittivity ϵ_2 and permeability μ_2, such that the wave impedance in Region 2 is $\eta_2 = \sqrt{\mu_2/\epsilon_2}$. Region 3 is characterized by its permittivity ϵ_3 and permeability μ_3, such that the wave impedance in Region 3 is $\eta_3 = \sqrt{\mu_3/\epsilon_3}$. The analysis in this section also depends on β_2, the phase propagation constant in Region 2, which is given by $\omega\sqrt{\mu_2\epsilon_2}$.

Recall that reflection from the slab is quantified by

the reflection coefficient

$$\Gamma_{1,eq} = \frac{\eta_{eq} - \eta_1}{\eta_{eq} + \eta_1} \tag{5.67}$$

where η_{eq} is given by

$$\eta_{eq} = \eta_2 \frac{1 + \Gamma_{23} e^{-j2\beta_2 d}}{1 - \Gamma_{23} e^{-j2\beta_2 d}} \tag{5.68}$$

and where Γ_{23} is given by

$$\Gamma_{23} = \frac{\eta_3 - \eta_2}{\eta_3 + \eta_2} \tag{5.69}$$

Total transmission requires that $\Gamma_{1,eq} = 0$. From Equation 5.67 we see that $\Gamma_{1,eq}$ is zero when $\eta_1 = \eta_{eq}$. Now employing Equation 5.68, we see that total transmission requires:

$$\eta_1 = \eta_2 \frac{1 + \Gamma_{23} e^{-j2\beta_2 d}}{1 - \Gamma_{23} e^{-j2\beta_2 d}} \tag{5.70}$$

For convenience and clarity, let us define the quantity

$$P \triangleq e^{-j2\beta_2 d} \tag{5.71}$$

Using this definition, Equation 5.70 becomes

$$\eta_1 = \eta_2 \frac{1 + \Gamma_{23} P}{1 - \Gamma_{23} P} \tag{5.72}$$

Also, let us substitute Equation 5.69 for Γ_{23}, and multiply numerator and denominator by $\eta_3 + \eta_2$ (the denominator of Equation 5.69). We obtain:

$$\eta_1 = \eta_2 \frac{\eta_3 + \eta_2 + (\eta_3 - \eta_2)P}{\eta_3 + \eta_2 - (\eta_3 - \eta_2)P} \tag{5.73}$$

Rearranging the numerator and denominator, we obtain:

$$\boxed{\eta_1 = \eta_2 \frac{(1+P)\eta_3 + (1-P)\eta_2}{(1-P)\eta_3 + (1+P)\eta_2}} \tag{5.74}$$

> The parameters η_1, η_2, η_3, β_2, and d defining any single-slab structure that exhibits total transmission must satisfy Equation 5.74.

Our challenge now is to identify combinations of parameters that satisfy this condition. There are two general categories of solutions. These categories are known as *half-wave matching* and *quarter-wave matching*.

Half-wave matching applies when we have the same material on either side of the slab; i.e., $\eta_1 = \eta_3$. Let us refer to this common value of η_1 and η_3 as η_{ext}. Then the condition for total transmission becomes:

$$\eta_{ext} = \eta_2 \frac{(1+P)\eta_{ext} + (1-P)\eta_2}{(1-P)\eta_{ext} + (1+P)\eta_2} \tag{5.75}$$

For the above condition to be satisfied, we need the fraction on the right side of the equation to be equal to η_{ext}/η_2. From Equation 5.71, the magnitude of P is always 1, so the first value of P you might think to try is $P = +1$. In fact, this value satisfies Equation 5.75. Therefore, $e^{-j2\beta_2 d} = +1$. This new condition is satisfied when $2\beta_2 d = 2\pi m$, where $m = 1, 2, 3, ...$ (We do not consider $m \leq 0$ to be valid solutions since these would represent zero or negative values of d.) Thus, we find

$$d = \frac{\pi m}{\beta_2} = \frac{\lambda_2}{2} m \text{ , where } m = 1, 2, 3, ... \tag{5.76}$$

where $\lambda_2 = 2\pi/\beta_2$ is the wavelength inside the slab. Summarizing:

> Total transmission through a slab embedded in regions of material having equal wave impedance (i.e., $\eta_1 = \eta_3$) may be achieved by setting the thickness of the slab equal to an integer number of half-wavelengths at the frequency of interest. This is known as *half-wave matching*.

A remarkable feature of half-wave matching is that there is *no* restriction on the permittivity or permeability of the slab, and the only constraint on the media in Regions 1 and 3 is that they have equal wave impedance.

Example 5.4. Radome design by half-wave matching.

The antenna for a 60 GHz radar is to be protected from weather by a radome panel positioned directly in front of the radar. The panel is to be constructed from a low-loss material having $\mu_r \approx 1$ and $\epsilon_r = 4$. To have sufficient mechanical integrity, the panel must be at least 3 mm thick. What thickness should be used?

Solution. This is a good application for half-wave matching because the material on either side of the slab is the same (presumably free space) whereas the material used for the slab is unspecified. The phase velocity in the slab is

$$v_p = \frac{c}{\sqrt{\epsilon_r}} \cong 1.5 \times 10^8 \text{ m/s} \tag{5.77}$$

so the wavelength in the slab is

$$\lambda_2 = \frac{v_p}{f} \cong 2.5 \text{ mm} \tag{5.78}$$

Thus, the minimum thickness of the slab that satisfies the half-wave matching condition is $d = \lambda_2/2 \cong 1.25$ mm. However, this does not meet the 3 mm minimum-thickness requirement. Neither does the next available thickness, $d = \lambda_2 \cong 2.5$ mm. The next-thickest option, $d = 3\lambda_2/2 \cong 3.75$ mm, does meet the requirement. Therefore, we select $\underline{d \cong 3.75 \text{ mm}}$.

It should be emphasized that designs employing half-wave matching will be *narrowband* – that is, total only for the design frequency. As frequency increases or decreases from the design frequency, there will be increasing reflection and decreasing transmission.

Quarter-wave matching requires that the wave impedances in each region are different and related in a particular way. The quarter-wave solution is obtained by requiring $P = -1$, so that

$$\eta_1 = \eta_2 \frac{(1+P)\eta_3 + (1-P)\eta_2}{(1-P)\eta_3 + (1+P)\eta_2} = \eta_2 \frac{\eta_2}{\eta_3} \tag{5.79}$$

Solving this equation for wave impedance of the slab material, we find

$$\eta_2 = \sqrt{\eta_1 \eta_3} \tag{5.80}$$

Note that $P = -1$ is obtained when $2\beta_2 d = \pi + 2\pi m$ where $m = 0, 1, 2, ...$ Thus, we find

$$\begin{aligned} d &= \frac{\pi}{2\beta_2} + \frac{\pi}{\beta_2} m \\ &= \frac{\lambda_2}{4} + \frac{\lambda_2}{2} m \text{ , where } m = 0, 1, 2, ... \end{aligned} \tag{5.81}$$

Summarizing:

Total transmission is achieved through a slab by selecting $\eta_2 = \sqrt{\eta_1 \eta_3}$ and making the slab one-quarter wavelength at the frequency of interest, or some integer number of half-wavelengths thicker if needed. This is known as *quarter-wave matching*.

Example 5.5. Radome design by quarter-wave matching.

The antenna for a 60 GHz radar is to be protected from weather by a radome panel positioned directly in front of the radar. In this case, however, the antenna is embedded in a lossless material having $\mu_r \approx 1$ and $\epsilon_r = 2$, and the radome panel is to be placed between this material and the outside, which we presume is free space. The material in which the antenna is embedded, and against which the radome panel is installed, is quite rigid so there is no minimum thickness requirement. However, the radome panel must be made from a material which is lossless and non-magnetic. Design the radome panel.

Solution. The radome panel must be comprised of a material having

$$\eta_2 = \sqrt{\eta_1 \eta_3} = \sqrt{\frac{\eta_0}{\sqrt{2}} \cdot \eta_0} \cong 317\ \Omega \tag{5.82}$$

Since the radome panel is required to be non-magnetic, the relative permittivity must be given by

$$\eta_2 = \frac{\eta_0}{\sqrt{\epsilon_r}} \quad \Rightarrow \quad \epsilon_r = \left(\frac{\eta_0}{\eta_2}\right)^2 \cong 1.41 \tag{5.83}$$

The phase velocity in the slab will be

$$v_p = \frac{c}{\sqrt{\epsilon_r}} \cong \frac{3 \times 10^8 \text{ m/s}}{\sqrt{1.41}} \cong 2.53 \times 10^8 \text{ m/s} \tag{5.84}$$

so the wavelength in the slab is

$$\lambda_2 = \frac{v_p}{f} \cong \frac{2.53 \times 10^8 \text{ m/s}}{60 \times 10^9 \text{ Hz}} \cong 4.20 \text{ mm} \tag{5.85}$$

Thus, the minimum possible thickness of the radome panel is $d = \lambda_2/4 \cong 1.05$ mm, and the relative permittivity of the radome panel must be $\epsilon_r \cong 1.41$.

Additional Reading:

- "Radome" on Wikipedia.

5.4 Propagation of a Uniform Plane Wave in an Arbitrary Direction

[m0165]

An example of a uniform plane wave propagating in a lossless medium is shown in Figure 5.4. This wave is expressed in the indicated coordinate system as follows:

$$\widetilde{\mathbf{E}} = \hat{\mathbf{x}} E_0 e^{-j\beta z} \quad (5.86)$$

This is a phasor-domain expression for the electric field intensity, so E_0 is a complex-valued number representing the magnitude and reference phase of the sinusoidally-varying wave. The term "reference phase" is defined as the phase of $\widetilde{\mathbf{E}}$ at the origin of the coordinate system. Since the phase propagation constant β is real and positive, this wave is traveling in the $+\hat{\mathbf{z}}$ direction through simple lossless media.

Note that electric field intensity vector is linearly polarized in a direction parallel to $\hat{\mathbf{x}}$. Depending on the position in space (and, for the physical time-domain waveform, time), $\widetilde{\mathbf{E}}$ points either in the $+\hat{\mathbf{x}}$ direction or the $-\hat{\mathbf{x}}$ direction. Let us be a bit more specific about the direction of the vector $\widetilde{\mathbf{E}}$. To do this, let us define the *reference polarization* to be the direction in which $\widetilde{\mathbf{E}}$ points when $\text{Re}\left\{E_0 e^{-j\beta z}\right\} \geq 0$; i.e., when the phase of $\widetilde{\mathbf{E}}$ is between $-\pi/2$ and $+\pi/2$ radians. Thus, the reference polarization of $\widetilde{\mathbf{E}}$ in Equation 5.86 is always $+\hat{\mathbf{x}}$.

Note that Equation 5.86 indicates a specific combination of reference polarization and direction of propagation. However, we may obtain any other combination of reference polarization and direction of

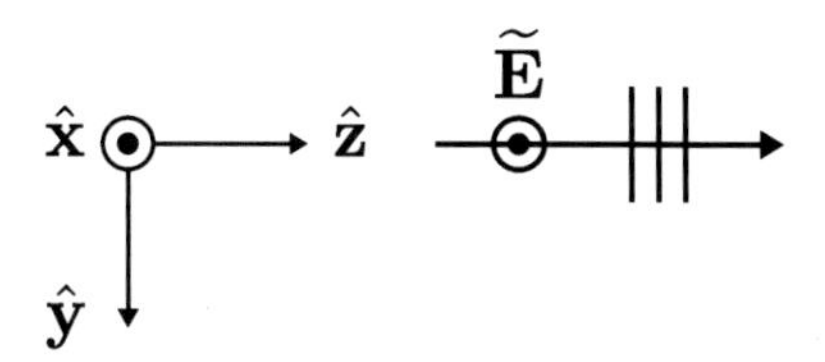

© C. Wang CC BY-SA 4.0

Figure 5.4: The plane wave described by Equation 5.86.

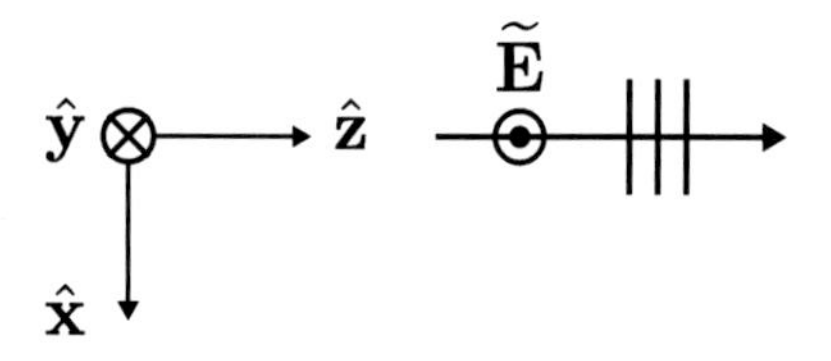

© C. Wang CC BY-SA 4.0

Figure 5.5: The same plane wave described in a rotated coordinate system, yielding Equation 5.87.

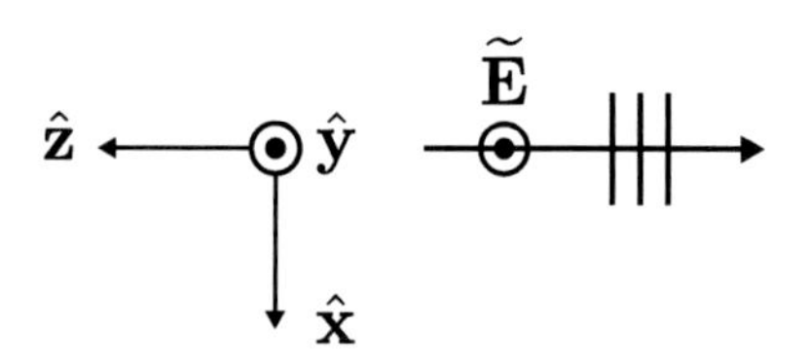

© C. Wang CC BY-SA 4.0

Figure 5.6: The same plane wave described in yet another rotation of the coordinate system, yielding Equation 5.88.

propagation by rotation of the Cartesian coordinate system. For example, if we rotate the $+x$ axis of the coordinate system into the position originally occupied by the $+y$ axis, then the very same wave is expressed as

$$\widetilde{\mathbf{E}} = -\hat{\mathbf{y}} E_0 e^{-j\beta z} \tag{5.87}$$

This is illustrated in Figure 5.5. At first glance, it appears that the reference polarization has changed; however, this is due entirely to our choice of coordinate system. That is, the reference polarization is precisely the same; it is only the coordinate system used to describe the reference polarization that has changed.

Let us now rotate the $+z$ axis of the coordinate system around the x axis into the position originally occupied by the $-z$ axis. Now the very same wave is expressed as

$$\widetilde{\mathbf{E}} = +\hat{\mathbf{y}} E_0 e^{+j\beta z} \tag{5.88}$$

This is illustrated in Figure 5.6. At first glance, it appears that the direction of propagation has reversed; but, again, it is only the coordinate system that has changed, and not the direction of propagation. Summarizing: Equations 5.86, 5.87, and 5.88 all represent the same wave. They only appear to be different due to our choice for the orientation of the coordinate system in each case.

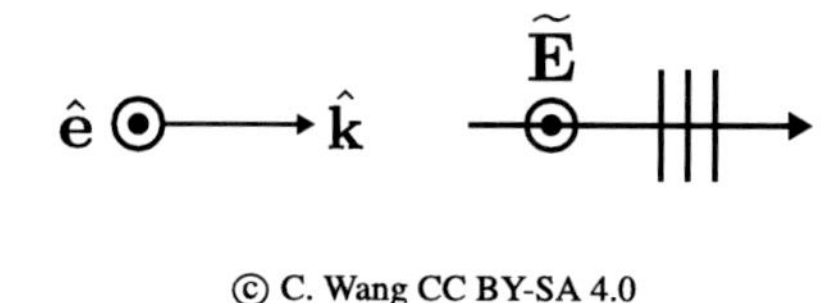

© C. Wang CC BY-SA 4.0

Figure 5.7: A plane wave described in ray-fixed coordinates, yielding Equation 5.89.

Now consider the same thought experiment for the infinite number of cases in which the wave does not propagate in one of the three basis directions of the Cartesian coordinate system. One situation in which we face this complication is when the wave is obliquely incident on a surface. In this case, it is impossible to select a single orientation of the coordinate system in which the directions of propagation, reference polarization, and surface normal can all be described in terms of one basis vector each. To be clear: There is no fundamental limitation imposed by this slipperiness of the coordinate system. However, practical problems such as the oblique-incidence scenario described above are much easier to analyze if we are able to express waves in a system of coordinates which always yields the same expressions.

Fortunately, this is easily accomplished using *ray-fixed coordinates*. Ray-fixed coordinates are a unique set of coordinates that are determined from the characteristics of the wave, as opposed to being determined arbitrarily and separately from the characteristics of the wave. The ray-fixed representation of a uniform plane wave is:

$$\boxed{\widetilde{\mathbf{E}}(\mathbf{r}) = \hat{\mathbf{e}} E_0 e^{-j\mathbf{k}\cdot\mathbf{r}}} \tag{5.89}$$

This is illustrated in Figure 5.7. In this representation, $\mathbf{r}$ is the position at which $\widetilde{\mathbf{E}}$ is evaluated, $\hat{\mathbf{e}}$ is the reference polarization expressed as a unit vector, and $\mathbf{k}$ is the unit vector $\hat{\mathbf{k}}$ in the direction of propagation, times β; i.e.:

$$\mathbf{k} \triangleq \hat{\mathbf{k}}\beta \tag{5.90}$$

Consider Equation 5.86 as an example. In this case, $\hat{\mathbf{e}} = \hat{\mathbf{x}}$, $\mathbf{k} = \hat{\mathbf{z}}\beta$, and (as always)

$$\mathbf{r} = \hat{\mathbf{x}}x + \hat{\mathbf{y}}y + \hat{\mathbf{z}}z \tag{5.91}$$

Thus, $\mathbf{k} \cdot \mathbf{r} = \beta z$, as expected.

In ray-fixed coordinates, a wave can be represented by one – and only one – expression, which is the same expression regardless of the orientation of the "global" coordinate system. Moreover, only two basis directions (namely, $\hat{\mathbf{k}}$ and $\hat{\mathbf{e}}$) must be defined. Should a third coordinate be required, either $\hat{\mathbf{k}} \times \hat{\mathbf{e}}$ or $\hat{\mathbf{e}} \times \hat{\mathbf{k}}$ may be selected as the additional basis direction. Note that the first choice has the possibly-useful feature that is the reference polarization of the magnetic field intensity $\widetilde{\mathbf{H}}$.

A general procedure for recasting the ray-fixed representation into a "coordinate-bound" representation is as follows. First, we represent $\mathbf{k}$ in the new fixed coordinate system; e.g.:

$$\mathbf{k} = k_x\hat{\mathbf{x}} + k_y\hat{\mathbf{y}} + k_z\hat{\mathbf{z}} \tag{5.92}$$

where

$$k_x \triangleq \beta\hat{\mathbf{k}} \cdot \hat{\mathbf{x}} \tag{5.93}$$

$$k_y \triangleq \beta\hat{\mathbf{k}} \cdot \hat{\mathbf{y}} \tag{5.94}$$

$$k_z \triangleq \beta\hat{\mathbf{k}} \cdot \hat{\mathbf{z}} \tag{5.95}$$

Then,

$$\mathbf{k} \cdot \mathbf{r} = k_x x + k_y y + k_z z \tag{5.96}$$

With this expression in hand, Equation 5.89 may be rewritten as:

$$\widetilde{\mathbf{E}} = \hat{\mathbf{e}}E_0 e^{-jk_x x} e^{-jk_y y} e^{-jk_z z} \tag{5.97}$$

If desired, one can similarly decompose $\hat{\mathbf{e}}$ into its Cartesian components as follows:

$$\hat{\mathbf{e}} = (\hat{\mathbf{e}} \cdot \hat{\mathbf{x}})\,\hat{\mathbf{x}} + (\hat{\mathbf{e}} \cdot \hat{\mathbf{y}})\,\hat{\mathbf{y}} + (\hat{\mathbf{e}} \cdot \hat{\mathbf{z}})\,\hat{\mathbf{z}} \tag{5.98}$$

Thus, we see that the ray-fixed representation of Equation 5.89 accommodates all possible combinations of direction of propagation and reference polarization.

Example 5.6. Plane wave propagating away from the z-axis.

A uniform plane wave exhibiting a reference polarization of $\hat{\mathbf{z}}$ propagates away from the z-axis. Develop representations of this wave in ray-fixed and global Cartesian coordinates.

Solution. As always, the ray-fixed representation is given by Equation 5.89. Since the reference polarization is $\hat{\mathbf{z}}$, $\hat{\mathbf{e}} = \hat{\mathbf{z}}$. Propagating away from the z-axis means

$$\hat{\mathbf{k}} = \hat{\mathbf{x}}\cos\phi + \hat{\mathbf{y}}\sin\phi \tag{5.99}$$

where ϕ indicates the specific direction of propagation. For example, $\phi = 0$ yields $\hat{\mathbf{k}} = +\hat{\mathbf{x}}$, $\phi = \pi/2$ yields $\hat{\mathbf{k}} = +\hat{\mathbf{y}}$, and so on. Therefore,

$$\mathbf{k} \triangleq \beta\hat{\mathbf{k}} = \beta\left(\hat{\mathbf{x}}\cos\phi + \hat{\mathbf{y}}\sin\phi\right) \tag{5.100}$$

For completeness, note that the following factor appears in the phase-determining exponent in Equation 5.89:

$$\mathbf{k} \cdot \mathbf{r} = \beta\left(x\cos\phi + y\sin\phi\right) \tag{5.101}$$

In this case, we see $k_x = \beta\cos\phi$, $k_y = \beta\sin\phi$, and $k_z = 0$. Thus, the wave may be expressed in Cartesian coordinates as follows:

$$\widetilde{\mathbf{E}} = \hat{\mathbf{z}}E_0 e^{-j\beta x\cos\phi} e^{-j\beta y\sin\phi} \tag{5.102}$$

5.5 Decomposition of a Wave into TE and TM Components

[m0166]

A broad range of problems in electromagnetics involve scattering of a plane wave by a planar boundary between dissimilar media. Section 5.1 ("Plane Waves at Normal Incidence on a Planar Boundary Between Lossless Media") addressed the special case in which the wave arrives in a direction which is perpendicular to the boundary (i.e., "normal incidence"). Analysis of the normal incidence case is simplified by the fact that the directions of field vectors associated with the reflected and transmitted are the same (except possibly with a sign change) as those of the incident wave. For the more general case in which the incident wave is *obliquely* incident (i.e., not necessarily normally-incident), the directions of the field vectors will generally be different. This added complexity is easily handled if we take the effort to represent the incident wave as the sum of two waves having particular polarizations. These polarizations are referred to as *transverse electric* (TE) and *transverse magnetic* (TM). This section describes these polarizations and the method for decomposition of a plane wave into TE and TM components. We will then be prepared to address the oblique incidence case in a later section.

To begin, we define the ray-fixed coordinate system shown in Figure 5.8. In this figure, $\hat{\mathbf{k}}^i$ is a unit vector indicating the direction in which the incident wave propagates. The unit normal $\hat{\mathbf{n}}$ is perpendicular to the boundary, and points into the region from which the wave is incident. We now make the following definition:

> The plane of incidence is the plane in which *both* the normal to the surface ($\hat{\mathbf{n}}$) and the direction of propagation ($\hat{\mathbf{k}}^i$) lie.

The TE-TM decomposition consists of finding the components of the electric and magnetic fields which are perpendicular ("transverse") to the plane of incidence. Of the two possible directions that are perpendicular to the plane of incidence, we choose $\hat{\mathbf{e}}_\perp$, defined as shown in Figure 5.8. From the figure, we see that:

$$\hat{\mathbf{e}}_\perp \triangleq \frac{\hat{\mathbf{k}}^i \times \hat{\mathbf{n}}}{\left|\hat{\mathbf{k}}^i \times \hat{\mathbf{n}}\right|} \tag{5.103}$$

Defined in this manner, $\hat{\mathbf{e}}_\perp$ is a unit vector which is perpendicular to both $\hat{\mathbf{k}}^i$, and so may serve as a basis vector of a coordinate system which is attached to the incident ray. The remaining basis vector for this ray-fixed coordinate system is chosen as follows:

$$\hat{\mathbf{e}}^i_\parallel \triangleq \hat{\mathbf{e}}_\perp \times \hat{\mathbf{k}}^i \tag{5.104}$$

Defined in this manner, $\hat{\mathbf{e}}^i_\parallel$ is a unit vector which is perpendicular to both $\hat{\mathbf{e}}_\perp$ and $\hat{\mathbf{k}}^i$, and parallel to the plane of incidence.

Let us now examine an incident uniform plane wave in the new, ray-fixed coordinate system. We begin with the following phasor representation of the electric field intensity:

$$\widetilde{\mathbf{E}}^i = \hat{\mathbf{e}}^i E^i_0 e^{-j\mathbf{k}^i\cdot\mathbf{r}} \tag{5.105}$$

where $\hat{\mathbf{e}}^i$ is a unit vector indicating the reference polarization, E^i_0 is a complex-valued scalar, and $\mathbf{r}$ is a vector indicating the position at which $\widetilde{\mathbf{E}}^i$ is evaluated. We may express $\hat{\mathbf{e}}^i$ in the ray-fixed coordinate system of Figure 5.8 as follows:

$$\begin{aligned}\hat{\mathbf{e}}^i = & \left(\hat{\mathbf{e}}^i\cdot\hat{\mathbf{e}}_\perp\right)\hat{\mathbf{e}}_\perp \\ & + \left(\hat{\mathbf{e}}^i\cdot\hat{\mathbf{e}}^i_\parallel\right)\hat{\mathbf{e}}^i_\parallel \\ & + \left(\hat{\mathbf{e}}^i\cdot\hat{\mathbf{k}}^i\right)\hat{\mathbf{k}}^i\end{aligned} \tag{5.106}$$

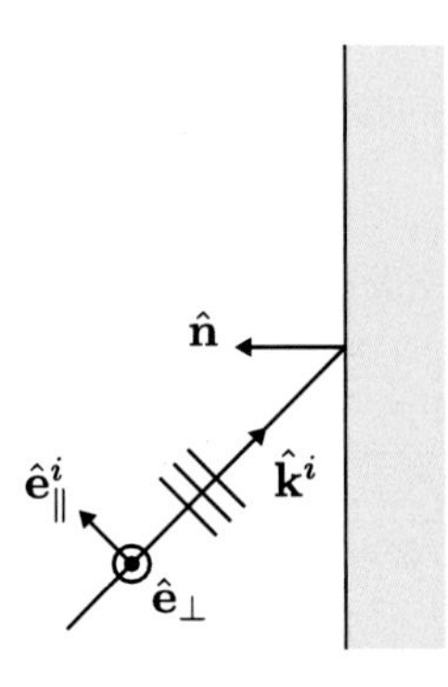

© C. Wang CC BY-SA 4.0

Figure 5.8: Coordinate system for TE-TM decomposition. Since both $\hat{\mathbf{k}}^i$ and $\hat{\mathbf{n}}$ lie in the plane of the page, this is also the plane of incidence.

The electric field vector is always perpendicular to the direction of propagation, so $\hat{\mathbf{e}}^i \cdot \hat{\mathbf{k}}^i = 0$. This leaves:

$$\hat{\mathbf{e}}^i = \left(\hat{\mathbf{e}}^i \cdot \hat{\mathbf{e}}_\perp\right)\hat{\mathbf{e}}_\perp + \left(\hat{\mathbf{e}}^i \cdot \hat{\mathbf{e}}^i_\parallel\right)\hat{\mathbf{e}}^i_\parallel \tag{5.107}$$

Substituting this expression into Equation 5.105, we obtain:

$$\widetilde{\mathbf{E}}^i = \hat{\mathbf{e}}_\perp E^i_{TE} e^{-j\mathbf{k}^i\cdot\mathbf{r}} + \hat{\mathbf{e}}^i_\parallel E^i_{TM} e^{-j\mathbf{k}^i\cdot\mathbf{r}} \tag{5.108}$$

where

$$E^i_{TE} \triangleq E^i_0\, \hat{\mathbf{e}}^i \cdot \hat{\mathbf{e}}_\perp \tag{5.109}$$

$$E^i_{TM} \triangleq E^i_0\, \hat{\mathbf{e}}^i \cdot \hat{\mathbf{e}}^i_\parallel \tag{5.110}$$

The first term in Equation 5.108 is the transverse electric (TE) component of $\widetilde{\mathbf{E}}^i$, so-named because it is the component which is perpendicular to the plane of incidence. The second term in Equation 5.108 is the transverse magnetic (TM) component of $\widetilde{\mathbf{E}}^i$. The term "TM" refers to the fact that the magnetic field associated with this component of the electric field is perpendicular to the plane of incidence. This is apparent since the magnetic field vector is perpendicular to both the direction of propagation and the electric field vector.

Summarizing:

> The TE component is the component for which $\widetilde{\mathbf{E}}^i$ is perpendicular to the plane of incidence.

> The TM component is the component for which $\widetilde{\mathbf{H}}^i$ is perpendicular to the plane of incidence; i.e., the component for which $\widetilde{\mathbf{E}}^i$ is parallel to the plane of incidence.

Finally, observe that the total wave is the sum of its TE and TM components. Therefore, we may analyze the TE and TM components separately, and know that the result for the combined wave is simply the sum of the results for the TE and TM components.

As stated at the beginning of this section, the utility of the TE-TM decomposition is that it simplifies the analysis of wave reflection. This is because the analysis of the TE and TM cases is relatively simple, whereas direct analysis of the scattering of arbitrarily-polarized waves is relatively difficult.

Note that the nomenclature "TE" and "TM" is commonly but not universally used. Sometimes "TE" is referred to as "perpendicular" polarization, indicated using the subscript "$\perp$" or "s" (short for *senkrecht*, German for "perpendicular"). Correspondingly, "TM" is sometimes referred to as "parallel" polarization, indicated using the subscript "$\parallel$" or "p."

Also, note that the TE component and TM component are sometimes referred to as the TE *mode* and TM *mode*, respectively. While the terms "component" and "mode" are synonymous for the single plane wave scenarios considered in this section, the terms are not synonymous in general. For example, the wave inside a waveguide may consist of multiple unique TE modes which collectively comprise the TE component of the field, and similarly the wave inside a waveguide may consist of multiple unique TM modes which collectively comprise the TM component of the field.

Finally, consider what happens when a plane wave is normally-incident upon the boundary; i.e., when $\hat{\mathbf{k}}^i = -\hat{\mathbf{n}}$. In this case, Equation 5.103 indicates that $\hat{\mathbf{e}}_\perp = 0$, so the TE-TM decomposition is undefined. The situation is simply that both $\mathbf{E}^i$ and $\mathbf{H}^i$ are already both perpendicular to the boundary, and there is no single plane that can be uniquely identified as the plane of incidence. We refer to this case as *transverse electromagnetic* (TEM).

> A wave which is normally-incident on a planar surface is said to be transverse electromagnetic (TEM) with respect to that boundary. There is no unique TE-TM decomposition in this case.

The fact that a unique TE-TM decomposition does not exist in the TEM case is of no consequence, because the TEM case is easily handled as a separate condition (see Section 5.1).

5.6 Plane Waves at Oblique Incidence on a Planar Boundary: TE Case

[m0167]

In this section, we consider the problem of reflection and transmission from a planar boundary between semi-infinite media for a transverse electric (TE) uniform plane wave. Before attempting this section, a review of Sections 5.1 ("Plane Waves at Normal Incidence on a Planar Boundary Between Lossless Media") and 5.5 ("Decomposition of a Wave into TE and TM Components") is recommended. Also, note that this section has much in common with Section 5.7 ("Plane Waves at Oblique Incidence on a Planar Boundary: TM Case"), although it is recommended to attempt the TE case first.

The TE case is illustrated in Figure 5.9. The boundary between the two semi-infinite and lossless regions is located at the $z = 0$ plane. The wave is incident from Region 1. The electric field intensity $\widetilde{\mathbf{E}}^i_{TE}$ of this wave is given by

$$\widetilde{\mathbf{E}}^i_{TE}(\mathbf{r}) = \hat{\mathbf{y}} E^i_{TE} e^{-j\mathbf{k}^i \cdot \mathbf{r}} \tag{5.111}$$

In this expression, $\mathbf{r}$ is the position at which $\widetilde{\mathbf{E}}^i_{TE}$ is evaluated, and

$$\mathbf{k}^i = \hat{\mathbf{k}}^i \beta_1 \tag{5.112}$$

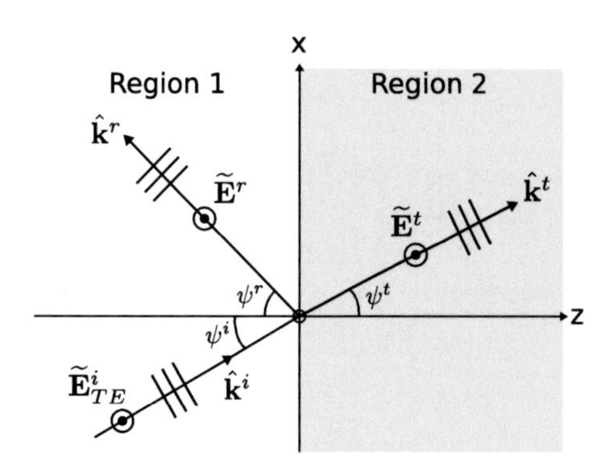

© C. Wang CC BY-SA 4.0

Figure 5.9: A TE uniform plane wave obliquely incident on the planar boundary between two semi-infinite material regions.

where $\hat{\mathbf{k}}^i$ is the unit vector indicating the direction of propagation and $\beta_1 = \omega\sqrt{\mu_1 \epsilon_1}$ is the phase propagation constant in Region 1. $\widetilde{\mathbf{E}}^i_{TE}$ serves as the "stimulus" in this problem, so all other contributions to the total field will be expressed in terms of quantities appearing in Equation 5.111.

The presence of reflected and transmitted uniform plane waves is inferred from our experience with the normal incidence scenario (Section 5.1). There, as here, the symmetry of the problem indicates that the reflected and transmitted components of the electric field will have the same polarization as that of the incident electric field. This is because there is nothing present in the problem that could account for a change in polarization. Thus, the reflected and transmitted fields will also be TE. Therefore, we postulate the following expression for the reflected wave:

$$\widetilde{\mathbf{E}}^r(\mathbf{r}) = \hat{\mathbf{y}} B e^{-j\mathbf{k}^r \cdot \mathbf{r}} \tag{5.113}$$

where B is an unknown, possibly complex-valued constant to be determined and

$$\mathbf{k}^r = \hat{\mathbf{k}}^r \beta_1 \tag{5.114}$$

indicates the direction of propagation, which is also currently unknown.

Similarly, we postulate the following expression for the transmitted wave:

$$\widetilde{\mathbf{E}}^t(\mathbf{r}) = \hat{\mathbf{y}} C e^{-j\mathbf{k}^t \cdot \mathbf{r}} \tag{5.115}$$

where C is an unknown, possibly complex-valued constant to be determined;

$$\mathbf{k}^t = \hat{\mathbf{k}}^t \beta_2 \tag{5.116}$$

where $\hat{\mathbf{k}}^t$ is the unit vector indicating the direction of propagation; and $\beta_2 = \omega\sqrt{\mu_2 \epsilon_2}$ is the phase propagation constant in Region 2.

At this point, the unknowns in this problem are the constants B and C, as well as the directions $\hat{\mathbf{k}}^r$ and $\hat{\mathbf{k}}^t$. We may establish a relationship between E^i_{TE}, B, and C by application of boundary conditions at $z = 0$. First, recall that the tangential component of the total electric field intensity must be continuous across material boundaries. To apply this boundary condition, let us define $\widetilde{\mathbf{E}}_1$ and $\widetilde{\mathbf{E}}_2$ to be the total electric fields in Regions 1 and 2, respectively. The total field in Region 1 is the sum of incident and reflected fields, so

$$\widetilde{\mathbf{E}}_1(\mathbf{r}) = \widetilde{\mathbf{E}}^i_{TE}(\mathbf{r}) + \widetilde{\mathbf{E}}^r(\mathbf{r}) \quad (5.117)$$

The total field in Region 2 is simply

$$\widetilde{\mathbf{E}}_2(\mathbf{r}) = \widetilde{\mathbf{E}}^t(\mathbf{r}) \quad (5.118)$$

Next, note that all electric field components are already tangent to the boundary. Thus, continuity of the tangential component of the electric field across the boundary requires $\widetilde{\mathbf{E}}_1(0) = \widetilde{\mathbf{E}}_2(0)$, and therefore

$$\widetilde{\mathbf{E}}^i_{TE}(\mathbf{r}_0) + \widetilde{\mathbf{E}}^r(\mathbf{r}_0) = \widetilde{\mathbf{E}}^t(\mathbf{r}_0) \quad (5.119)$$

where $\mathbf{r} = \mathbf{r}_0 \triangleq \hat{\mathbf{x}}x + \hat{\mathbf{y}}y$ since $z = 0$ on the boundary. Now employing Equations 5.111, 5.113, and 5.115, we obtain:

$$\hat{\mathbf{y}}E^i_{TE}e^{-j\mathbf{k}^i\cdot\mathbf{r}_0} + \hat{\mathbf{y}}Be^{-j\mathbf{k}^r\cdot\mathbf{r}_0} = \hat{\mathbf{y}}Ce^{-j\mathbf{k}^t\cdot\mathbf{r}_0} \quad (5.120)$$

Dropping the vector ($\hat{\mathbf{y}}$) since it is the same in each term, we obtain:

$$E^i_{TE}e^{-j\mathbf{k}^i\cdot\mathbf{r}_0} + Be^{-j\mathbf{k}^r\cdot\mathbf{r}_0} = Ce^{-j\mathbf{k}^t\cdot\mathbf{r}_0} \quad (5.121)$$

For Equation 5.121 to be true at every point $\mathbf{r}_0$ on the boundary, it must be true that

$$\mathbf{k}^i \cdot \mathbf{r}_0 = \mathbf{k}^r \cdot \mathbf{r}_0 = \mathbf{k}^t \cdot \mathbf{r}_0 \quad (5.122)$$

Essentially, we are requiring the phases of each field in Regions 1 and 2 to be matched at every point along the boundary. Any other choice will result in a violation of boundary conditions at some point along the boundary. This phase matching criterion will determine the directions of propagation of the reflected and transmitted fields, which we shall do later.

First, let us use the phase matching criterion to complete the solution for the coefficients B and C. Enforcing Equation 5.122, we observe that Equation 5.121 reduces to:

$$E^i_{TE} + B = C \quad (5.123)$$

A second equation is needed since we currently have only one equation (Equation 5.123) and two unknowns (B and C). The second equation is

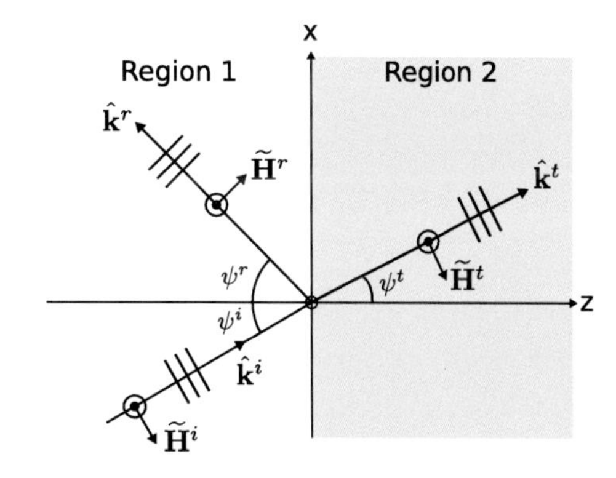

© C. Wang CC BY-SA 4.0

Figure 5.10: Incident, reflected, and transmitted magnetic field components associated with the TE electric field components shown in Figure 5.9.

obtained by applying the appropriate boundary conditions to the magnetic field. The magnetic field associated with each of the electric field components is identified in Figure 5.10. Note the orientations of the magnetic field vectors may be confirmed using the *plane wave relationships*: Specifically, the cross product of the electric and magnetic fields should point in the direction of propagation. Expressions for each of the magnetic field components is determined formally below.

From the plane wave relationships, we determine that the incident magnetic field intensity is

$$\widetilde{\mathbf{H}}^i(\mathbf{r}) = \frac{1}{\eta_1}\hat{\mathbf{k}}^i \times \widetilde{\mathbf{E}}^i_{TE} \quad (5.124)$$

where $\eta_1 = \sqrt{\mu_1/\epsilon_1}$ is the wave impedance in Region 1. To make progress requires that we express $\hat{\mathbf{k}}^i$ in the global fixed coordinate system. Here it is:

$$\hat{\mathbf{k}}^i = \hat{\mathbf{x}}\sin\psi^i + \hat{\mathbf{z}}\cos\psi^i \quad (5.125)$$

Thus:

$$\widetilde{\mathbf{H}}^i(\mathbf{r}) = \left(\hat{\mathbf{z}}\sin\psi^i - \hat{\mathbf{x}}\cos\psi^i\right)\frac{E^i_{TE}}{\eta_1}e^{-j\mathbf{k}^i\cdot\mathbf{r}} \quad (5.126)$$

Similarly, we determine that the reflected magnetic field has the form:

$$\widetilde{\mathbf{H}}^r(\mathbf{r}) = \frac{1}{\eta_1}\hat{\mathbf{k}}^r \times \widetilde{\mathbf{E}}^r \quad (5.127)$$

In the global coordinate system:

$$\hat{\mathbf{k}}^r = \hat{\mathbf{x}}\sin\psi^r - \hat{\mathbf{z}}\cos\psi^r \quad (5.128)$$

Thus:

$$\widetilde{\mathbf{H}}^r(\mathbf{r}) = (\hat{\mathbf{z}}\sin\psi^r + \hat{\mathbf{x}}\cos\psi^r)\frac{B}{\eta_1}e^{-j\mathbf{k}^r\cdot\mathbf{r}} \quad (5.129)$$

The transmitted magnetic field has the form:

$$\widetilde{\mathbf{H}}^t(\mathbf{r}) = \frac{1}{\eta_2}\hat{\mathbf{k}}^t \times \widetilde{\mathbf{E}}^t \quad (5.130)$$

In the global coordinate system:

$$\hat{\mathbf{k}}^t = \hat{\mathbf{x}}\sin\psi^t + \hat{\mathbf{z}}\cos\psi^t \quad (5.131)$$

Thus:

$$\widetilde{\mathbf{H}}^t(\mathbf{r}) = \left(\hat{\mathbf{z}}\sin\psi^t - \hat{\mathbf{x}}\cos\psi^t\right)\frac{C}{\eta_2}e^{-j\mathbf{k}^t\cdot\mathbf{r}} \quad (5.132)$$

The total magnetic field in Region 1 is the sum of incident and reflected fields, so

$$\widetilde{\mathbf{H}}_1(\mathbf{r}) = \widetilde{\mathbf{H}}^i(\mathbf{r}) + \widetilde{\mathbf{H}}^r(\mathbf{r}) \quad (5.133)$$

The magnetic field in Region 2 is simply

$$\widetilde{\mathbf{H}}_2(\mathbf{r}) = \widetilde{\mathbf{H}}^t(\mathbf{r}) \quad (5.134)$$

Since there is no current on the boundary, the tangential component of the total magnetic field intensity must be continuous across the boundary. Expressed in terms of the quantities already established, this boundary condition requires:

$$\hat{\mathbf{x}}\cdot\widetilde{\mathbf{H}}^i(\mathbf{r}_0) + \hat{\mathbf{x}}\cdot\widetilde{\mathbf{H}}^r(\mathbf{r}_0) = \hat{\mathbf{x}}\cdot\widetilde{\mathbf{H}}^t(\mathbf{r}_0) \quad (5.135)$$

where "$\hat{\mathbf{x}}\cdot$" selects the component of the magnetic field that is tangent to the boundary. Evaluating this expression, we obtain:

$$\begin{aligned} &-\left(\cos\psi^i\right)\frac{E^i_{TE}}{\eta_1}e^{-j\mathbf{k}^i\cdot\mathbf{r}_0} \\ &+\left(\cos\psi^r\right)\frac{B}{\eta_1}e^{-j\mathbf{k}^r\cdot\mathbf{r}_0} \\ &= -\left(\cos\psi^t\right)\frac{C}{\eta_2}e^{-j\mathbf{k}^t\cdot\mathbf{r}_0} \end{aligned} \quad (5.136)$$

Now employing the phase matching condition expressed in Equation 5.122, we find:

$$\begin{aligned} &-\left(\cos\psi^i\right)\frac{E^i_{TE}}{\eta_1} \\ &+\left(\cos\psi^r\right)\frac{B}{\eta_1} \\ &= -\left(\cos\psi^t\right)\frac{C}{\eta_2} \end{aligned} \quad (5.137)$$

Equations 5.123 and 5.137 comprise a linear system of equations with unknowns B and C. This system of equations is easily solved for B as follows. First, use Equation 5.123 to eliminate C in Equation 5.137. The result is:

$$\begin{aligned} &-\left(\cos\psi^i\right)\frac{E^i_{TE}}{\eta_1} \\ &+\left(\cos\psi^r\right)\frac{B}{\eta_1} \\ &= -\left(\cos\psi^t\right)\frac{E^i_{TE}+B}{\eta_2} \end{aligned} \quad (5.138)$$

Solving this equation for B, we obtain:

$$B = \frac{\eta_2\cos\psi^i - \eta_1\cos\psi^t}{\eta_2\cos\psi^r + \eta_1\cos\psi^t}E^i_{TE} \quad (5.139)$$

We can express this result as a reflection coefficient as follows:

$$B = \Gamma_{TE}E^i_{TE} \quad (5.140)$$

where

$$\Gamma_{TE} \triangleq \frac{\eta_2\cos\psi^i - \eta_1\cos\psi^t}{\eta_2\cos\psi^r + \eta_1\cos\psi^t} \quad (5.141)$$

It is worth noting that Equation 5.141 becomes the reflection coefficient for normal (TEM) incidence when $\psi^i = \psi^r = \psi^t = 0$, as expected.

Returning to Equation 5.123, we now find

$$C = (1+\Gamma_{TE})\,E^i_{TE} \quad (5.142)$$

Let us now summarize the solution. Given the TE electric field intensity expressed in Equation 5.111, we find:

$$\boxed{\widetilde{\mathbf{E}}^r(\mathbf{r}) = \hat{\mathbf{y}}\Gamma_{TE}E^i_{TE}e^{-j\mathbf{k}^r\cdot\mathbf{r}}} \quad (5.143)$$

$$\boxed{\widetilde{\mathbf{E}}^t(\mathbf{r}) = \hat{\mathbf{y}}\,(1+\Gamma_{TE})\,E^i_{TE}e^{-j\mathbf{k}^t\cdot\mathbf{r}}} \quad (5.144)$$

This solution is complete except that we have not yet determined $\hat{\mathbf{k}}^r$, which is now completely determined by ψ^r via Equation 5.128, and $\hat{\mathbf{k}}^t$, which is now completely determined by ψ^t via Equation 5.131. In other words, we have not yet determined the directions of propagation ψ^r for the reflected wave and ψ^t for the transmitted wave. However, ψ^r and ψ^i can be found using Equation 5.122. Here we shall simply state the result, and in Section 5.8 we shall perform this part of the derivation in detail and with greater attention to the implications. One finds:

$$\psi^r = \psi^i \tag{5.145}$$

and

$$\psi^t = \arcsin\left(\frac{\beta_1}{\beta_2}\sin\psi^i\right) \tag{5.146}$$

Equation 5.145 is the unsurprising result that angle of reflection equals angle of incidence. Equation 5.146 – addressing angle of transmission – is a bit more intriguing. Astute readers may notice that there is something fishy about this equation: It seems possible for the argument of arcsin to be greater than one. This oddity is addressed in Section 5.8.

Finally, note that Equation 5.145 allows us to eliminate ψ^r from Equation 5.141, yielding:

$$\boxed{\Gamma_{TE} = \frac{\eta_2\cos\psi^i - \eta_1\cos\psi^t}{\eta_2\cos\psi^i + \eta_1\cos\psi^t}} \tag{5.147}$$

Thus, we obtain what is perhaps the most important finding of this section:

The electric field reflection coefficient for oblique TE incidence, Γ_{TE}, is given by Equation 5.147.

The following example demonstrates the utility of this result.

Example 5.7. Power transmission at an air-to-glass interface (TE case).

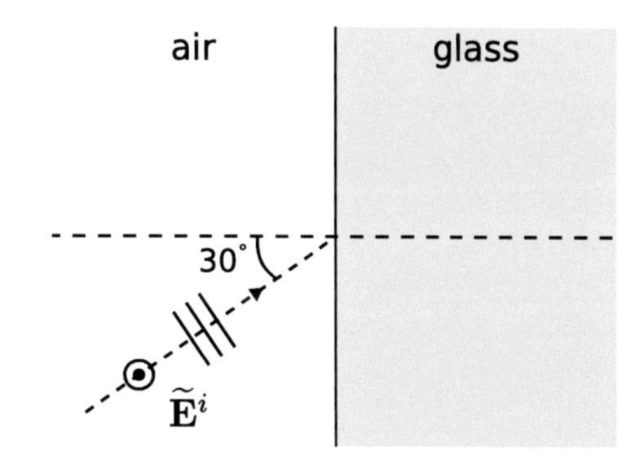

© C. Wang CC BY-SA 4.0

Figure 5.11: A TE uniform plane wave incident from air to glass.

Figure 5.11 illustrates a TE plane wave incident from air onto the planar boundary with glass. The glass exhibits relative permittivity of 2.1. Determine the power reflected and transmitted relative to power incident on the boundary.

Solution. The power reflected relative to power incident is $|\Gamma_{TE}|^2$ whereas the power transmitted relative to power incident is $1 - |\Gamma_{TE}|^2$. Γ_{TE} may be calculated using Equation 5.147. Calculating the quantities that enter into this expression:

$$\eta_1 \approx \eta_0 \cong 376.7~\Omega~~\text{(air)} \tag{5.148}$$

$$\eta_2 \approx \frac{\eta_0}{\sqrt{2.1}} \cong 260.0~\Omega~~\text{(glass)} \tag{5.149}$$

$$\psi^i = 30^\circ \tag{5.150}$$

Note

$$\frac{\beta_1}{\beta_2} \approx \frac{\omega\sqrt{\mu_0\epsilon_0}}{\omega\sqrt{\mu_0\cdot 2.1\epsilon_0}} \cong 0.690 \tag{5.151}$$

so

$$\psi^t = \arcsin\left(\frac{\beta_1}{\beta_2}\sin\psi^i\right) \cong 20.2^\circ \tag{5.152}$$

Now substituting these values into Equation 5.147, we obtain

$$\Gamma_{TE} \cong -0.2220 \tag{5.153}$$

Subsequently, the fraction of power reflected relative to power incident is $|\Gamma_{TE}|^2 \cong 0.049$; i.e., about <u>4.9%</u>. $1 - |\Gamma_{TE}|^2 \cong$ <u>95.1%</u> of the power is transmitted into the glass.

5.7 Plane Waves at Oblique Incidence on a Planar Boundary: TM Case

[m0164]

In this section, we consider the problem of reflection and transmission from a planar boundary between semi-infinite media for a transverse magnetic (TM) uniform plane wave. Before attempting this section, a review of Sections 5.1 ("Plane Waves at Normal Incidence on a Planar Boundary Between Lossless Media") and 5.5 ("Decomposition of a Wave into TE and TM Components") is recommended. Also, note that this section has much in common with Section 5.6 ("Plane Waves at Oblique Incidence on a Planar Boundary: TE Case"), and it is recommended to attempt the TE case first.

In this section, we consider the scenario illustrated in Figure 5.12. The boundary between the two semi-infinite and lossless regions is located at the $z = 0$ plane. The wave is incident from Region 1. The magnetic field intensity $\widetilde{\mathbf{H}}^i_{TM}$ of this wave is given by

$$\widetilde{\mathbf{H}}^i_{TM}(\mathbf{r}) = \hat{\mathbf{y}} H^i_{TM} e^{-j\mathbf{k}^i\cdot\mathbf{r}} \tag{5.154}$$

In this expression, $\mathbf{r}$ is the position at which $\widetilde{\mathbf{H}}^i_{TM}$ is evaluated. Also,

$$\mathbf{k}^i = \hat{\mathbf{k}}^i \beta_1 \tag{5.155}$$

where $\hat{\mathbf{k}}^i$ is the unit vector indicating the direction of propagation and $\beta_1 = \omega\sqrt{\mu_1\epsilon_1}$ is the phase propagation constant in Region 1. $\widetilde{\mathbf{H}}^i_{TM}$ serves as the "stimulus" in this problem, and all other contributions to the total field may be expressed in terms of parameters associated with Equation 5.154.

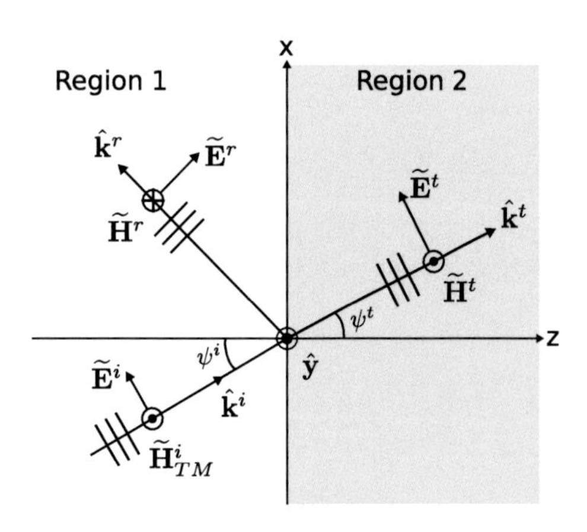

© C. Wang CC BY-SA 4.0

Figure 5.12: A TM uniform plane wave obliquely incident on the planar boundary between two semi-infinite material regions.

The presence of reflected and transmitted uniform plane waves is inferred from our experience with the normal incidence scenario (Section 5.1). There, as here, the symmetry of the problem indicates that the reflected and transmitted components of the magnetic field will have the same polarization as that of the incident electric field. This is because there is nothing present in the problem that could account for a change in polarization. Thus, the reflected and transmitted fields will also be TM. So we postulate the following expression for the reflected wave:

$$\widetilde{\mathbf{H}}^r(\mathbf{r}) = -\hat{\mathbf{y}} B e^{-j\mathbf{k}^r\cdot\mathbf{r}} \tag{5.156}$$

where B is an unknown, possibly complex-valued constant to be determined and

$$\mathbf{k}^r = \hat{\mathbf{k}}^r \beta_1 \tag{5.157}$$

indicates the direction of propagation.

The reader may wonder why we have chosen $-\hat{\mathbf{y}}$, as opposed to $+\hat{\mathbf{y}}$, as the reference polarization for $\widetilde{\mathbf{H}}^r$. In fact, either $+\hat{\mathbf{y}}$ or $-\hat{\mathbf{y}}$ could be used. However, the choice is important because the form of the results we obtain in this section – specifically, the reflection coefficient – will be determined with respect to this specific convention, and will be incorrect with respect to the opposite convention. We choose $-\hat{\mathbf{y}}$ because it has a particular advantage which we shall point out at the end of this section.

Continuing, we postulate the following expression for the transmitted wave:

$$\widetilde{\mathbf{H}}^t(\mathbf{r}) = \hat{\mathbf{y}} C e^{-j\mathbf{k}^t\cdot\mathbf{r}} \tag{5.158}$$

where C is an unknown, possibly complex-valued constant to be determined and

$$\mathbf{k}^t = \hat{\mathbf{k}}^t \beta_2 \tag{5.159}$$

where $\hat{\mathbf{k}}^t$ is the unit vector indicating the direction of propagation and $\beta_2 = \omega\sqrt{\mu_2\epsilon_2}$ is the phase propagation constant in Region 2.

At this point, the unknowns in this problem are the constants B and C, as well as the unknown directions $\hat{\mathbf{k}}^r$ and $\hat{\mathbf{k}}^t$. We may establish a relationship between H^i_{TM}, B, and C by application of boundary conditions at $z = 0$. First, we presume no impressed current at the boundary. Thus, the tangential component of the total magnetic field intensity must be continuous across the boundary. To apply this boundary condition, let us define $\widetilde{\mathbf{H}}_1$ and $\widetilde{\mathbf{H}}_2$ to be the total magnetic fields in Regions 1 and 2, respectively. The total field in Region 1 is the sum of incident and reflected fields, so

$$\widetilde{\mathbf{H}}_1(\mathbf{r}) = \widetilde{\mathbf{H}}^i_{TM}(\mathbf{r}) + \widetilde{\mathbf{H}}^r(\mathbf{r}) \tag{5.160}$$

The field in Region 2 is simply

$$\widetilde{\mathbf{H}}_2(\mathbf{r}) = \widetilde{\mathbf{H}}^t(\mathbf{r}) \tag{5.161}$$

Also, we note that all magnetic field components are already tangent to the boundary. Thus, continuity of the tangential component of the magnetic field across the boundary requires $\widetilde{\mathbf{H}}_1(\mathbf{r}_0) = \widetilde{\mathbf{H}}_2(\mathbf{r}_0)$, where $\mathbf{r}_0 \triangleq \hat{\mathbf{x}}x + \hat{\mathbf{y}}y$ since $z = 0$ on the boundary. Therefore,

$$\widetilde{\mathbf{H}}^i_{TM}(\mathbf{r}_0) + \widetilde{\mathbf{H}}^r(\mathbf{r}_0) = \widetilde{\mathbf{H}}^t(\mathbf{r}_0) \tag{5.162}$$

Now employing Equations 5.154, 5.156, and 5.158, we obtain:

$$\hat{\mathbf{y}}H^i_{TM}e^{-j\mathbf{k}^i\cdot\mathbf{r}_0} - \hat{\mathbf{y}}Be^{-j\mathbf{k}^r\cdot\mathbf{r}_0} = \hat{\mathbf{y}}Ce^{-j\mathbf{k}^t\cdot\mathbf{r}_0} \tag{5.163}$$

Dropping the vector ($\hat{\mathbf{y}}$) since it is the same in each term, we obtain:

$$H^i_{TM}e^{-j\mathbf{k}^i\cdot\mathbf{r}_0} - Be^{-j\mathbf{k}^r\cdot\mathbf{r}_0} = Ce^{-j\mathbf{k}^t\cdot\mathbf{r}_0} \tag{5.164}$$

For this to be true at every point $\mathbf{r}_0$ on the boundary, it must be true that

$$\mathbf{k}^i\cdot\mathbf{r}_0 = \mathbf{k}^r\cdot\mathbf{r}_0 = \mathbf{k}^t\cdot\mathbf{r}_0 \tag{5.165}$$

Essentially, we are requiring the phases of each field in Regions 1 and 2 to be matched at every point along the boundary. Any other choice will result in a violation of boundary conditions at some point along the boundary. This expression allows us to solve for the directions of propagation of the reflected and transmitted fields, which we shall do later. Our priority for now shall be to solve for the coefficients B and C.

Enforcing Equation 5.165, we observe that Equation 5.164 reduces to:

$$H^i_{TM} - B = C \tag{5.166}$$

A second equation is needed since we currently have only one equation (Equation 5.166) and two unknowns (B and C). The second equation is obtained by applying the appropriate boundary conditions to the electric field. The electric field associated with each of the magnetic field components is identified in Figure 5.12. Note the orientations of the electric field vectors may be confirmed using the *plane wave relationships*: Specifically, the cross product of the electric and magnetic fields should point in the direction of propagation. Expressions for each of the electric field components is determined formally below.

From the plane wave relationships, we determine that the incident electric field intensity is

$$\widetilde{\mathbf{E}}^i(\mathbf{r}) = -\eta_1\hat{\mathbf{k}}^i \times \widetilde{\mathbf{H}}^i_{TM} \tag{5.167}$$

where $\eta_1 = \sqrt{\mu_1/\epsilon_1}$ is the wave impedance in Region 1. To make progress requires that we express $\hat{\mathbf{k}}^i$ in the global fixed coordinate system. Here it is:

$$\hat{\mathbf{k}}^i = \hat{\mathbf{x}}\sin\psi^i + \hat{\mathbf{z}}\cos\psi^i \tag{5.168}$$

Thus:

$$\widetilde{\mathbf{E}}^i(\mathbf{r}) = \left(\hat{\mathbf{x}}\cos\psi^i - \hat{\mathbf{z}}\sin\psi^i\right)\eta_1 H^i_{TM}e^{-j\mathbf{k}^i\cdot\mathbf{r}} \tag{5.169}$$

Similarly we determine that the reflected electric field has the form:

$$\widetilde{\mathbf{E}}^r(\mathbf{r}) = -\eta_1\hat{\mathbf{k}}^r \times \widetilde{\mathbf{H}}^r \tag{5.170}$$

In the global coordinate system:

$$\hat{\mathbf{k}}^r = \hat{\mathbf{x}}\sin\psi^r - \hat{\mathbf{z}}\cos\psi^r \tag{5.171}$$

Thus:

$$\widetilde{\mathbf{E}}^r(\mathbf{r}) = \left(\hat{\mathbf{x}}\cos\psi^r + \hat{\mathbf{z}}\sin\psi^r\right)\eta_1 Be^{-j\mathbf{k}^r\cdot\mathbf{r}} \tag{5.172}$$

The transmitted magnetic field has the form:

$$\widetilde{\mathbf{E}}^t(\mathbf{r}) = -\eta_2 \hat{\mathbf{k}}^t \times \widetilde{\mathbf{H}}^t \tag{5.173}$$

In the global coordinate system:

$$\hat{\mathbf{k}}^t = \hat{\mathbf{x}} \sin\psi^t + \hat{\mathbf{z}} \cos\psi^t \tag{5.174}$$

Thus:

$$\widetilde{\mathbf{E}}^t(\mathbf{r}) = \left(\hat{\mathbf{x}} \cos\psi^t - \hat{\mathbf{z}} \sin\psi^t\right) \eta_2 C e^{-j\mathbf{k}^t \cdot \mathbf{r}} \tag{5.175}$$

The total electric field in Region 1 is the sum of incident and reflected fields, so

$$\widetilde{\mathbf{E}}_1(\mathbf{r}) = \widetilde{\mathbf{E}}^i(\mathbf{r}) + \widetilde{\mathbf{E}}^r(\mathbf{r}) \tag{5.176}$$

The electric field in Region 2 is simply

$$\widetilde{\mathbf{E}}_2(\mathbf{r}) = \widetilde{\mathbf{E}}^t(\mathbf{r}) \tag{5.177}$$

The tangential component of the total electric field intensity must be continuous across the boundary. Expressed in terms of the quantities already established, this boundary condition requires:

$$\hat{\mathbf{x}} \cdot \widetilde{\mathbf{E}}^i(\mathbf{r}_0) + \hat{\mathbf{x}} \cdot \widetilde{\mathbf{E}}^r(\mathbf{r}_0) = \hat{\mathbf{x}} \cdot \widetilde{\mathbf{E}}^t(\mathbf{r}_0) \tag{5.178}$$

where "$\hat{\mathbf{x}}\cdot$" selects the component of the electric field that is tangent to the boundary. Evaluating this expression, we obtain:

$$\begin{aligned} &+ \left(\cos\psi^i\right) \eta_1 H_{TM}^i e^{-j\mathbf{k}^i \cdot \mathbf{r}_0} \\ &+ \left(\cos\psi^r\right) \eta_1 B e^{-j\mathbf{k}^r \cdot \mathbf{r}_0} \\ &= + \left(\cos\psi^t\right) \eta_2 C e^{-j\mathbf{k}^t \cdot \mathbf{r}_0} \end{aligned} \tag{5.179}$$

Now employing the "phase matching" condition expressed in Equation 5.165, we find:

$$\begin{aligned} &+ \left(\cos\psi^i\right) \eta_1 H_{TM}^i \\ &+ \left(\cos\psi^r\right) \eta_1 B \\ &= + \left(\cos\psi^t\right) \eta_2 C \end{aligned} \tag{5.180}$$

Equations 5.166 and 5.180 comprise a linear system of equations with unknowns B and C. This system of equations is easily solved for B as follows. First, use Equation 5.166 to eliminate C in Equation 5.180. The result is:

$$\begin{aligned} &+ \left(\cos\psi^i\right) \eta_1 H_{TM}^i \\ &+ \left(\cos\psi^r\right) \eta_1 B \\ &= + \left(\cos\psi^t\right) \eta_2 \left(H_{TM}^i - B\right) \end{aligned} \tag{5.181}$$

Solving this equation for B, we obtain:

$$B = \frac{-\eta_1 \cos\psi^i + \eta_2 \cos\psi^t}{+\eta_1 \cos\psi^r + \eta_2 \cos\psi^t} H_{TM}^i \tag{5.182}$$

We can express this result as follows:

$$B = \Gamma_{TM} H_{TM}^i \tag{5.183}$$

where we have made the definition

$$\Gamma_{TM} \triangleq \frac{-\eta_1 \cos\psi^i + \eta_2 \cos\psi^t}{+\eta_1 \cos\psi^r + \eta_2 \cos\psi^t} \tag{5.184}$$

We are now able to express the complete solution in terms of the electric field intensity. First we make the substitution $E_{TM}^i \triangleq \eta_1 H_{TM}^i$ in Equation 5.169, yielding:

$$\widetilde{\mathbf{E}}^i(\mathbf{r}) = \left(\hat{\mathbf{x}} \cos\psi^i - \hat{\mathbf{z}} \sin\psi^i\right) E_{TM}^i e^{-j\mathbf{k}^i \cdot \mathbf{r}} \tag{5.185}$$

The factor $\eta_1 B$ in Equation 5.172 becomes $\Gamma_{TM} E_{TM}^i$, so we obtain:

$$\begin{aligned} \widetilde{\mathbf{E}}^r(\mathbf{r}) = &\left(\hat{\mathbf{x}} \cos\psi^r + \hat{\mathbf{z}} \sin\psi^r\right) \\ &\cdot \Gamma_{TM} E_{TM}^i e^{-j\mathbf{k}^r \cdot \mathbf{r}} \end{aligned} \tag{5.186}$$

Thus, we see Γ_{TM} is the reflection coefficient for the electric field intensity.

Returning to Equation 5.166, we now find

$$\begin{aligned} C &= H_{TM}^i - B \\ &= H_{TM}^i - \Gamma_{TM} H_{TM}^i \\ &= \left(1 - \Gamma_{TM}\right) H_{TM}^i \\ &= \left(1 - \Gamma_{TM}\right) E_{TM}^i / \eta_1 \end{aligned} \tag{5.187}$$

Subsequently, Equation 5.175 becomes

$$\begin{aligned} \widetilde{\mathbf{E}}^t(\mathbf{r}) = &\left(\hat{\mathbf{x}} \cos\psi^t - \hat{\mathbf{z}} \sin\psi^t\right) \\ &\cdot \left(1 - \Gamma_{TM}\right) \frac{\eta_2}{\eta_1} E_{TM}^i e^{-j\mathbf{k}^t \cdot \mathbf{r}} \end{aligned} \tag{5.188}$$

This solution is complete except that we have not yet determined $\hat{\mathbf{k}}^r$, which is now completely determined by ψ^r via Equation 5.171, and $\hat{\mathbf{k}}^t$, which is now completely determined by ψ^t via Equation 5.174. In other words, we have not yet determined the directions of propagation ψ^r for the reflected wave and ψ^t for the transmitted wave. However, ψ^r and ψ^i

can be found using Equation 5.165. Here we shall simply state the result, and in Section 5.8 we shall perform this part of the derivation in detail and with greater attention to the implications. One finds:

$$\psi^r = \psi^i \tag{5.189}$$

i.e., angle of reflection equals angle of incidence. Also,

$$\psi^t = \arcsin\left(\frac{\beta_1}{\beta_2}\sin\psi^i\right) \tag{5.190}$$

Astute readers may notice that there is something fishy about Equation 5.190. Namely, it seems possible for the argument of arcsin to be greater than one. This oddity is addressed in Section 5.8.

Now let us return to the following question, raised near the beginning of this section: Why choose $-\hat{\mathbf{y}}$, as opposed to $+\hat{\mathbf{y}}$, as the reference polarization for $\mathbf{H}^r$, as shown in Figure 5.12? To answer this question, first note that Γ_{TM} (Equation 5.184) becomes the reflection coefficient for normal (TEM) incidence when $\psi^i = \psi^t = 0$. If we had chosen $+\hat{\mathbf{y}}$ as the reference polarization for $\mathbf{H}^r$, we would have instead obtained an expression for Γ_{TM} that has the opposite sign for TEM incidence.[3] There is nothing wrong with this answer, but it is awkward to have different values of the reflection coefficient for the same physical scenario. By choosing $-\hat{\mathbf{y}}$, the reflection coefficient for the oblique incidence case computed for $\psi^i = 0$ converges to the reflection coefficient previously computed for the normal-incidence case. It is important to be aware of this issue, as one occasionally encounters work in which the opposite ("$+\hat{\mathbf{y}}$") reference polarization has been employed.

Finally, note that Equation 5.189 allows us to eliminate ψ^r from Equation 5.184, yielding:

$$\boxed{\Gamma_{TM} = \frac{-\eta_1\cos\psi^i + \eta_2\cos\psi^t}{+\eta_1\cos\psi^i + \eta_2\cos\psi^t}} \tag{5.191}$$

Thus, we obtain what is perhaps the most important finding of this section:

> The electric field reflection coefficient for oblique TM incidence, Γ_{TM}, is given by Equation 5.191.

[3]Obtaining this result is an excellent way for the student to confirm their understanding of the derivation presented in this section.

The following example demonstrates the utility of this result.

Example 5.8. Power transmission at an air-to-glass interface (TM case).

Figure 5.13 illustrates a TM plane wave incident from air onto the planar boundary with a glass region. The glass exhibits relative permittivity of 2.1. Determine the power reflected and transmitted relative to power incident on the boundary.

Solution. The power reflected relative to power incident is $|\Gamma_{TM}|^2$ whereas the power transmitted relative to power incident is $1 - |\Gamma_{TM}|^2$. Γ_{TM} may be calculated using Equation 5.191. Calculating the quantities that enter into this expression:

$$\eta_1 \approx \eta_0 \cong 376.7\ \Omega \text{ (air)} \tag{5.192}$$

$$\eta_2 \approx \frac{\eta_0}{\sqrt{2.1}} \cong 260.0\ \Omega \text{ (glass)} \tag{5.193}$$

$$\psi^i = 30^\circ \tag{5.194}$$

Note

$$\frac{\beta_1}{\beta_2} \approx \frac{\omega\sqrt{\mu_0\epsilon_0}}{\omega\sqrt{\mu_0 \cdot 2.1\epsilon_0}} \cong 0.690 \tag{5.195}$$

so

$$\psi^t = \arcsin\left(\frac{\beta_1}{\beta_2}\sin\psi^i\right) \cong 20.2^\circ \tag{5.196}$$

Now substituting these values into Equation 5.191, we obtain

$$\Gamma_{TM} \cong -0.1442 \tag{5.197}$$

(Did you get an answer closer to -0.1323? If so, you probably did not use sufficient precision to represent intermediate results. This is a good example of a problem in which three significant figures for results that are used in subsequent calculations is not sufficient.)

The fraction of power reflected relative to power incident is now determined to be

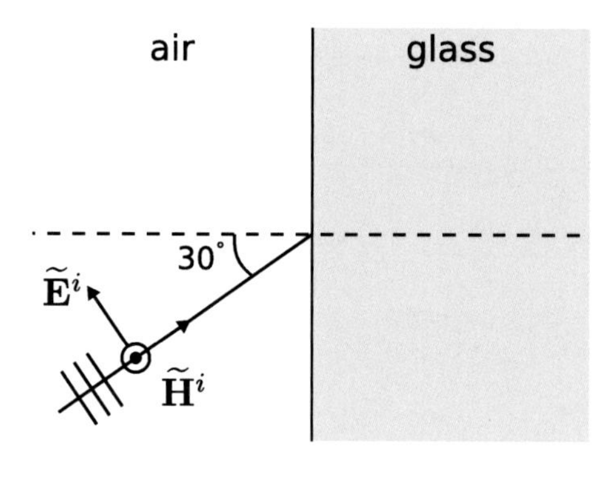

© C. Wang CC BY-SA 4.0

Figure 5.13: A TM uniform plane wave incident from air to glass.

$|\Gamma_{TM}|^2 \cong 0.021$; i.e., about 2.1%.
$1 - |\Gamma_{TM}|^2 \cong$ 97.9% of the power is transmitted into the glass.

Note that the result obtained in the preceding example is different from the result for a TE wave incident from the same direction (Example 5.7). In other words:

> The fraction of power reflected and transmitted from the planar boundary between dissimilar media depends on the polarization of the incident wave relative to the boundary, as well as the angle of incidence.

5.8 Angles of Reflection and Refraction

[m0168]

Consider the situation shown in Figure 5.14: A uniform plane wave obliquely incident on the planar boundary between two semi-infinite material regions. Let a point on the boundary be represented as the position vector

$$\mathbf{r}_0 = \hat{\mathbf{x}}x + \hat{\mathbf{y}}y \quad (5.198)$$

In both Sections 5.6 ("Plane Waves at Oblique Incidence on a Planar Boundary: TE Case") and 5.7 ("Plane Waves at Oblique Incidence on a Planar Boundary: TM Case"), it is found that

$$\mathbf{k}^i \cdot \mathbf{r}_0 = \mathbf{k}^r \cdot \mathbf{r}_0 = \mathbf{k}^t \cdot \mathbf{r}_0 \quad (5.199)$$

In this expression,

$$\mathbf{k}^i = \beta_1 \hat{\mathbf{k}}^i \quad (5.200)$$

$$\mathbf{k}^r = \beta_1 \hat{\mathbf{k}}^r \quad (5.201)$$

$$\mathbf{k}^t = \beta_2 \hat{\mathbf{k}}^t \quad (5.202)$$

where $\hat{\mathbf{k}}^i$, $\hat{\mathbf{k}}^r$, and $\hat{\mathbf{k}}^t$ are unit vectors in the direction of incidence, reflection, and transmission,

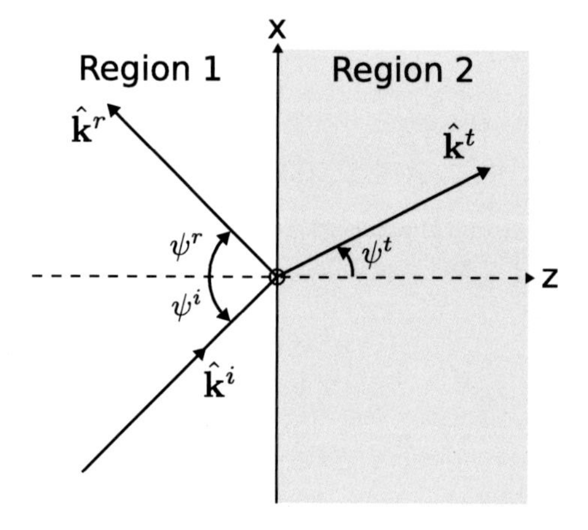

© C. Wang CC BY-SA 4.0

Figure 5.14: A uniform plane wave obliquely incident on the planar boundary between two semi-infinite material regions.

respectively; and β_1 and β_2 are the phase propagation constants in Region 1 (from which the wave is incident) and Region 2, respectively. Equation 5.199 is essentially a boundary condition that enforces continuity of the phase of the electric and magnetic fields across the boundary, and is sometimes referred to as the "phase matching" requirement. Since the same requirement emerges independently in the TE and TM cases, and since any plane wave may be decomposed into TE and TM components, the requirement must apply to any incident plane wave regardless of polarization.

Equation 5.199 is the key to finding the direction of reflection ψ^r and direction of transmission ψ^t. First, observe:

$$\hat{\mathbf{k}}^i = \hat{\mathbf{x}} \sin\psi^i + \hat{\mathbf{z}} \cos\psi^i \quad (5.203)$$

$$\hat{\mathbf{k}}^r = \hat{\mathbf{x}} \sin\psi^r - \hat{\mathbf{z}} \cos\psi^r \quad (5.204)$$

$$\hat{\mathbf{k}}^t = \hat{\mathbf{x}} \sin\psi^t + \hat{\mathbf{z}} \cos\psi^t \quad (5.205)$$

Therefore, we may express Equation 5.199 in the following form

$$\begin{aligned} &\beta_1 \left(\hat{\mathbf{x}} \sin\psi^i + \hat{\mathbf{z}} \cos\psi^i\right) \cdot (\hat{\mathbf{x}}x + \hat{\mathbf{y}}y) \\ &= \beta_1 \left(\hat{\mathbf{x}} \sin\psi^r - \hat{\mathbf{z}} \cos\psi^r\right) \cdot (\hat{\mathbf{x}}x + \hat{\mathbf{y}}y) \\ &= \beta_2 \left(\hat{\mathbf{x}} \sin\psi^t + \hat{\mathbf{z}} \cos\psi^t\right) \cdot (\hat{\mathbf{x}}x + \hat{\mathbf{y}}y) \end{aligned} \quad (5.206)$$

which reduces to

$$\beta_1 \sin\psi^i = \beta_1 \sin\psi^r = \beta_2 \sin\psi^t \quad (5.207)$$

Examining the first and second terms of Equation 5.207, and noting that ψ^i and ψ^r are both limited to the range $-\pi/2$ to $+\pi/2$, we find that:

$$\boxed{\psi^r = \psi^i} \quad (5.208)$$

In plain English:

Angle of reflection equals angle of incidence.

Examining the first and third terms of Equation 5.207, we find that

$$\beta_1 \sin\psi^i = \beta_2 \sin\psi^t \quad (5.209)$$

Since $\beta_1 = \omega\sqrt{\mu_1\epsilon_1}$ and $\beta_2 = \omega\sqrt{\mu_2\epsilon_2}$, Equation 5.209 expressed explicitly in terms of the constitutive parameters is:

$$\sqrt{\mu_1\epsilon_1} \sin\psi^i = \sqrt{\mu_2\epsilon_2} \sin\psi^t \quad (5.210)$$

Thus, we see that ψ^t does not depend on frequency, except to the extent that the constitutive parameters might. We may also express this relationship in terms of the *relative* values of constitutive parameters; i.e., $\mu_1 = \mu_{r1}\mu_0$, $\epsilon_1 = \epsilon_{r1}\epsilon_0$, $\mu_2 = \mu_{r2}\mu_0$, and $\epsilon_2 = \epsilon_{r2}\epsilon_0$. In terms of the relative parameters:

$$\boxed{\sqrt{\mu_{r1}\epsilon_{r1}} \sin\psi^i = \sqrt{\mu_{r2}\epsilon_{r2}} \sin\psi^t} \quad (5.211)$$

This is known as *Snell's law* or the *law of refraction*. Refraction is simply transmission with the result that the direction of propagation is changed.

Snell's law (Equation 5.211) determines the angle of refraction (transmission).

The associated formula for ψ^t explicitly is:

$$\psi^t = \arcsin\left(\sqrt{\frac{\mu_{r1}\epsilon_{r1}}{\mu_{r2}\epsilon_{r2}}} \sin\psi^i\right) \quad (5.212)$$

For the common special case of non-magnetic media, one assumes $\mu_{r1} = \mu_{r2} = 1$. In this case, Snell's law simplifies to:

$$\sqrt{\epsilon_{r1}} \sin\psi^i = \sqrt{\epsilon_{r2}} \sin\psi^t \quad (5.213)$$

In optics, it is common to express permittivities in terms of indices of refraction; e.g., $n_1 \triangleq \sqrt{\epsilon_{r1}}$ and $n_2 \triangleq \sqrt{\epsilon_{r2}}$. Thus, Snell's law in optics is often expressed as:

$$n_1 \sin\psi^i = n_2 \sin\psi^t \quad (5.214)$$

When both media are non-magnetic, Equation 5.212 simplifies to

$$\psi^t = \arcsin\left(\sqrt{\frac{\epsilon_{r1}}{\epsilon_{r2}}} \sin\psi^i\right) \quad (5.215)$$

When $\epsilon_{r2} > \epsilon_{r1}$, we observe that $\psi^t < \psi^i$. In other words, the transmitted wave travels in a direction that is closer to the surface normal than the angle of incidence. This scenario is demonstrated in the following example.

Example 5.9. Refraction of light at an air-glass boundary.

Figure 5.15 shows a narrow beam of light that is incident from air to glass at an angle $\psi^i = 60°$.

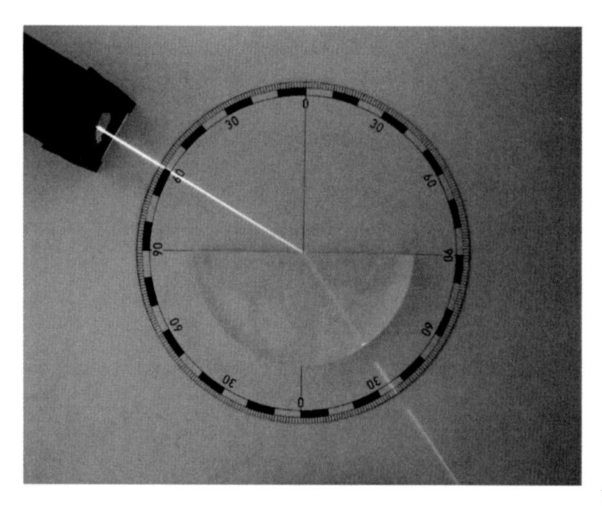

© Z. Sándor CC BY-SA 3.0

Figure 5.15: Angles of reflection and refraction for a light wave incident from air onto glass.

As expected, the angle of reflection ψ^r is observed to be equal to ψ^i. The angle of refraction ψ^t is observed to be 35°. What is the relative permittivity of the glass?

Solution. Since the permittivity of glass is greater than that of air, we observe the expected result $\psi^t < \psi^i$. Since glass is non-magnetic, the expected relationship between these angles is given by Equation 5.213. Solving that equation for the relative permittivity of the glass, we obtain:

$$\epsilon_{r2} = \epsilon_{r1} \left(\frac{\sin \psi^i}{\sin \psi^t} \right)^2 \cong \underline{2.28} \qquad (5.216)$$

When a wave travels in the reverse direction – i.e., from a non-magnetic medium of higher permittivity to a medium of lower permittivity – one finds $\psi^t > \psi^r$. In other words, the refraction is *away* from the surface normal. Figure 5.16 shows an example from common experience.

In non-magnetic media, when $\epsilon_{r1} < \epsilon_{r2}$, $\psi_t < \psi_i$ (refraction toward the surface normal). When $\epsilon_{r1} > \epsilon_{r2}$, $\psi_t > \psi_i$ (refraction away from the surface normal).

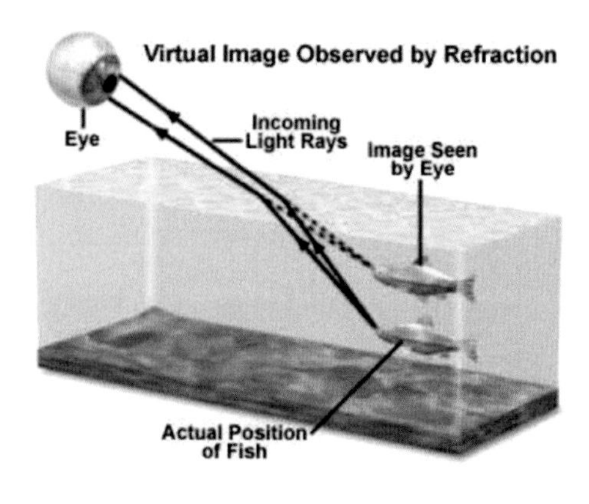

© G. Saini CC BY-SA 4.0

Figure 5.16: Refraction accounts for the apparent displacement of an underwater object from the perspective of an observer above the water.

Under certain conditions, the $\epsilon_{r2} < \epsilon_{r1}$ case leads to the following surprising observation: When calculating ψ^t using, for example, Equation 5.212, one finds that $\sqrt{\epsilon_{r1}/\epsilon_{r2}} \sin \psi^i$ can be greater than 1. Since the sin function yields values between -1 and $+1$, the result of the arcsin function is undefined. This odd situation is addressed in Section 5.11. For now, we will simply note that this condition leads to the phenomenon of *total internal reflection*. For now, all we can say is that when $\epsilon_{r2} < \epsilon_{r1}$, ψ^t is able to reach $\pi/2$ radians, which corresponds to propagation parallel to the boundary. Beyond that threshold, we must account for the unique physical considerations associated with total internal reflection.

We conclude this section with a description of the common waveguiding device known as the *prism*, shown in Figure 5.17. This particular device uses refraction to change the direction of light waves (similar devices can be used to manipulate radio waves as well). Many readers are familiar with the use of prisms to separate white light into its constituent colors (frequencies), as shown in Figure 5.18. The separation of colors is due to frequency dependence of the material comprising the prism. Specifically, the permittivity of the material is a function of frequency, and therefore the angle of refraction is a function of frequency. Thus, each frequency is refracted by a different amount. Conversely, a prism comprised of a material whose permittivity exhibits negligible variation with frequency will not separate incident

© D-Kuru CC BY-SA 3.0

Figure 5.17: A typical triangular prism.

white light into its constituent colors since each color will be refracted by the same amount.

Additional Reading:

- "Prism" on Wikipedia.
- "Refraction" on Wikipedia.
- "Refractive index" on Wikipedia.
- "Snell's law" on Wikipedia.
- "Total internal reflection" on Wikipedia.

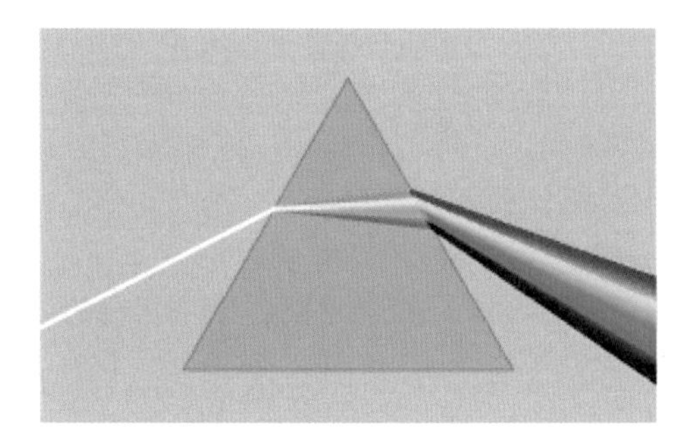

© Suidroot CC BY-SA 4.0

Figure 5.18: A color-separating prism.

5.9 TE Reflection in Non-magnetic Media

[m0171]

Figure 5.19 shows a TE uniform plane wave incident on the planar boundary between two semi-infinite material regions. In this case, the reflection coefficient is given by:

$$\Gamma_{TE} = \frac{\eta_2 \cos\psi^i - \eta_1 \cos\psi^t}{\eta_2 \cos\psi^i + \eta_1 \cos\psi^t} \tag{5.217}$$

where ψ^i and ψ^t are the angles of incidence and transmission (refraction), respectively; and η_1 and η_2 are the wave impedances in Regions 1 and 2, respectively. Many materials of practical interest are non-magnetic; that is, they have permeability that is not significantly different from the permeability of free space. In this section, we consider the behavior of the reflection coefficient for this class of materials.

To begin, recall the general form of Snell's law:

$$\sin\psi^t = \frac{\beta_1}{\beta_2}\sin\psi^i \tag{5.218}$$

In non-magnetic media, the permeabilities μ_1 and μ_2 are assumed equal to μ_0. Thus:

$$\frac{\beta_1}{\beta_2} = \frac{\omega\sqrt{\mu_1\epsilon_1}}{\omega\sqrt{\mu_2\epsilon_2}} = \sqrt{\frac{\epsilon_1}{\epsilon_2}} \tag{5.219}$$

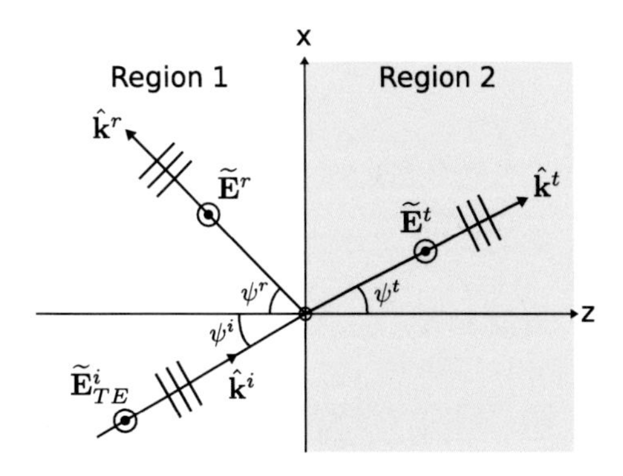

© C. Wang CC BY-SA 4.0

Figure 5.19: A TE uniform plane wave obliquely incident on the planar boundary between two semi-infinite regions of lossless non-magnetic material.

Since permittivity ϵ can be expressed as ϵ_0 times the relative permittivity ϵ_r, we may reduce further to:

$$\frac{\beta_1}{\beta_2} = \sqrt{\frac{\epsilon_{r1}}{\epsilon_{r2}}} \tag{5.220}$$

Now Equation 5.218 reduces to:

$$\sin \psi^t = \sqrt{\frac{\epsilon_{r1}}{\epsilon_{r2}}} \sin \psi^i \tag{5.221}$$

Next, note that for any value ψ, one may write cosine in terms of sine as follows:

$$\cos \psi = \sqrt{1 - \sin^2 \psi} \tag{5.222}$$

Therefore,

$$\cos \psi^t = \sqrt{1 - \frac{\epsilon_{r1}}{\epsilon_{r2}} \sin^2 \psi^i} \tag{5.223}$$

Also we note that in non-magnetic media

$$\eta_1 = \sqrt{\frac{\mu_1}{\epsilon_1}} = \sqrt{\frac{\mu_0}{\epsilon_{r1}\epsilon_0}} = \frac{\eta_0}{\sqrt{\epsilon_{r1}}} \tag{5.224}$$

$$\eta_2 = \sqrt{\frac{\mu_2}{\epsilon_2}} = \sqrt{\frac{\mu_0}{\epsilon_{r2}\epsilon_0}} = \frac{\eta_0}{\sqrt{\epsilon_{r2}}} \tag{5.225}$$

where η_0 is the wave impedance in free space. Making substitutions into Equation 5.217, we obtain:

$$\Gamma_{TE} = \frac{\left(\eta_0/\sqrt{\epsilon_{r2}}\right) \cos \psi^i - \left(\eta_0/\sqrt{\epsilon_{r1}}\right) \cos \psi^t}{\left(\eta_0/\sqrt{\epsilon_{r2}}\right) \cos \psi^i + \left(\eta_0/\sqrt{\epsilon_{r1}}\right) \cos \psi^t} \tag{5.226}$$

Multiplying numerator and denominator by $\sqrt{\epsilon_{r2}}/\eta_0$, we obtain:

$$\Gamma_{TE} = \frac{\cos \psi^i - \sqrt{\epsilon_{r2}/\epsilon_{r1}} \cos \psi^t}{\cos \psi^i + \sqrt{\epsilon_{r2}/\epsilon_{r1}} \cos \psi^t} \tag{5.227}$$

Finally, by substituting Equation 5.223, we obtain:

$$\boxed{\Gamma_{TE} = \frac{\cos \psi^i - \sqrt{\epsilon_{r2}/\epsilon_{r1} - \sin^2 \psi^i}}{\cos \psi^i + \sqrt{\epsilon_{r2}/\epsilon_{r1} - \sin^2 \psi^i}}} \tag{5.228}$$

This expression has the advantage that it is now entirely in terms of ψ^i, with no need to first calculate ψ^t.

Using Equation 5.228, we can see how different combinations of material affect the reflection coefficient. First, we note that when $\epsilon_{r1} = \epsilon_{r2}$ (i.e., same media on both sides of the boundary), $\Gamma_{TE} = 0$ as expected. When $\epsilon_{r1} > \epsilon_{r2}$ (e.g., wave traveling in glass toward air), we see that it is possible for $\epsilon_{r2}/\epsilon_{r1} - \sin^2 \psi^i$ to be negative, which makes Γ_{TE} complex-valued. This results in *total internal reflection*, and is addressed elsewhere in another section. When $\epsilon_{r1} < \epsilon_{r2}$ (e.g., wave traveling in air toward glass), we see that $\epsilon_{r2}/\epsilon_{r1} - \sin^2 \psi^i$ is always positive, so Γ_{TE} is always real-valued.

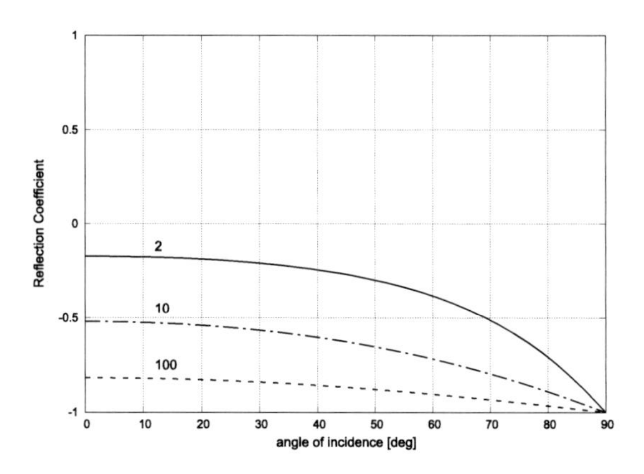

Figure 5.20: The reflection coefficient Γ_{TE} as a function of angle of incidence ψ^i for various media combinations. Curves are labeled with the ratio $\epsilon_{r2}/\epsilon_{r1}$.

Let us continue with the $\epsilon_{r1} < \epsilon_{r2}$ condition. Figure 5.20 shows Γ_{TE} plotted for various combinations of media over all possible angles of incidence from 0 (normal incidence) to $\pi/2$ (grazing incidence). We observe:

> In non-magnetic media with $\epsilon_{r1} < \epsilon_{r2}$, Γ_{TE} is real-valued, negative, and decreases to -1 as ψ^i approaches grazing incidence.

Also note that at any particular angle of incidence, Γ_{TE} trends toward -1 as $\epsilon_{r2}/\epsilon_{r1}$ increases. Thus, we observe that as $\epsilon_{r2}/\epsilon_{r1} \to \infty$, the result is increasingly similar to the result we would obtain for a perfect conductor in Region 2.

5.10 TM Reflection in Non-magnetic Media

[m0172]

Figure 5.21 shows a TM uniform plane wave incident on the planar boundary between two semi-infinite material regions. In this case, the reflection coefficient is given by:

$$\Gamma_{TM} = \frac{-\eta_1 \cos\psi^i + \eta_2 \cos\psi^t}{+\eta_1 \cos\psi^i + \eta_2 \cos\psi^t} \tag{5.229}$$

where ψ^i and ψ^t are the angles of incidence and transmission (refraction), respectively; and η_1 and η_2 are the wave impedances in Regions 1 and 2, respectively. Many materials of practical interest are non-magnetic; that is, they have permeability that is not significantly different from the permeability of free space. In this section, we consider the behavior of the reflection coefficient for this class of materials.

To begin, recall the general form of Snell's law:

$$\sin\psi^t = \frac{\beta_1}{\beta_2}\sin\psi^i \tag{5.230}$$

In non-magnetic media, the permeabilities μ_1 and μ_2 are assumed equal to μ_0. Thus:

$$\frac{\beta_1}{\beta_2} = \frac{\omega\sqrt{\mu_1\epsilon_1}}{\omega\sqrt{\mu_2\epsilon_2}} = \sqrt{\frac{\epsilon_1}{\epsilon_2}} \tag{5.231}$$

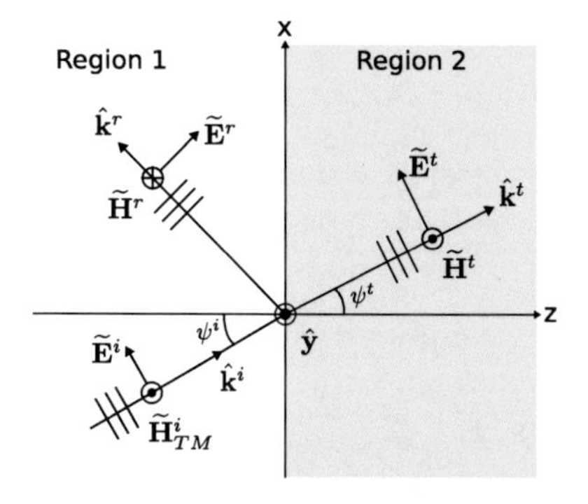

© C. Wang CC BY-SA 4.0

Figure 5.21: A transverse magnetic uniform plane wave obliquely incident on the planar boundary between two semi-infinite material regions.

Since permittivity ϵ can be expressed as ϵ_0 times the relative permittivity ϵ_r, we may reduce further to:

$$\frac{\beta_1}{\beta_2} = \sqrt{\frac{\epsilon_{r1}}{\epsilon_{r2}}} \tag{5.232}$$

Now Equation 5.230 reduces to:

$$\sin\psi^t = \sqrt{\frac{\epsilon_{r1}}{\epsilon_{r2}}}\sin\psi^i \tag{5.233}$$

Next, note that for any value ψ, one may write cosine in terms of sine as follows:

$$\cos\psi = \sqrt{1-\sin^2\psi} \tag{5.234}$$

Therefore,

$$\cos\psi^t = \sqrt{1-\frac{\epsilon_{r1}}{\epsilon_{r2}}\sin^2\psi^i} \tag{5.235}$$

Also we note that in non-magnetic media

$$\eta_1 = \sqrt{\frac{\mu_1}{\epsilon_1}} = \sqrt{\frac{\mu_0}{\epsilon_{r1}\epsilon_0}} = \frac{\eta_0}{\sqrt{\epsilon_{r1}}} \tag{5.236}$$

$$\eta_2 = \sqrt{\frac{\mu_2}{\epsilon_2}} = \sqrt{\frac{\mu_0}{\epsilon_{r2}\epsilon_0}} = \frac{\eta_0}{\sqrt{\epsilon_{r2}}} \tag{5.237}$$

where η_0 is the wave impedance in free space. Making substitutions into Equation 5.229, we obtain:

$$\Gamma_{TM} = \frac{-\left(\eta_0/\sqrt{\epsilon_{r1}}\right)\cos\psi^i + \left(\eta_0/\sqrt{\epsilon_{r2}}\right)\cos\psi^t}{+\left(\eta_0/\sqrt{\epsilon_{r1}}\right)\cos\psi^i + \left(\eta_0/\sqrt{\epsilon_{r2}}\right)\cos\psi^t} \tag{5.238}$$

Multiplying numerator and denominator by $\sqrt{\epsilon_{r2}}/\eta_0$, we obtain:

$$\Gamma_{TM} = \frac{-\sqrt{\epsilon_{r2}/\epsilon_{r1}}\cos\psi^i + \cos\psi^t}{+\sqrt{\epsilon_{r2}/\epsilon_{r1}}\cos\psi^i + \cos\psi^t} \tag{5.239}$$

Substituting Equation 5.235, we obtain:

$$\Gamma_{TM} = \frac{-\sqrt{\epsilon_{r2}/\epsilon_{r1}}\cos\psi^i + \sqrt{1-(\epsilon_{r1}/\epsilon_{r2})\sin^2\psi^i}}{+\sqrt{\epsilon_{r2}/\epsilon_{r1}}\cos\psi^i + \sqrt{1-(\epsilon_{r1}/\epsilon_{r2})\sin^2\psi^i}} \tag{5.240}$$

This expression has the advantage that it is now entirely in terms of ψ^i, with no need to first calculate ψ^t.

Finally, multiplying numerator and denominator by $\sqrt{\epsilon_{r2}/\epsilon_{r1}}$, we obtain:

$$\boxed{\Gamma_{TM} = \frac{-(\epsilon_{r2}/\epsilon_{r1})\cos\psi^i + \sqrt{\epsilon_{r2}/\epsilon_{r1}-\sin^2\psi^i}}{+(\epsilon_{r2}/\epsilon_{r1})\cos\psi^i + \sqrt{\epsilon_{r2}/\epsilon_{r1}-\sin^2\psi^i}}} \tag{5.241}$$

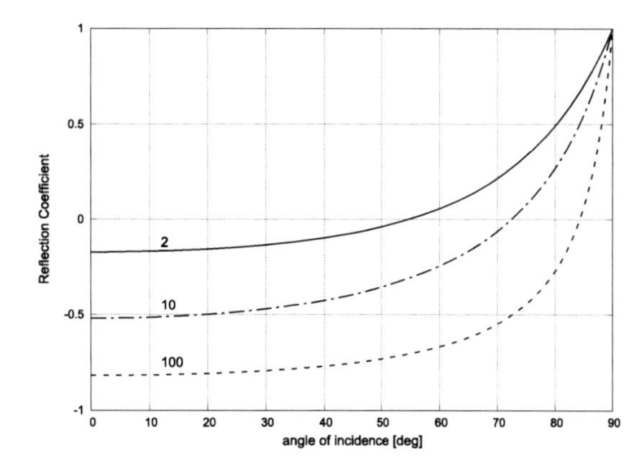

Figure 5.22: The reflection coefficient Γ_{TM} as a function of angle of incidence ψ^i for various media combinations, parameterized as $\epsilon_{r2}/\epsilon_{r1}$.

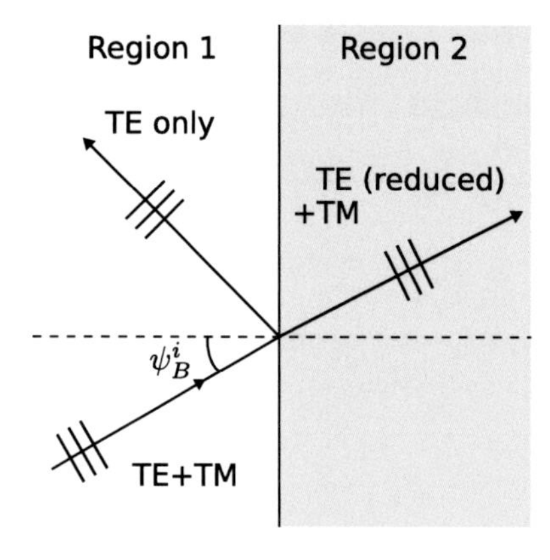

© C. Wang CC BY-SA 4.0

Figure 5.23: Reflection of a plane wave with angle of incidence ψ^i equal to the polarizing angle ψ_B^i. Here the media are non-magnetic with $\epsilon_{r1} < \epsilon_{r2}$.

Using Equation 5.241, we can easily see how different combinations of material affect the reflection coefficient. First, we note that when $\epsilon_{r1} = \epsilon_{r2}$ (i.e., same media on both sides of the boundary), $\Gamma_{TM} = 0$ as expected. When $\epsilon_{r1} > \epsilon_{r2}$ (e.g., wave traveling in glass toward air), we see that it is possible for $\epsilon_{r2}/\epsilon_{r1} - \sin^2\psi^i$ to be negative, which makes Γ_{TM} complex-valued. This results in *total internal reflection*, and is addressed in another section. When $\epsilon_{r1} < \epsilon_{r2}$ (e.g., wave traveling in air toward glass), we see that $\epsilon_{r2}/\epsilon_{r1} - \sin^2\psi^i$ is always positive, so Γ_{TM} is always real-valued.

Let us continue with the $\epsilon_{r1} < \epsilon_{r2}$ condition. Figure 5.22 shows Γ_{TM} plotted for various combinations of media over all possible angles of incidence from 0 (normal incidence) to $\pi/2$ (grazing incidence). We observe:

> In non-magnetic media with $\epsilon_{r1} < \epsilon_{r2}$, Γ_{TM} is real-valued and increases from a negative value for normal incidence to $+1$ as ψ^i approaches grazing incidence.

Note that at any particular angle of incidence, Γ_{TM} trends toward -1 as $\epsilon_{r2}/\epsilon_{r1} \to \infty$. In this respect, the behavior of the TM component is similar to that of the TE component. In other words: As $\epsilon_{r2}/\epsilon_{r1} \to \infty$, the result for both the TE and TM components are increasingly similar to the result we would obtain for a perfect conductor in Region 2.

Also note that when $\epsilon_{r1} < \epsilon_{r2}$, Γ_{TM} changes sign from negative to positive as angle of incidence increases from 0 to $\pi/2$. This behavior is quite different from that of the TE component, which is always negative for $\epsilon_{r1} < \epsilon_{r2}$. The angle of incidence at which $\Gamma_{TM} = 0$ is referred to as *Brewster's angle*, which we assign the symbol ψ_B^i. Thus:

$$\boxed{\psi_B^i \triangleq \psi^i \text{ at which } \Gamma_{TM} = 0} \tag{5.242}$$

In the discussion that follows, here is the key point to keep in mind:

> Brewster's angle ψ_B^i is the angle of incidence at which $\Gamma_{TM} = 0$.

Brewster's angle is also referred to as the *polarizing angle*. The motivation for the term "polarizing angle" is demonstrated in Figure 5.23. In this figure, a plane wave is incident with $\psi^i = \psi_B^i$. The wave may contain TE and TM components in any combination. Applying the principle of superposition, we may consider these components separately. The TE component of the incident wave will scatter as reflected and transmitted waves which are also TE. However, $\Gamma_{TM} = 0$ when $\psi^i = \psi_B^i$, so the TM component of the transmitted wave will be TM, but the TM component of the reflected wave will be zero. Thus, the total (TE+TM) reflected wave will be purely TE, regardless of the TM component of the incident wave. This principle can be exploited to suppress the TM component of a wave having both TE and TM components. This method can be used to isolate the TE and TM components of a wave.

Derivation of a formula for Brewster's angle. Brewster's angle for any particular combination of non-magnetic media may be determined as follows. $\Gamma_{TM} = 0$ when the numerator of Equation 5.241 equals zero, so:

$$-R\cos\psi_B^i + \sqrt{R - \sin^2\psi_B^i} = 0 \tag{5.243}$$

where we have made the substitution $R \triangleq \epsilon_{r2}/\epsilon_{r1}$ to improve clarity. Moving the second term to the right side of the equation and squaring both sides, we obtain:

$$R^2\cos^2\psi_B^i = R - \sin^2\psi_B^i \tag{5.244}$$

Now employing a trigonometric identity on the left side of the equation, we obtain:

$$R^2\left(1 - \sin^2\psi_B^i\right) = R - \sin^2\psi_B^i \tag{5.245}$$

$$R^2 - R^2\sin^2\psi_B^i = R - \sin^2\psi_B^i \tag{5.246}$$

$$\left(1 - R^2\right)\sin^2\psi_B^i = R - R^2 \tag{5.247}$$

and finally

$$\sin\psi_B^i = \sqrt{\frac{R - R^2}{1 - R^2}} \tag{5.248}$$

Although this equation gets the job done, it is possible to simplify further. Note that Equation 5.248 can be interpreted as a description of the right triangle shown in Figure 5.24. In the figure, we have identified the length h of the vertical side and the length d of the hypotenuse as:

$$h \triangleq \sqrt{R - R^2} \tag{5.249}$$

$$d \triangleq \sqrt{1 - R^2} \tag{5.250}$$

The length b of the horizontal side is therefore

$$b = \sqrt{d^2 - h^2} = \sqrt{1 - R} \tag{5.251}$$

Subsequently, we observe

$$\tan\psi_B^i = \frac{h}{b} = \frac{\sqrt{R - R^2}}{\sqrt{1 - R}} = \sqrt{R} \tag{5.252}$$

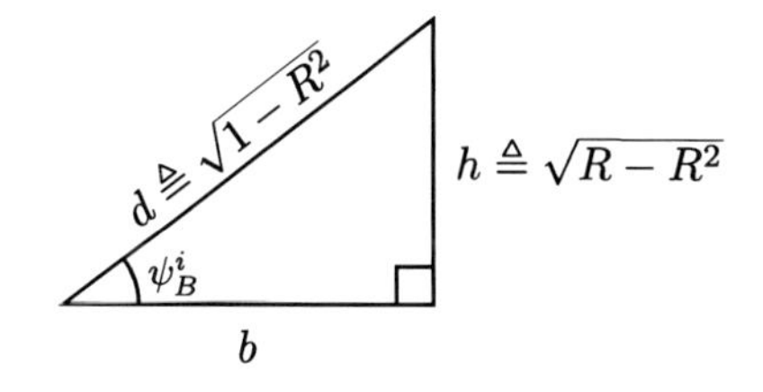

© C. Wang CC BY-SA 4.0

Figure 5.24: Derivation of a simple formula for Brewster's angle for non-magnetic media.

Thus, we have found

$$\boxed{\tan\psi_B^i = \sqrt{\frac{\epsilon_{r2}}{\epsilon_{r1}}}} \tag{5.253}$$

Example 5.10. Polarizing angle for an air-to-glass interface.

A plane wave is incident from air onto the planar boundary with a glass region. The glass exhibits relative permittivity of 2.1. The incident wave contains both TE and TM components. At what angle of incidence ψ^i will the reflected wave be purely TE?

Solution. Using Equation 5.253:

$$\tan\psi_B^i = \sqrt{\frac{\epsilon_{r2}}{\epsilon_{r1}}} = \sqrt{\frac{2.1}{1}} \cong 1.449 \tag{5.254}$$

Therefore, Brewster's angle is $\psi_B^i \cong \underline{55.4^\circ}$. This is the angle ψ^i at which $\Gamma_{TM} = 0$. Therefore, when $\psi^i = \psi_B^i$, the reflected wave contains no TM component and therefore must be purely TE.

Additional Reading:

- "Brewster's angle" on Wikipedia.

5.11 Total Internal Reflection

[m0169]

Total internal reflection refers to a particular condition resulting in the complete reflection of a wave at the boundary between two media, with no power transmitted into the second region. One way to achieve complete reflection with zero transmission is simply to require the second material to be a perfect conductor. However, total *internal* reflection is a distinct phenomenon in which neither of the two media are perfect conductors. Total internal reflection has a number of practical applications; notably, it is the enabling principle of fiber optics.

Consider the situation shown in Figure 5.25: A uniform plane wave is obliquely incident on the planar boundary between two semi-infinite material regions. In Section 5.8, it is found that

$$\psi^r = \psi^i \tag{5.255}$$

i.e., angle of reflection equals angle of incidence. Also, from Snell's law:

$$\sqrt{\mu_{r1}\epsilon_{r1}}\sin\psi^i = \sqrt{\mu_{r2}\epsilon_{r2}}\sin\psi^t \tag{5.256}$$

where "r" in the subscripts indicates the relative (unitless) quantities. The associated formula for ψ^t explicitly is:

$$\psi^t = \arcsin\left(\sqrt{\frac{\mu_{r1}\epsilon_{r1}}{\mu_{r2}\epsilon_{r2}}}\sin\psi^i\right) \tag{5.257}$$

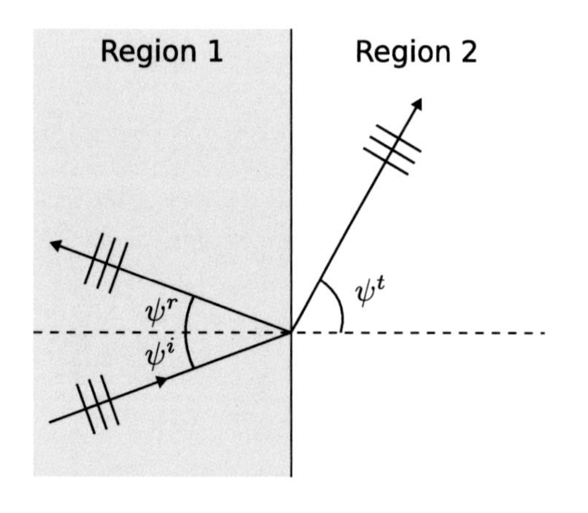

© C. Wang CC BY-SA 4.0 (modified)

Figure 5.25: A uniform plane wave obliquely incident on the planar boundary between two semi-infinite material regions. Here $\mu_{r1}\epsilon_{r1} > \mu_{r2}\epsilon_{r2}$, so $\psi^t > \psi^i$.

From Equation 5.257, it is apparent that when $\mu_{r1}\epsilon_{r1} > \mu_{r2}\epsilon_{r2}$, $\psi^t > \psi^r$; i.e., the transmitted wave appears to bend away from the surface normal, as shown in Figure 5.25. In fact, ψ^t can be as large as $\pi/2$ (corresponding to propagation parallel to the boundary) for angles of incidence which are less than $\pi/2$. What happens if the angle of incidence is further increased? When calculating ψ^t using Equation 5.257, one finds that the argument of the arcsine function becomes greater than 1. Since the possible values of the sine function are between -1 and $+1$, the arcsine function is undefined. Clearly our analysis is inadequate in this situation.

To make sense of this, let us begin by identifying the threshold angle of incidence ψ^i_c at which the trouble begins. From the analysis in the previous paragraph,

$$\sqrt{\frac{\mu_{r1}\epsilon_{r1}}{\mu_{r2}\epsilon_{r2}}}\sin\psi^i_c = 1 \tag{5.258}$$

therefore,

$$\boxed{\psi^i_c = \arcsin\sqrt{\frac{\mu_{r2}\epsilon_{r2}}{\mu_{r1}\epsilon_{r1}}}} \tag{5.259}$$

This is known as the *critical angle*. When $\psi^i < \psi^i_c$, our existing theory applies. When $\psi^i \geq \psi^i_c$, the situation is, at present, unclear. For non-magnetic materials, Equation 5.259 simplifies to

$$\psi^i_c = \arcsin\sqrt{\frac{\epsilon_{r2}}{\epsilon_{r1}}} \tag{5.260}$$

Now let us examine the behavior of the reflection coefficient. For example, the reflection coefficient for TE component and non-magnetic materials is

$$\Gamma_{TE} = \frac{\cos\psi^i - \sqrt{\epsilon_{r2}/\epsilon_{r1} - \sin^2\psi^i}}{\cos\psi^i + \sqrt{\epsilon_{r2}/\epsilon_{r1} - \sin^2\psi^i}} \tag{5.261}$$

From Equation 5.260, we see that

$$\sin^2\psi^i_c = \frac{\epsilon_{r2}}{\epsilon_{r1}} \tag{5.262}$$

So, when $\psi^i > \psi_c^i$, we see that

$$\epsilon_{r2}/\epsilon_{r1} - \sin^2 \psi^i < 0 \quad (\psi^i > \psi_c^i) \tag{5.263}$$

and therefore

$$\sqrt{\epsilon_{r2}/\epsilon_{r1} - \sin^2 \psi^i} = jB \quad (\psi^i > \psi_c^i) \tag{5.264}$$

where B is a positive real-valued number. Now we may write Equation 5.261 as follows:

$$\Gamma_{TE} = \frac{A - jB}{A + jB} \quad (\psi^i > \psi_c^i) \tag{5.265}$$

where $A \triangleq \cos \psi^i$ is also a positive real-valued number. Note that the numerator and denominator in Equation 5.265 have equal magnitude. Therefore, the magnitude of $|\Gamma_{TE}| = 1$ and

$$\Gamma_{TE} = e^{j\zeta} \quad (\psi^i > \psi_c^i) \tag{5.266}$$

where ζ is a real-valued number indicating the phase of Γ_{TE}. In other words,

> When the angle of incidence ψ^i exceeds the critical angle ψ_c^i, the magnitude of the reflection coefficient is 1. In this case, all power is reflected, and no power is transmitted into the second medium. This is *total internal reflection.*

Although we have obtained this result for TE component, the identical conclusion is obtained for TM component as well. This is left as an exercise for the student.

Example 5.11. Total internal reflection in glass.

Figure 5.15 (Section 5.8) shows a demonstration of refraction of a beam of light incident from air onto a planar boundary with glass. Analysis of that demonstration revealed that the relative permittivity of the glass was $\cong 2.28$. Figure 5.26 shows a modification of the demonstration: In this case, a beam of light incident from glass onto a planar boundary with air. Confirm that total internal reflection is the expected result in this demonstration.

Solution. Assuming the glass is non-magnetic, the critical angle is given by Equation 5.260. In the present example, $\epsilon_{r1} \cong 2.28$ (glass), $\epsilon_{r2} \cong 1$ (air). Therefore, the critical angle $\psi_c^i \cong 41.5°$.

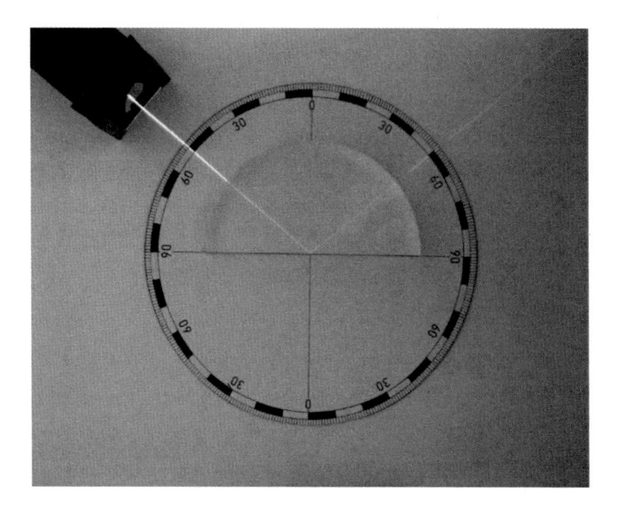

© Z. Sándor CC BY-SA 3.0

Figure 5.26: Total internal reflection of a light wave incident on a planar boundary between glass and air.

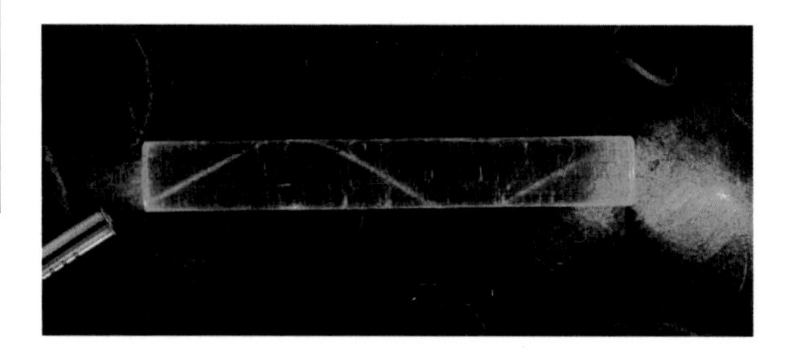

© Timwether CC BY-SA 3.0

Figure 5.27: Laser light in a dielectric rod exhibiting the Goos-Hänchen effect.

The angle of incidence in Figure 5.26 is seen to be about $\cong 50°$, which is greater than the critical angle. Therefore, total internal reflection is expected.

Note also that the phase ζ of the reflection coefficient is precisely zero unless $\psi^i > \psi_c^i$, at which point it is both non-zero and varies with ψ^i. This is known as the *Goos-Hänchen effect*. This leads to the startling phenomenon shown in Figure 5.27. In this figure, the Goos-Hänchen phase shift is apparent as a displacement between the point of incidence and the point of reflection.

The presence of an imaginary component in the reflection coefficient is odd for two reasons. First, we are not accustomed to seeing a complex-valued reflection coefficient emerge when the wave impedances of the associated media are real-valued. Second, the *total* reflection of the incident wave seems to contradict the boundary condition that requires the tangential components of the electric and magnetic fields to be continuous across the boundary. That is, how can these components of the fields be continuous across the boundary if no power is transmitted across the boundary? These considerations suggest that there *is* a field on the opposite side of the boundary, but – somehow – it must have zero power. This is exactly the case, as is explained in Section 5.12.

Additional Reading:

- "Goos-Hänchen effect" on Wikipedia.
- "Snell's law" on Wikipedia.
- "Total internal reflection" on Wikipedia.

5.12 Evanescent Waves

[m0170]

Consider the situation shown in Figure 5.28: A uniform plane wave obliquely incident on the planar boundary between two semi-infinite material regions, and total internal reflection occurs because the angle of incidence ψ^i is greater than the critical angle

$$\psi_c^i = \arcsin\sqrt{\frac{\mu_{r2}\epsilon_{r2}}{\mu_{r1}\epsilon_{r1}}} \tag{5.267}$$

Therefore, the reflection coefficient is complex-valued with magnitude equal to 1 and phase that depends on polarization and the constitutive parameters of the media.

The total reflection of the incident wave seems to contradict the boundary conditions that require the tangential components of the electric and magnetic fields to be continuous across the boundary. How can these components of the fields be continuous across the boundary if no power is transmitted across the boundary? There must be a field on the opposite side of the boundary, but – somehow – it must have zero power. To make sense of this, let us attempt to find a solution for the transmitted field.

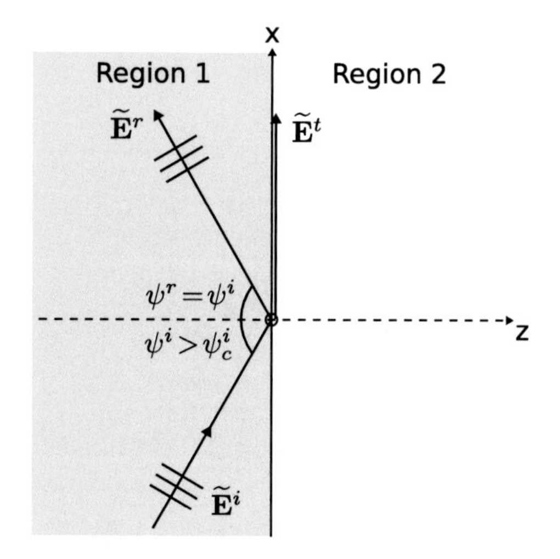

© C. Wang CC BY-SA 4.0

Figure 5.28: A uniform plane wave obliquely incident on the planar boundary between two semi-infinite material regions. Here $\mu_{r1}\epsilon_{r1} > \mu_{r2}\epsilon_{r2}$ and $\psi^i > \psi^i_c$.

We begin by postulating a complex-valued angle of transmission ψ^{tc}. Although the concept of a complex-valued angle may seem counterintuitive, there is mathematical support for this concept. For example, consider the well-known trigonometric identities:

$$\sin\theta = \frac{1}{j2}\left(e^{j\theta} - e^{-j\theta}\right) \tag{5.268}$$

$$\cos\theta = \frac{1}{2}\left(e^{j\theta} + e^{-j\theta}\right) \tag{5.269}$$

These identities allow us to compute values for sine and cosine even when θ is complex-valued. One may conclude that the sine and cosine of a complex-valued angle exist, although the results may also be complex-valued.

Based on the evidence established so far, we presume that ψ^{tc} behaves as follows:

$$\psi^{tc} \triangleq \psi^t\,, \qquad \psi^i < \psi^i_c \tag{5.270}$$

$$\psi^{tc} \triangleq \pi/2\,, \qquad \psi^i = \psi^i_c \tag{5.271}$$

$$\psi^{tc} \triangleq \pi/2 + j\psi''\,, \quad \psi^i > \psi^i_c \tag{5.272}$$

In other words, ψ^{tc} is identical to ψ^t for $\psi^i \leq \psi^i_c$, but when total internal reflection occurs, we presume the real part of ψ^{tc} remains fixed (parallel to the boundary) and that an imaginary component $j\psi''$ emerges to satisfy the boundary conditions.

For clarity, let us assign the variable ψ' to represent the real part of ψ^{tc} in Equations 5.270–5.272. Then we may refer to all three cases using a single expression as follows:

$$\psi^{tc} = \psi' + j\psi'' \tag{5.273}$$

Now we use a well-known trigonometric identity as follows:

$$\sin\psi^{tc} = \sin\left(\psi' + j\psi''\right) \tag{5.274}$$

$$= \sin\psi' \cos j\psi'' + \cos\psi' \sin j\psi'' \tag{5.275}$$

Using Equation 5.269, we find:

$$\cos j\psi'' = \frac{1}{2}\left(e^{j(j\psi'')} + e^{-j(j\psi'')}\right) \tag{5.276}$$

$$= \frac{1}{2}\left(e^{-\psi''} + e^{+\psi''}\right) \tag{5.277}$$

$$= \cosh\psi'' \tag{5.278}$$

In other words, the cosine of $j\psi''$ is simply the hyperbolic cosine ("cosh") of ψ''. Interestingly, cosh of a real-valued argument is real-valued, so $\cos j\psi''$ is real-valued.

Using Equation 5.268, we find:

$$\sin j\psi'' = \frac{1}{j2}\left(e^{j(j\psi'')} - e^{-j(j\psi'')}\right) \tag{5.279}$$

$$= \frac{1}{j2}\left(e^{-\psi''} - e^{+\psi''}\right) \tag{5.280}$$

$$= j\frac{1}{2}\left(e^{+\psi''} - e^{-\psi''}\right) \tag{5.281}$$

$$= j\sinh\psi'' \tag{5.282}$$

In other words, the sine of $j\psi''$ is j times hyperbolic sine ("sinh") of ψ''. Now note that sinh of a real-valued argument is real-valued, so $\sin j\psi''$ is imaginary-valued.

Using these results, we find Equation 5.275 may be written as follows:

$$\sin\psi^{tc} = \sin\psi' \cosh\psi'' + j\cos\psi' \sinh\psi'' \tag{5.283}$$

Using precisely the same approach, we find:

$$\cos\psi^{tc} = \cos\psi' \cosh\psi'' - j\sin\psi' \sinh\psi'' \tag{5.284}$$

Before proceeding, let's make sure Equations 5.283 and 5.284 exhibit the expected behavior before the onset of total internal reflection. For $\psi^i < \psi^i_c$, $\psi' = \psi^t$ and $\psi'' = 0$. In this case, $\sinh\psi'' = 0$, $\cosh\psi'' = 1$, and Equations 5.283 and 5.284 yield

$$\sin\psi^{tc} = \sin\psi^t \tag{5.285}$$

$$\cos\psi^{tc} = \cos\psi^t \tag{5.286}$$

as expected.

When total internal reflection is in effect, $\psi^i > \psi^i_c$, so $\psi' = \pi/2$. In this case, Equations 5.283 and 5.284 yield

$$\sin\psi^{tc} = \cosh\psi'' \tag{5.287}$$

$$\cos\psi^{tc} = -j\sinh\psi'' \tag{5.288}$$

Let us now consider what this means for the field in Region 2. According to the formalism adopted in previous sections, the propagation of wave components in this region is described by the factor $e^{-j\mathbf{k}^t\cdot\mathbf{r}}$ where

$$\begin{aligned}\mathbf{k}^t &= \beta_2 \hat{\mathbf{k}}^t \\ &= \beta_2 \left(\hat{\mathbf{x}} \sin\psi^{tc} + \hat{\mathbf{z}} \cos\psi^{tc}\right)\end{aligned} \quad (5.289)$$

and

$$\mathbf{r} = \hat{\mathbf{x}}x + \hat{\mathbf{y}}y + \hat{\mathbf{z}}z \quad (5.290)$$

so

$$\begin{aligned}\mathbf{k}^t \cdot \mathbf{r} &= \left(\beta_2 \sin\psi^{tc}\right) x + \left(\beta_2 \cos\psi^{tc}\right) z \\ &= \left(\beta_2 \cosh\psi''\right) x + \left(-j\beta_2 \sinh\psi''\right) z\end{aligned} \quad (5.291)$$

Therefore, the wave in Region 2 propagates according to

$$e^{-j\mathbf{k}^t\cdot\mathbf{r}} = e^{-j\left(\beta_2 \cosh\psi''\right)x} e^{-\left(\beta_2 \sinh\psi''\right)z} \quad (5.292)$$

Note that the constants $\beta_2 \cosh\psi''$ and $\beta_2 \sinh\psi''$ are both real-valued and positive. Therefore, Equation 5.292 describes a wave which propagates in the $+\hat{\mathbf{x}}$ direction, but which is not uniform. Specifically, the magnitude of the transmitted field decreases exponentially with increasing z; i.e., maximum at the boundary, asymptotically approaching zero with increasing distance from the boundary. This wave is unlike the incident or reflected waves (both uniform plane waves), and is unlike the transmitted wave in the $\psi^i < \psi^i_c$ case (also a uniform plane wave). The transmitted wave that we have derived in the $\psi^i > \psi^i_c$ case gives the impression of being somehow attached to the boundary, and so may be described as a *surface wave*. However, in this case we have a particular kind of surface wave, known as an *evanescent wave*. Summarizing:

> When total internal reflection occurs, the transmitted field is an evanescent wave; i.e., a surface wave which conveys no power and whose magnitude decays exponentially with increasing distance into Region 2.

At this point, we could enforce the "phase matching" condition at the boundary, which would lead us to a new version of Snell's law that would allow us to solve for ψ'' in terms of ψ^i and the constitutive properties of the media comprising Regions 1 and 2. We could subsequently determine values for the phase propagation and attenuation constants for the evanescent wave. It suffices to say that the magnitude of the evanescent field becomes negligible beyond a few wavelengths of the boundary.

Finally, we return to the strangest characteristic of this field: It acts like a wave, but conveys no power. This field exists solely to enforce the electromagnetic boundary conditions at the boundary, and does not exist independently of the incident and reflected field. The following thought experiment may provide some additional insight.

In this experiment, a laser illuminates a planar boundary between two material regions, with conditions such that total internal reflection occurs. Thus, all incident power is reflected, and an evanescent wave exists on the opposite side of the boundary. Next, the laser is turned off. All the light incident on the boundary reflects from the boundary and continues to propagate to infinity, even after light is no longer incident on the boundary. In contrast, the evanescent wave vanishes at the moment laser light ceases to illuminate the boundary. In other words, the evanescent field does not continue to propagate along the boundary to infinity. The reason for this is simply that there is no power – hence, no energy – in the evanescent wave.

Additional Reading:

- "Evanescent field" on Wikipedia.
- "Hyperbolic function" on Wikipedia.
- "Total internal reflection" on Wikipedia.

[m0185]

Image Credits

Fig. 5.1: © Sevenchw (C. Wang),
https://commons.wikimedia.org/wiki/File:Upw_incident_on_planar_boundary.svg,
CC BY-SA 4.0 (https://creativecommons.org/licenses/by-sa/4.0/).

Fig. 5.2: © Sevenchw (C. Wang), https://commons.wikimedia.org/wiki/File:Upw_incident_on_a_slab.svg,
CC BY-SA 4.0 (https://creativecommons.org/licenses/by-sa/4.0/).

Fig. 5.3: © Sevenchw (C. Wang),
https://commons.wikimedia.org/wiki/File:Double-boundary_problem_equivalent.svg,
CC BY-SA 4.0 (https://creativecommons.org/licenses/by-sa/4.0/).

Fig. 5.4: © Sevenchw (C. Wang), https://commons.wikimedia.org/wiki/File:Plane_wave_in_basic_coord.svg,
CC BY-SA 4.0 (https://creativecommons.org/licenses/by-sa/4.0/).

Fig. 5.5: © Sevenchw (C. Wang), https://commons.wikimedia.org/wiki/File:Plane_wave_in_rotated_coord.svg,
CC BY-SA 4.0 (https://creativecommons.org/licenses/by-sa/4.0/).

Fig. 5.6: © Sevenchw (C. Wang),
https://commons.wikimedia.org/wiki/File:Plane_wave_in_another_rotation_coord.svg,
CC BY-SA 4.0 (https://creativecommons.org/licenses/by-sa/4.0/).

Fig. 5.7: © Sevenchw (C. Wang),
https://commons.wikimedia.org/wiki/File:Plane_wave_in_ray-fixed_coord.svg,
CC BY-SA 4.0 (https://creativecommons.org/licenses/by-sa/4.0/).

Fig. 5.8: © Sevenchw (C. Wang),
https://commons.wikimedia.org/wiki/File:Coord_system_for_TE-TM_decomposition.svg,
CC BY-SA 4.0 (https://creativecommons.org/licenses/by-sa/4.0/).

Fig. 5.9: © Sevenchw (C. Wang),
https://commons.wikimedia.org/wiki/File:TE-polarized_upw_incident_on_planar_boundary.svg,
CC BY-SA 4.0 (https://creativecommons.org/licenses/by-sa/4.0/).

Fig. 5.10: © Sevenchw (C. Wang),
https://commons.wikimedia.org/wiki/File:Incident_reflected_and_transmitted_magnetic_field_components.svg,
CC BY-SA 4.0 (https://creativecommons.org/licenses/by-sa/4.0/).

Fig. 5.11: © Sevenchw (C. Wang),
https://commons.wikimedia.org/wiki/File:TE-polarized_upw_incident_from_air_to_glass.svg,
CC BY-SA 4.0 (https://creativecommons.org/licenses/by-sa/4.0/).

Fig. 5.12: © Sevenchw (C. Wang),
https://commons.wikimedia.org/wiki/File:TM-polarized_upw_incident_on_planar_boundary.svg,
CC BY-SA 4.0 (https://creativecommons.org/licenses/by-sa/4.0/).

Fig. 5.13: © Sevenchw (C. Wang),
https://commons.wikimedia.org/wiki/File:TM-polarized_upw_incident_from_air_to_glass.svg,
CC BY-SA 4.0 (https://creativecommons.org/licenses/by-sa/4.0/).

Fig. 5.14: © Sevenchw (C. Wang),
https://commons.wikimedia.org/wiki/File:Upw_incident_obliquely_on_planar_boundary.svg,
CC BY-SA 4.0 (https://creativecommons.org/licenses/by-sa/4.0/).

Fig. 5.15: © Z. Sándor, https://commons.wikimedia.org/wiki/File:F%C3%A9nyt%C3%B6r%C3%A9s.jpg,
CC BY-SA 3.0 (https://creativecommons.org/licenses/by-sa/3.0/).

Fig. 5.16: © G. Saini, https://kids.kiddle.co/Image:Refractionn.jpg,
CC BY-SA 4.0 (https://creativecommons.org/licenses/by-sa/4.0/).

Fig. 5.17: © D-Kuru, https://commons.wikimedia.org/wiki/File:Prism-side-fs_PNr%C2%B00117.jpg,
CC BY-SA 3.0 (https://creativecommons.org/licenses/by-sa/3.0/).

Fig. 5.18: © Suidroot, https://commons.wikimedia.org/wiki/File:Prism-rainbow.svg,
CC BY-SA 4.0 (https://creativecommons.org/licenses/by-sa/4.0/).

Fig. 5.19: © Sevenchw (C. Wang),
https://commons.wikimedia.org/wiki/File:TE-polarized_upw_incident_on_planar_boundary.svg,
CC BY-SA 4.0 (https://creativecommons.org/licenses/by-sa/4.0/).

Fig. 5.21: © Sevenchw (C. Wang),
https://commons.wikimedia.org/wiki/File:TM-polarized_upw_incident_on_planar_boundary.svg,
CC BY-SA 4.0 (https://creativecommons.org/licenses/by-sa/4.0/).

Fig. 5.23: © Sevenchw (C. Wang),
https://commons.wikimedia.org/wiki/File:Reflection_of_plane_wave_incidence_angle_equals_polarizing_angle.svg,
CC BY-SA 4.0 (https://creativecommons.org/licenses/by-sa/4.0/).

Fig. 5.24: © Sevenchw (C. Wang),
https://commons.wikimedia.org/wiki/File:Brewster%E2%80%99s_angle_for_non-magnetic_media.svg,
CC BY-SA 4.0 (https://creativecommons.org/licenses/by-sa/4.0/).

Fig. 5.25: © Sevenchw (C. Wang),
https://commons.wikimedia.org/wiki/File:Upw_incident_on_planar_boundary_angle_reflection_equals_incidence.svg,
CC BY-SA 4.0 (https://creativecommons.org/licenses/by-sa/4.0/), modified.

Fig. 5.26: © Z. Sándor,
https://en.wikipedia.org/wiki/File:Teljes_f%C3%A9nyvisszaver%C5%91d%C3%A9s.jpg,
CC BY-SA 3.0 (https://creativecommons.org/licenses/by-sa/3.0/).

Fig. 5.27: © Timwether, https://en.wikipedia.org/wiki/File:Laser_in_fibre.jpg,
CC BY-SA 3.0 (https://creativecommons.org/licenses/by-sa/3.0/).

Fig. 5.28: © Sevenchw (C. Wang),
https://commons.wikimedia.org/wiki/File:Upw_incident_on_planar_boundary_total_internal_reflection.svg,
CC BY-SA 4.0 (https://creativecommons.org/licenses/by-sa/4.0/).

Chapter 6

Waveguides

6.1 Phase and Group Velocity

[m0176]

Phase velocity is the speed at which a point of constant phase travels as the wave propagates.[1] For a sinusoidally-varying wave, this speed is easy to quantify. To see this, consider the wave:

$$A \cos(\omega t - \beta z + \psi) \tag{6.1}$$

where $\omega = 2\pi f$ is angular frequency, z is position, and β is the phase propagation constant. At any given time, the distance between points of constant phase is one wavelength λ. Therefore, the phase velocity v_p is

$$v_p = \lambda f \tag{6.2}$$

Since $\beta = 2\pi/\lambda$, this may also be written as follows:

$$\boxed{v_p = \frac{\omega}{\beta}} \tag{6.3}$$

Noting that $\beta = \omega\sqrt{\mu\epsilon}$ for simple matter, we may also express v_p in terms of the constitutive parameters μ and ϵ as follows:

$$v_p = \frac{1}{\sqrt{\mu\epsilon}} \tag{6.4}$$

Since v_p in this case depends *only* on the constitutive properties μ and ϵ, it is reasonable to view phase velocity also as a property of matter.

[1] Formally, "velocity" is a vector which indicates both the direction and rate of motion. It is common practice to use the terms "phase velocity" and "group velocity" even though we are actually referring merely to rate of motion. The direction is, of course, in the direction of propagation.

Central to the concept of phase velocity is uniformity over space and time. Equations 6.2–6.4 presume a wave having the form of Equation 6.1, which exhibits precisely the same behavior over all possible time t from $-\infty$ to $+\infty$ and over all possible z from $-\infty$ to $+\infty$. This uniformity over all space and time precludes the use of such a wave to send information. To send information, the source of the wave needs to vary at least one parameter as a function of time; for example A (resulting in amplitude modulation), ω (resulting in frequency modulation), or ψ (resulting in phase modulation). In other words, information can be transmitted only by making the wave non-uniform in some respect. Furthermore, some materials and structures can cause changes in ψ or other combinations of parameters which vary with position or time. Examples include dispersion and propagation within waveguides. Regardless of the cause, varying the parameters ω or ψ as a function of time means that the instantaneous distance between points of constant phase may be very different from λ. Thus, the *instantaneous* frequency of variation as a function of time and position may be very different from f. In this case Equations 6.2–6.4 may not necessarily provide a meaningful value for the speed of propagation.

Some other concept is required to describe the speed of propagation of such waves. That concept is *group velocity*, v_g, defined as follows:

> *Group velocity*, v_g, is the ratio of the apparent change in frequency ω to the associated change in the phase propagation constant β; i.e., $\Delta\omega/\Delta\beta$.

Letting $\Delta\beta$ become vanishingly small, we obtain

$$\boxed{v_g \triangleq \frac{\partial \omega}{\partial \beta}} \tag{6.5}$$

Note the similarity to the definition of phase velocity in Equation 6.3. Group velocity can be interpreted as the speed at which a *disturbance* in the wave propagates. Information may be conveyed as meaningful disturbances relative to a steady-state condition, so group velocity is also the speed of information in a wave.

Note Equation 6.5 yields the expected result for waves in the form of Equation 6.1:

$$v_g = \left(\frac{\partial \beta}{\partial \omega}\right)^{-1} = \left(\frac{\partial}{\partial \omega}\omega\sqrt{\mu\epsilon}\right)^{-1}$$
$$= \frac{1}{\sqrt{\mu\epsilon}} = v_p \tag{6.6}$$

In other words, the group velocity of a wave in the form of Equation 6.1 is equal to its phase velocity.

To observe a difference between v_p and v_g, β must somehow vary as a function of something other than just ω and the constitutive parameters. Again, modulation (introduced by the source of the wave) and dispersion (frequency-dependent constitutive parameters) are examples in which v_g is not necessarily equal to v_p. Here's an example involving dispersion:

Example 6.1. Phase and group velocity for a material exhibiting square-law dispersion.

A broad class of non-magnetic dispersive media exhibit relative permittivity ϵ_r that varies as the square of frequency over a narrow range of frequencies centered at ω_0. For these media we presume

$$\epsilon_r = K\left(\frac{\omega}{\omega_0}\right)^2 \tag{6.7}$$

where K is a real-valued positive constant. What is the phase and group velocity for a sinusoidally-varying wave in this material?

Solution. First, note

$$\beta = \omega\sqrt{\mu_0\epsilon} = \omega\sqrt{\mu_0\epsilon_0}\sqrt{\epsilon_r}$$
$$= \frac{\sqrt{K}\cdot\omega^2}{\omega_0}\sqrt{\mu_0\epsilon_0} \tag{6.8}$$

The phase velocity is:

$$v_p = \frac{\omega}{\beta} = \frac{\omega_0}{\sqrt{K}\cdot\omega\sqrt{\mu_0\epsilon_0}} \tag{6.9}$$

Whereas the group velocity is:

$$v_g = \frac{\partial \omega}{\partial \beta} = \left(\frac{\partial \beta}{\partial \omega}\right)^{-1} \tag{6.10}$$
$$= \left(\frac{\partial}{\partial \omega}\frac{\sqrt{K}\cdot\omega^2}{\omega_0}\sqrt{\mu_0\epsilon_0}\right)^{-1} \tag{6.11}$$
$$= \left(2\frac{\sqrt{K}\cdot\omega}{\omega_0}\sqrt{\mu_0\epsilon_0}\right)^{-1} \tag{6.12}$$

Now simplifying using Equation 6.8:

$$v_g = \left(2\frac{\beta}{\omega}\right)^{-1} \tag{6.13}$$
$$= \frac{1}{2}\frac{\omega}{\beta} \tag{6.14}$$
$$= \frac{1}{2}v_p \tag{6.15}$$

Thus, we see that in this case the group velocity is always half the phase velocity.

Another commonly-encountered example for which v_g is not necessarily equal to v_p is the propagation of guided waves; e.g., waves within a waveguide. In fact, such waves may exhibit phase velocity greater than the speed of light in a vacuum, c. However, the group velocity remains less than c, which means the speed at which information may propagate in a waveguide is less than c. No physical laws are violated, since the universal "speed limit" c applies to information, and not simply points of constant phase. (See "Additional Reading" at the end of this section for more on this concept.)

Additional Reading:

- "Group velocity" on Wikipedia.

- "Phase velocity" on Wikipedia.
- "Speed of light" on Wikipedia.

6.2 Parallel Plate Waveguide: Introduction

[m0173]

A parallel plate waveguide is a device for guiding the propagation of waves between two perfectly-conducting plates. Our primary interest in this structure is as a rudimentary model applicable to a broad range of engineering problems. Examples of such problems include analysis of the fields within microstrip line and propagation of radio waves in the ionosphere.

Figure 6.1 shows the geometry of interest. Here the plates are located at $z = 0$ and $z = a$. The plates are assumed to be infinite in extent, and therefore there is no need to consider fields in the regions $z < 0$ or $z > a$. For this analysis, the region between the plates is assumed to consist of an ideal (lossless) material exhibiting real-valued permeability μ and real-valued permittivity ϵ.

Let us limit our attention to a region within the waveguide which is free of sources. Expressed in phasor form, the electric field intensity is governed by the wave equation

$$\nabla^2 \widetilde{\mathbf{E}} + \beta^2 \widetilde{\mathbf{E}} = 0 \tag{6.16}$$

where

$$\beta = \omega\sqrt{\mu\epsilon} \tag{6.17}$$

Equation 6.16 is a partial differential equation. This equation, combined with boundary conditions

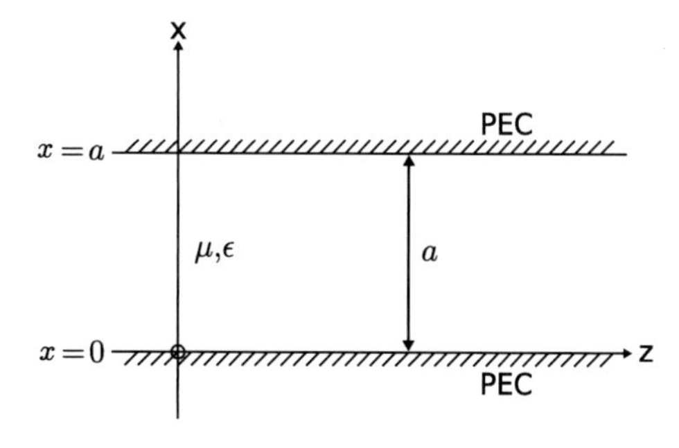

© C. Wang CC BY-SA 4.0 (modified)

Figure 6.1: Geometry for analysis of fields in a parallel plate waveguide.

imposed by the perfectly-conducting plates, is sufficient to determine a unique solution. This is most easily done in Cartesian coordinates, as we shall now demonstrate. First we express $\widetilde{\mathbf{E}}$ in Cartesian coordinates:

$$\widetilde{\mathbf{E}} = \hat{\mathbf{x}}\widetilde{E}_x + \hat{\mathbf{y}}\widetilde{E}_y + \hat{\mathbf{z}}\widetilde{E}_z \quad (6.18)$$

This facilitates the decomposition of Equation 6.16 into separate equations governing the $\hat{\mathbf{x}}$, $\hat{\mathbf{y}}$, $\hat{\mathbf{z}}$ components of $\widetilde{\mathbf{E}}$:

$$\nabla^2\widetilde{E}_x + \beta^2\widetilde{E}_x = 0 \quad (6.19)$$

$$\nabla^2\widetilde{E}_y + \beta^2\widetilde{E}_y = 0 \quad (6.20)$$

$$\nabla^2\widetilde{E}_z + \beta^2\widetilde{E}_z = 0 \quad (6.21)$$

Next we observe that the operator ∇^2 may be expressed in Cartesian coordinates as follows:

$$\nabla^2 = \frac{\partial^2}{\partial x^2} + \frac{\partial^2}{\partial y^2} + \frac{\partial^2}{\partial z^2} \quad (6.22)$$

so the equations governing the Cartesian components of $\widetilde{\mathbf{E}}$ may be written as follows:

$$\frac{\partial^2}{\partial x^2}\widetilde{E}_x + \frac{\partial^2}{\partial y^2}\widetilde{E}_x + \frac{\partial^2}{\partial z^2}\widetilde{E}_x = -\beta^2\widetilde{E}_x \quad (6.23)$$

$$\frac{\partial^2}{\partial x^2}\widetilde{E}_y + \frac{\partial^2}{\partial y^2}\widetilde{E}_y + \frac{\partial^2}{\partial z^2}\widetilde{E}_y = -\beta^2\widetilde{E}_y \quad (6.24)$$

$$\frac{\partial^2}{\partial x^2}\widetilde{E}_z + \frac{\partial^2}{\partial y^2}\widetilde{E}_z + \frac{\partial^2}{\partial z^2}\widetilde{E}_z = -\beta^2\widetilde{E}_z \quad (6.25)$$

Let us restrict our attention to scenarios that can be completely described in two dimensions; namely x and z, and for which there is no variation in y. This is not necessarily required, however, it is representative of a broad class of relevant problems, and allows Equations 6.23–6.25 to be considerably simplified. If there is no variation in y, then partial derivatives with respect to y are zero, yielding:

$$\frac{\partial^2}{\partial x^2}\widetilde{E}_x + \frac{\partial^2}{\partial z^2}\widetilde{E}_x = -\beta^2\widetilde{E}_x \quad (6.26)$$

$$\frac{\partial^2}{\partial x^2}\widetilde{E}_y + \frac{\partial^2}{\partial z^2}\widetilde{E}_y = -\beta^2\widetilde{E}_y \quad (6.27)$$

$$\frac{\partial^2}{\partial x^2}\widetilde{E}_z + \frac{\partial^2}{\partial z^2}\widetilde{E}_z = -\beta^2\widetilde{E}_z \quad (6.28)$$

The solution to the parallel plate waveguide problem may now be summarized as follows: The electric field $\widetilde{\mathbf{E}}$ (Equation 6.18) is the solution to simultaneous Equations 6.26–6.28 subject to the boundary conditions that apply at the PEC surfaces at $z = 0$ and $z = d$; namely, that the tangent component of $\widetilde{\mathbf{E}}$ is zero at these surfaces.

At this point, the problem has been reduced to a routine exercise in the solution of partial differential equations. However, a somewhat more useful approach is to first decompose the total electric field into transverse electric (TE) and transverse magnetic (TM) components,[2] and determine the solutions to these components separately. The TE component of the electric field is parallel to the plates, and therefore transverse (perpendicular) to the plane shown in Figure 6.1. Thus, the TE component has $\widetilde{E}_x = \widetilde{E}_z = 0$, and only $\widetilde{E}_y$ may be non-zero. The TM component of the magnetic field intensity ($\widetilde{\mathbf{H}}$) is parallel to the plates, and therefore transverse to the plane shown in Figure 6.1. Thus, the TM component has $\widetilde{H}_x = \widetilde{H}_z = 0$, and only $\widetilde{H}_y$ may be non-zero. As always, the total field is the sum of the TE and TM components.

The TE and TM solutions are presented in Sections 6.3 (Electric component of the TE solution), 6.4 (Magnetic component of the TE solution), and 6.5 (Electric component of the TM solution). The magnetic component of the TM solution can be determined via a straightforward variation of the preceding three cases, and so is not presented here.

Presentation of the solution for the fields in a parallel plate waveguide under the conditions described in the section continues in Section 6.3.

[2]For a refresher on TE-TM decomposition, see Section 5.5.

6.3 Parallel Plate Waveguide: TE Case, Electric Field

[m0174]

In Section 6.2, the parallel plate waveguide was introduced. At the end of that section, we described the decomposition of the problem into its TE and TM components. In this section, we find the electric field component of the TE field in the waveguide.

Figure 6.2 shows the problem addressed in this section. (Additional details and assumptions are addressed in Section 6.2.)

Since $\widetilde{E}_x = \widetilde{E}_z = 0$ for the TE component of the electric field, Equations 6.26 and 6.28 are irrelevant, leaving only:

$$\frac{\partial^2}{\partial x^2}\widetilde{E}_y + \frac{\partial^2}{\partial z^2}\widetilde{E}_y = -\beta^2 \widetilde{E}_y \tag{6.29}$$

The general solution to this partial differential equation is:

$$\begin{aligned}\widetilde{E}_y = \; & e^{-jk_z z}\left[Ae^{-jk_x x} + Be^{+jk_x x}\right] \\ & + e^{+jk_z z}\left[Ce^{-jk_x x} + De^{+jk_x x}\right]\end{aligned} \tag{6.30}$$

where A, B, C, and D are complex-valued constants and k_x and k_z are real-valued constants. We have assigned variable names to these constants with advance knowledge of their physical interpretation; however, at this moment they remain simply unknown constants whose values must be determined by enforcement of boundary conditions.

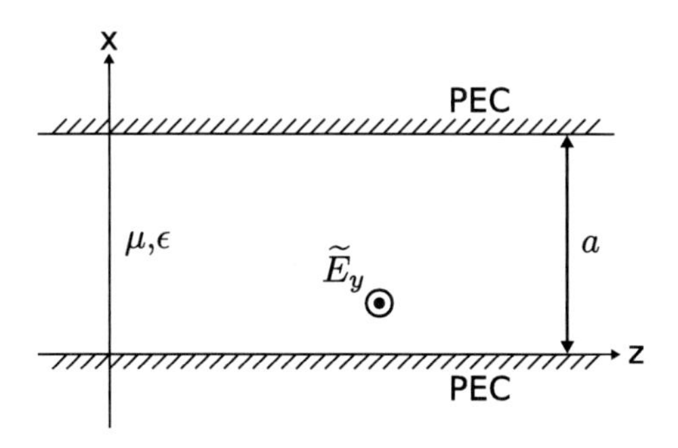

© C. Wang CC BY-SA 4.0

Figure 6.2: TE component of the electric field in a parallel plate waveguide.

Note that Equation 6.30 consists of two terms. The first term includes the factor $e^{-jk_z z}$, indicating a wave propagating in the $+\hat{\mathbf{z}}$ direction, and the second term includes the factor $e^{+jk_z z}$, indicating a wave propagating in the $-\hat{\mathbf{z}}$ direction. If we impose the restriction that sources exist only on the left ($z < 0$) side of Figure 6.2, and that there be no structure capable of wave scattering (in particular, reflection) on the right ($z > 0$) side of Figure 6.2, then there can be no wave components propagating in the $-\hat{\mathbf{z}}$ direction. In this case, $C = D = 0$ and Equation 6.30 simplifies to:

$$\widetilde{E}_y = e^{-jk_z z}\left[Ae^{-jk_x x} + Be^{+jk_x x}\right] \tag{6.31}$$

Before proceeding, let's make sure that Equation 6.31 is actually a solution to Equation 6.29. As we shall see in a moment, performing this check will reveal some additional useful information. First, note:

$$\frac{\partial \widetilde{E}_y}{\partial x} = e^{-jk_z z}\left[-Ae^{-jk_x x} + Be^{+jk_x x}\right](jk_x) \tag{6.32}$$

So:

$$\frac{\partial^2 \widetilde{E}_y}{\partial x^2} = e^{-jk_z z}\left[Ae^{-jk_x x} + Be^{+jk_x x}\right]\left(-k_x^2\right) \tag{6.33}$$

Comparing this to Equation 6.31, we observe the remarkable fact that

$$\frac{\partial^2 \widetilde{E}_y}{\partial x^2} = -k_x^2 \widetilde{E}_y \tag{6.34}$$

Similarly, note:

$$\frac{\partial \widetilde{E}_y}{\partial z} = e^{-jk_z z}\left[Ae^{-jk_x x} + Be^{+jk_x x}\right](-jk_z) \tag{6.35}$$

So:

$$\begin{aligned}\frac{\partial^2 \widetilde{E}_y}{\partial z^2} &= e^{-jk_z z}\left[Ae^{-jk_x x} + Be^{+jk_x x}\right]\left(-k_z^2\right) \\ &= -k_z^2 \widetilde{E}_y\end{aligned} \tag{6.36}$$

Now summing these results:

$$\frac{\partial^2 \widetilde{E}_y}{\partial x^2} + \frac{\partial^2 \widetilde{E}_y}{\partial z^2} = -\left(k_x^2 + k_z^2\right)\widetilde{E}_y \tag{6.37}$$

Comparing Equation 6.37 to Equation 6.29, we conclude that Equation 6.31 is indeed a solution to Equation 6.29, but only if:

$$\beta^2 = k_x^2 + k_z^2 \tag{6.38}$$

This confirms that k_x and k_z are in fact the components of the propagation vector

$$\mathbf{k} \triangleq \beta\hat{\mathbf{k}} = \hat{\mathbf{x}}k_x + \hat{\mathbf{y}}k_y + \hat{\mathbf{z}}k_z \tag{6.39}$$

where $\hat{\mathbf{k}}$ is the unit vector pointing in the direction of propagation, and $k_y = 0$ in this particular problem.

The solution has now been reduced to finding the constants A, B, and either k_x or k_z. This is accomplished by enforcing the relevant boundary conditions. In general, the component of $\widetilde{\mathbf{E}}$ that is tangent to a perfectly-conducting surface is zero. Applied to the present problem, this means $\widetilde{E}_y = 0$ at $x = 0$ and $\widetilde{E}_y = 0$ at $x = a$. Referring to Equation 6.31, the boundary condition at $x = 0$ means

$$e^{-jk_z z}\left[A \cdot 1 + B \cdot 1\right] = 0 \tag{6.40}$$

The factor $e^{-jk_z z}$ cannot be zero; therefore, $A + B = 0$. Since $B = -A$, we may rewrite Equation 6.31 as follows:

$$\widetilde{E}_y = e^{-jk_z z}B\left[e^{+jk_x x} - e^{-jk_x x}\right] \tag{6.41}$$

This expression is simplified using a trigonometric identity:

$$\frac{1}{2j}\left[e^{+jk_x x} - e^{-jk_x x}\right] = \sin k_x x \tag{6.42}$$

Let us now make the definition $E_{y0} \triangleq j2B$. Then:

$$\widetilde{E}_y = E_{y0}e^{-jk_z z}\sin k_x x \tag{6.43}$$

Now applying the boundary condition at $x = a$:

$$E_{y0}e^{-jk_z z}\sin k_x a = 0 \tag{6.44}$$

The factor $e^{-jk_z z}$ cannot be zero, and $E_{y0} = 0$ yields only trivial solutions; therefore:

$$\sin k_x a = 0 \tag{6.45}$$

This in turn requires that

$$k_x a = m\pi \tag{6.46}$$

where m is an integer. Note that $m = 0$ is not of interest since this yields $k_x = 0$, which according to Equation 6.43 yields the trivial solution $\widetilde{E}_y = 0$. Also each integer value of m that is less than zero is excluded because the associated solution is different from the solution for the corresponding positive value of m in sign only, which can be absorbed in the arbitrary constant E_{y0}.

At this point we have uncovered a family of solutions given by Equation 6.43 and Equation 6.46 with $m = 1, 2, ...$ Each solution associated with a particular value of m is referred to as a *mode*, which (via Equation 6.46) has a particular value of k_x. The value of k_z for mode m is obtained using Equation 6.38 as follows:

$$\begin{aligned} k_z &= \sqrt{\beta^2 - k_x^2} \\ &= \sqrt{\beta^2 - \left(\frac{m\pi}{a}\right)^2} \end{aligned} \tag{6.47}$$

Since k_z is specified to be real-valued, we require:

$$\beta^2 - \left(\frac{m\pi}{a}\right)^2 > 0 \tag{6.48}$$

This constrains β; specifically:

$$\beta > \frac{m\pi}{a} \tag{6.49}$$

Recall that $\beta = \omega\sqrt{\mu\epsilon}$ and $\omega = 2\pi f$ where f is frequency. Solving for f, we find:

$$f > \frac{m}{2a\sqrt{\mu\epsilon}} \tag{6.50}$$

Therefore, each mode exists only above a certain frequency, which is different for each mode. This *cutoff frequency* f_c for mode m is given by

$$\boxed{f_c^{(m)} \triangleq \frac{m}{2a\sqrt{\mu\epsilon}}} \tag{6.51}$$

At frequencies below the cutoff frequency for mode m, modes 1 through $m - 1$ exhibit imaginary-valued k_z. The propagation constant must have a real-valued component in order to propagate; therefore, these modes do not propagate and may be ignored.

Let us now summarize the solution. For the scenario depicted in Figure 6.2, the electric field component of the TE solution is given by:

$$\boxed{\hat{\mathbf{y}}\widetilde{E}_y = \hat{\mathbf{y}}\sum_{m=1}^{\infty}\widetilde{E}_y^{(m)}} \tag{6.52}$$

where

$$\widetilde{E}_y^{(m)} \triangleq \begin{cases} 0, & f < f_c^{(m)} \\ E_{y0}^{(m)} e^{-jk_z^{(m)} z} \sin k_x^{(m)} x, & f \geq f_c^{(m)} \end{cases} \quad (6.53)$$

where m enumerates modes ($m = 1, 2, ...$),

$$k_z^{(m)} \triangleq \sqrt{\beta^2 - \left[k_x^{(m)}\right]^2} \quad (6.54)$$

and

$$k_x^{(m)} \triangleq m\pi/a \quad (6.55)$$

Finally, $E_{y0}^{(m)}$ is a complex-valued constant that depends on sources or boundary conditions to the left of the region of interest.

For the scenario depicted in Figure 6.2, the electric field component of the TE solution is given by Equation 6.52 with modal components determined as indicated by Equations 6.51–6.55. This solution presumes all sources lie to the left of the region of interest, and no scattering occurs to the right of the region of interest.

To better understand this result, let us examine the lowest-order mode, $m = 1$. For this mode $f_c^{(1)} = 1/2a\sqrt{\mu\epsilon}$, so this mode can exist if $f > 1/2a\sqrt{\mu\epsilon}$. Also $k_x^{(1)} = \pi/a$, so

$$k_z^{(1)} = \sqrt{\beta^2 - \left(\frac{\pi}{a}\right)^2} \quad (6.56)$$

Subsequently,

$$\widetilde{E}_y^{(1)} = E_{y0}^{(1)} e^{-jk_z^{(1)} z} \sin \frac{\pi x}{a} \quad (6.57)$$

Note that this mode has the form of a plane wave. The plane wave propagates in the $+\hat{\mathbf{z}}$ direction with phase propagation constant $k_z^{(1)}$. Also, we observe that the apparent plane wave is non-uniform, exhibiting magnitude proportional to $\sin \pi x/a$ within the waveguide. This is shown in Figure 6.3 (left image). In particular, we observe that the magnitude of the wave is zero at the perfectly-conducting surfaces – as is necessary to satisfy the boundary conditions – and is maximum in the center of the waveguide.

Now let us examine the $m = 2$ mode. For this mode, $f_c^{(2)} = 1/a\sqrt{\mu\epsilon}$, so this mode can exist if

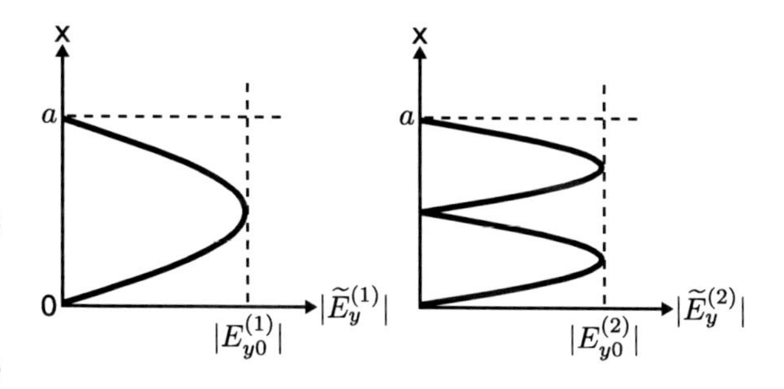

© C. Wang CC BY-SA 4.0

Figure 6.3: Magnitude of the two lowest-order TE modes in a parallel plate waveguide. *Left:* $m = 1$, *Right:* $m = 2$.

$f > 1/a\sqrt{\mu\epsilon}$. This frequency is higher than $f_c^{(1)}$, so the $m = 1$ mode can exist at any frequency at which the $m = 2$ mode exists. Also $k_x^{(2)} = 2\pi/a$, so

$$k_z^{(2)} = \sqrt{\beta^2 - \left(\frac{2\pi}{a}\right)^2} \quad (6.58)$$

Subsequently,

$$\widetilde{E}_y^{(2)} = E_{y0}^{(2)} e^{-jk_z^{(2)} z} \sin \frac{2\pi x}{a} \quad (6.59)$$

In this case, the apparent plane wave propagates in the $+\hat{\mathbf{z}}$ direction with phase propagation constant $k_z^{(2)}$, which is less than $k_z^{(1)}$. For $m = 2$, we find magnitude is proportional to $\sin 2\pi x/a$ within the waveguide (Figure 6.3, right image). As in the $m = 1$ case, we observe that the magnitude of the wave is zero at the PEC surfaces; however, for $m = 2$, there are *two* maxima with respect to x, and the magnitude in the center of the waveguide is zero.

This pattern continues for higher-order modes. In particular, each successive mode exhibits higher cutoff frequency, smaller propagation constant, and increasing integer number of sinusoidal half-periods in magnitude.

Example 6.2. Single-mode TE propagation in a parallel plate waveguide.

Consider an air-filled parallel plate waveguide consisting of plates separated by 1 cm. Determine the frequency range for which one (and only one) propagating TE mode is assured.

Solution. Single-mode TE propagation is assured by limiting frequency f to greater than the cutoff frequency for $m = 1$, but lower than the cutoff frequency for $m = 2$. (Any frequency higher than the cutoff frequency for $m = 2$ allows at least 2 modes to exist.) Calculating the applicable cutoff frequencies, we find:

$$f_c^{(1)} = \frac{1}{2a\sqrt{\mu_0\epsilon_0}} \cong 15.0 \text{ GHz} \tag{6.60}$$

$$f_c^{(2)} = \frac{2}{2a\sqrt{\mu_0\epsilon_0}} \cong 30.0 \text{ GHz} \tag{6.61}$$

Therefore, $\underline{15.0 \text{ GHz} \leq f \leq 30.0 \text{ GHz}}$.

Finally, let us consider the phase velocity v_p within the waveguide. For lowest-order mode $m = 1$, this is

$$v_p = \frac{\omega}{k_z^{(1)}} = \frac{\omega}{\sqrt{\omega^2\mu\epsilon - \left(\frac{\pi}{a}\right)^2}} \tag{6.62}$$

Recall that the speed of an electromagnetic wave in unbounded space (i.e., not in a waveguide) is $1/\sqrt{\mu\epsilon}$. For example, the speed of light in free space is $1/\sqrt{\mu_0\epsilon_0} = c$. However, the phase velocity indicated by Equation 6.62 is *greater* than $1/\sqrt{\mu\epsilon}$; e.g., faster than light would travel in the same material (presuming it were transparent). At first glance, this may seem to be impossible. However, recall that *information* travels at the group velocity v_g, and not necessarily the phase velocity. (See Section 6.1 for a refresher.) Although we shall not demonstrate this here, the group velocity in the parallel plate waveguide is always *less* than $1/\sqrt{\mu\epsilon}$, so no physical laws are broken, and signals travel somewhat slower than the speed of light, as they do in any other structure used to convey signals.

Also remarkable is that the speed of propagation is different for each mode. In fact, we find that the phase velocity increases and the group velocity decreases as m increases. This phenomenon is known as *dispersion*, and sometimes specifically as *mode dispersion* or *modal dispersion*.

6.4 Parallel Plate Waveguide: TE Case, Magnetic Field

[m0175]

In Section 6.2, the parallel plate waveguide was introduced. In Section 6.3, we determined the TE component of the electric field. In this section, we determine the TE component of the magnetic field. The reader should be familiar with Section 6.3 before attempting this section.

In Section 6.3, the TE component of the electric field was determined to be:

$$\hat{\mathbf{y}}\widetilde{E}_y = \hat{\mathbf{y}}\sum_{m=1}^{\infty}\widetilde{E}_y^{(m)} \tag{6.63}$$

The TE component of the magnetic field may be obtained from the Maxwell-Faraday equation:

$$\nabla \times \widetilde{\mathbf{E}} = -j\omega\mu\widetilde{\mathbf{H}} \tag{6.64}$$

Thus:

$$\begin{aligned}\widetilde{\mathbf{H}} &= \frac{j}{\omega\mu}\nabla\times\widetilde{\mathbf{E}} \\ &= \frac{j}{\omega\mu}\nabla\times\left(\hat{\mathbf{y}}\widetilde{E}_y\right)\end{aligned} \tag{6.65}$$

The relevant form of the curl operator is Equation B.16 (Appendix B.2). Although the complete expression consists of 6 terms, all but 2 of these terms are zero because the $\hat{\mathbf{x}}$ and $\hat{\mathbf{z}}$ components of $\widetilde{\mathbf{E}}$ are zero. The two remaining terms are $-\hat{\mathbf{x}}\partial\widetilde{E}_y/\partial z$ and $+\hat{\mathbf{z}}\partial\widetilde{E}_y/\partial x$. Thus:

$$\widetilde{\mathbf{H}} = \frac{j}{\omega\mu}\left(-\hat{\mathbf{x}}\frac{\partial\widetilde{E}_y}{\partial z} + \hat{\mathbf{z}}\frac{\partial\widetilde{E}_y}{\partial x}\right) \tag{6.66}$$

Recall that $\widetilde{E}_y$ is the sum of modes, as indicated in Equation 6.63. Since differentiation (i.e., $\partial/\partial z$ and $\partial/\partial x$) is a linear operator, we may evaluate Equation 6.66 for modes one at a time, and then sum the results. Using this approach, we find:

$$\begin{aligned}\frac{\partial\widetilde{E}_y^{(m)}}{\partial z} &= \frac{\partial}{\partial z}\,E_{y0}^{(m)}e^{-jk_z^{(m)}z}\sin k_x^{(m)}x \\ &= \left(E_{y0}^{(m)}e^{-jk_z^{(m)}z}\sin k_x^{(m)}x\right)\left(-jk_z^{(m)}\right)\end{aligned} \tag{6.67}$$

and

$$\frac{\partial \widetilde{E}_y^{(m)}}{\partial x} = \frac{\partial}{\partial x} E_{y0}^{(m)} e^{-jk_z^{(m)} z} \sin k_x^{(m)} x$$
$$= \left(E_{y0}^{(m)} e^{-jk_z^{(m)} z} \cos k_x^{(m)} x\right)\left(+k_x^{(m)}\right) \quad (6.68)$$

We may now assemble a solution for the magnetic field as follows:

$$\hat{\mathbf{x}}\widetilde{H}_x + \hat{\mathbf{z}}\widetilde{H}_z = \hat{\mathbf{x}} \sum_{m=1}^{\infty} \widetilde{H}_x^{(m)} + \hat{\mathbf{z}} \sum_{m=1}^{\infty} \widetilde{H}_z^{(m)} \quad (6.69)$$

where

$$\widetilde{H}_x^{(m)} = -\frac{k_z^{(m)}}{\omega\mu} E_{y0}^{(m)} e^{-jk_z^{(m)} z} \sin k_x^{(m)} x \quad (6.70)$$

$$\widetilde{H}_z^{(m)} = +j\frac{k_x^{(m)}}{\omega\mu} E_{y0}^{(m)} e^{-jk_z^{(m)} z} \cos k_x^{(m)} x \quad (6.71)$$

and modes may only exist at frequencies greater than the associated cutoff frequencies. Summarizing:

> The magnetic field component of the TE solution is given by Equation 6.69 with modal components as indicated by Equations 6.70 and 6.71. Caveats pertaining to the cutoff frequencies and the locations of sources and structures continue to apply.

This result is quite complex, yet some additional insight is possible. At the perfectly-conducting (PEC) surface at $x = 0$, we see

$$\widetilde{H}_x^{(m)}(x=0) = 0$$
$$\widetilde{H}_z^{(m)}(x=0) = +j\frac{k_x^{(m)}}{\omega\mu} E_{y0}^{(m)} e^{-jk_z^{(m)} z} \quad (6.72)$$

Similarly, on the PEC surface at $x = a$, we see

$$\widetilde{H}_x^{(m)}(x=a) = 0$$
$$\widetilde{H}_z^{(m)}(x=a) = -j\frac{k_x^{(m)}}{\omega\mu} E_{y0}^{(m)} e^{-jk_z^{(m)} z} \quad (6.73)$$

Thus, we see the magnetic field vector at the PEC surfaces is non-zero and parallel to the PEC surfaces.

Recall that the magnetic field is identically zero *inside* a PEC material. Also recall that boundary conditions require that discontinuity in the component of $\mathbf{H}$ tangent to a surface must be supported by a surface current. We conclude that

> Current flows on the PEC surfaces of the waveguide.

If this seems surprising, note that essentially the same thing happens in a coaxial transmission line. That is, signals in a coaxial transmission line can be described equally well in terms of either potentials and currents on the inner and outer conductors, or the electromagnetic fields between the conductors. The parallel plate waveguide is only slightly more complicated because the field in a properly-designed coaxial cable is a single transverse electromagnetic (TEM) mode, whereas the fields in a parallel plate waveguide are combinations of TE and TM modes.

Interestingly, we also find that the magnetic field vector points in different directions depending on position relative to the conducting surfaces. We just determined that the magnetic field is parallel to the conducting surfaces at those surfaces. However, the magnetic field is *perpendicular* to those surfaces at m locations between $x = 0$ and $x = a$. These locations correspond to maxima in the electric field.

6.5 Parallel Plate Waveguide: TM Case, Electric Field

[m0177]

In Section 6.2, the parallel plate waveguide shown in Figure 6.4 was introduced. At the end of that section, we decomposed the problem into its TE and TM components. In this section, we find the TM component of the fields in the waveguide.

"Transverse magnetic" means the magnetic field vector is perpendicular to the plane of interest, and is therefore parallel to the conducting surfaces. Thus, $\widetilde{\mathbf{H}} = \hat{\mathbf{y}}\widetilde{H}_y$, with no component in the $\hat{\mathbf{x}}$ or $\hat{\mathbf{z}}$ directions. Following precisely the same reasoning employed in Section 6.2, we find the governing equation for the magnetic component of TM field is:

$$\frac{\partial^2}{\partial x^2}\widetilde{H}_y + \frac{\partial^2}{\partial z^2}\widetilde{H}_y = -\beta^2\widetilde{H}_y \tag{6.74}$$

The general solution to this partial differential equation is:

$$\begin{aligned}\widetilde{H}_y = \ & e^{-jk_z z}\left[Ae^{-jk_x x} + Be^{+jk_x x}\right] \\ & + e^{+jk_z z}\left[Ce^{-jk_x x} + De^{+jk_x x}\right]\end{aligned} \tag{6.75}$$

where A, B, C, and D are complex-valued constants; and k_x and k_z are real-valued constants. We have assigned variable names to these constants with advance knowledge of their physical interpretation; however, at this moment they remain simply unknown constants whose values must be determined by enforcement of boundary conditions.

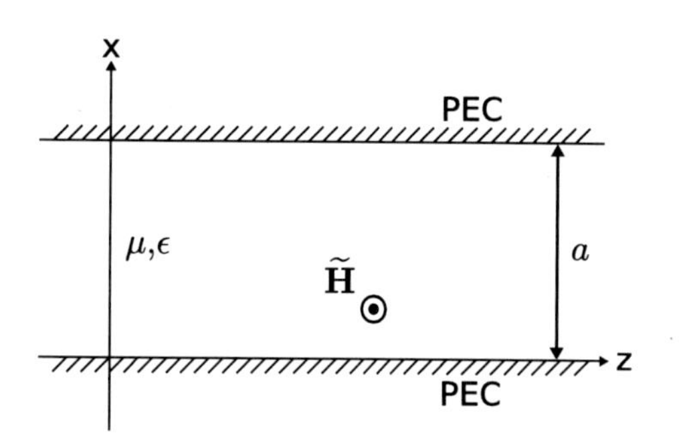

© C. Wang CC BY-SA 4.0

Figure 6.4: TM component of the electric field in a parallel plate waveguide.

Note that Equation 6.75 consists of two terms. The first term includes the factor $e^{-jk_z z}$, indicating a wave propagating in the $+\hat{\mathbf{z}}$ direction, and the second term includes the factor $e^{+jk_z z}$, indicating a wave propagating in the $-\hat{\mathbf{z}}$ direction. If we impose the restriction that sources exist only on the left ($z < 0$) side of Figure 6.4, and that there be no structure capable of wave scattering (in particular, reflection) on the right ($z > 0$) side of Figure 6.4, then there can be no wave components propagating in the $-\hat{\mathbf{z}}$ direction. In this case, $C = D = 0$ and Equation 6.75 simplifies to:

$$\widetilde{H}_y = e^{-jk_z z}\left[Ae^{-jk_x x} + Be^{+jk_x x}\right] \tag{6.76}$$

Before proceeding, let's make sure that Equation 6.76 is actually a solution to Equation 6.74. As in the TE case, this check yields a constraint (in fact, the same constraint) on the as-yet undetermined parameters k_x and k_z. First, note:

$$\frac{\partial \widetilde{H}_y}{\partial x} = e^{-jk_z z}\left[-Ae^{-jk_x x} + Be^{+jk_x x}\right](jk_x) \tag{6.77}$$

So:

$$\begin{aligned}\frac{\partial^2 \widetilde{H}_y}{\partial x^2} &= e^{-jk_z z}\left[Ae^{-jk_x x} + Be^{+jk_x x}\right]\left(-k_x^2\right) \\ &= -k_x^2\widetilde{H}_y\end{aligned} \tag{6.78}$$

Next, note:

$$\frac{\partial \widetilde{H}_y}{\partial z} = e^{-jk_z z}\left[Ae^{-jk_x x} + Be^{+jk_x x}\right](-jk_z) \tag{6.79}$$

So:

$$\begin{aligned}\frac{\partial^2 \widetilde{H}_y}{\partial z^2} &= e^{-jk_z z}\left[Ae^{-jk_x x} + Be^{+jk_x x}\right]\left(-k_z^2\right) \\ &= -k_z^2\widetilde{H}_y\end{aligned} \tag{6.80}$$

Now summing these results:

$$\frac{\partial^2 \widetilde{H}_y}{\partial x^2} + \frac{\partial^2 \widetilde{H}_y}{\partial z^2} = -\left(k_x^2 + k_z^2\right)\widetilde{H}_y \tag{6.81}$$

Comparing Equation 6.81 to Equation 6.74, we conclude that Equation 6.76 is a solution to Equation 6.74 under the constraint that:

$$\beta^2 = k_x^2 + k_z^2 \tag{6.82}$$

This is precisely the same constraint identified in the TE case, and confirms that k_x and k_y are in fact the components of the propagation vector

$$\mathbf{k} \triangleq \beta\hat{\mathbf{k}} = \hat{\mathbf{x}}k_x + \hat{\mathbf{y}}k_y + \hat{\mathbf{z}}k_z \tag{6.83}$$

where $\hat{\mathbf{k}}$ is the unit vector pointing in the direction of propagation, and $k_y = 0$ in this particular problem.

Our objective in this section is to determine the *electric* field component of the TM field. The electric field may be obtained from the magnetic field using Ampere's law:

$$\nabla \times \widetilde{\mathbf{H}} = j\omega\epsilon\widetilde{\mathbf{E}} \tag{6.84}$$

Thus:

$$\begin{aligned}\widetilde{\mathbf{E}} &= \frac{1}{j\omega\epsilon}\,\nabla \times \widetilde{\mathbf{H}} \\ &= \frac{1}{j\omega\epsilon}\,\nabla \times \left(\hat{\mathbf{y}}\widetilde{H}_y\right)\end{aligned} \tag{6.85}$$

The relevant form of the curl operator is Equation B.16 (Appendix B.2). Although the complete expression consists of 6 terms, all but 2 of these terms are zero because the $\hat{\mathbf{x}}$ and $\hat{\mathbf{z}}$ components of $\widetilde{\mathbf{H}}$ are zero. The two remaining terms are $-\hat{\mathbf{x}}\partial\widetilde{H}_y/\partial z$ and $+\hat{\mathbf{z}}\partial\widetilde{H}_y/\partial x$. Thus:

$$\widetilde{\mathbf{E}} = \frac{1}{j\omega\epsilon}\left(-\hat{\mathbf{x}}\frac{\partial\widetilde{H}_y}{\partial z} + \hat{\mathbf{z}}\frac{\partial\widetilde{H}_y}{\partial x}\right) \tag{6.86}$$

We may further develop this expression using Equations 6.77 and 6.79. We find the $\hat{\mathbf{x}}$ component of $\widetilde{\mathbf{E}}$ is:

$$\widetilde{E}_x = \frac{k_z}{\omega\epsilon}\,e^{-jk_z z}\left[Ae^{-jk_x x} + Be^{+jk_x x}\right] \tag{6.87}$$

and the $\hat{\mathbf{z}}$ component of $\widetilde{\mathbf{E}}$ is:

$$\widetilde{E}_z = \frac{k_x}{\omega\epsilon}\,e^{-jk_z z}\left[-Ae^{-jk_x x} + Be^{+jk_x x}\right] \tag{6.88}$$

The solution has now been reduced to the problem of finding the constants A, B, and either k_x or k_z. This is accomplished by enforcing the relevant boundary conditions. In general, the component of the electric field which is tangent to a perfectly-conducting surface is zero. Applied to the present (TM) case, this means $\widetilde{E}_z\,(x=0) = 0$ and $\widetilde{E}_z\,(x=a) = 0$.

Referring to Equation 6.88, the boundary condition at $x = 0$ means

$$\frac{k_x}{\omega\epsilon}\,e^{-jk_z z}\left[-A\,(1) + B\,(1)\right] = 0 \tag{6.89}$$

The factor $e^{-jk_z z}$ always has unit magnitude, and so cannot be zero. We could require k_x to be zero, but this is unnecessarily restrictive. Instead, we require $A = B$ and we may rewrite Equation 6.88 as follows:

$$\widetilde{E}_z = \frac{Bk_x}{\omega\epsilon}\,e^{-jk_z z}\left[e^{+jk_x x} - e^{-jk_x x}\right] \tag{6.90}$$

This expression is simplified using a trigonometric identity:

$$\sin k_x a = \frac{1}{2j}\left[e^{+jk_x a} - e^{-jk_x a}\right] \tag{6.91}$$

Thus:

$$\widetilde{E}_z = \frac{j2Bk_x}{\omega\epsilon}e^{-jk_z z}\sin k_x x \tag{6.92}$$

Now following up with $\widetilde{E}_x$, beginning from Equation 6.87:

$$\begin{aligned}\widetilde{E}_x &= \frac{k_z}{\omega\epsilon}\,e^{-jk_z z}\left[Ae^{-jk_x x} + Be^{+jk_x x}\right] \\ &= \frac{Bk_z}{\omega\epsilon}\,e^{-jk_z z}\left[e^{-jk_x x} + e^{+jk_x x}\right] \\ &= \frac{2Bk_z}{\omega\epsilon}\,e^{-jk_z z}\cos k_x x\end{aligned} \tag{6.93}$$

For convenience we define the following complex-valued constant:

$$E_{x0} \triangleq \frac{2Bk_z}{\omega\epsilon} \tag{6.94}$$

This yields the following simpler expression:

$$\widetilde{E}_x = E_{x0}\,e^{-jk_z z}\cos k_x x \tag{6.95}$$

Now let us apply the boundary condition at $x = a$ to $\widetilde{E}_z$:

$$\frac{j2Bk_z}{\omega\epsilon}e^{-jk_z z}\sin k_x a = 0 \tag{6.96}$$

Requiring $B = 0$ or $k_z = 0$ yields only trivial solutions, therefore, it must be true that

$$\sin k_x a = 0 \tag{6.97}$$

This in turn requires that

$$k_x a = m\pi \tag{6.98}$$

where m is an integer. Note that this is precisely the same relationship that we identified in the TE case. There is an important difference, however. In the TE case, $m = 0$ was not of interest because this yields $k_x = 0$, and the associated field turned out to be identically zero. In the present (TM) case, $m = 0$ also yields $k_x = 0$, but the associated field is not necessarily zero. That is, for $m = 0$, $\widetilde{E}_z = 0$ but $\widetilde{E}_x$ is not necessarily zero. Therefore, $m = 0$ as well as $m = 1$, $m = 2$, and so on are of interest in the TM case.

At this point, we have uncovered a family of solutions with $m = 0, 1, 2, ...$ Each solution is referred to as a *mode*, and is associated with a particular value of k_x. In the discussion that follows, we shall find that the consequences are identical to those identified in the TE case, except that $m = 0$ is now also allowed. Continuing: The value of k_z for mode m is obtained using Equation 6.82 as follows:

$$\begin{aligned} k_z &= \sqrt{\beta^2 - k_x^2} \\ &= \sqrt{\beta^2 - \left(\frac{m\pi}{a}\right)^2} \end{aligned} \tag{6.99}$$

Since k_z is specified to be real-valued, we require:

$$\beta^2 - \left(\frac{m\pi}{a}\right)^2 > 0 \tag{6.100}$$

This constrains β; specifically:

$$\beta > \frac{m\pi}{a} \tag{6.101}$$

Recall that $\beta = \omega\sqrt{\mu\epsilon}$ and $\omega = 2\pi f$ where f is frequency. Solving for f, we find:

$$f > \frac{m}{2a\sqrt{\mu\epsilon}} \tag{6.102}$$

Thus, each mode exists only above a certain frequency, which is different for each mode. This *cutoff frequency* f_c for mode m is given by

$$\boxed{f_c^{(m)} \triangleq \frac{m}{2a\sqrt{\mu\epsilon}}} \tag{6.103}$$

At frequencies below the cutoff frequency for mode m, modes 0 through $m - 1$ exhibit imaginary-valued k_z and therefore do no propagate. Also, note that the cutoff frequency for $m = 0$ is zero, and so this mode is always able to propagate. That is, the $m = 0$ mode may exist for any $a > 0$ and any $f > 0$. Once again, this is a remarkable difference from the TE case, for which $m = 0$ is not available.

Let us now summarize the solution. With respect to Figure 6.4, we find that the electric field component of the TM field is given by:

$$\boxed{\widetilde{\mathbf{E}} = \sum_{m=0}^{\infty} \left[\hat{\mathbf{x}}\widetilde{E}_x^{(m)} + \hat{\mathbf{z}}\widetilde{E}_z^{(m)}\right]} \tag{6.104}$$

where

$$\boxed{\widetilde{E}_x^{(m)} \triangleq \begin{cases} 0, & f < f_c^{(m)} \\ E_{x0}^{(m)} e^{-jk_z^{(m)}z} \cos k_x^{(m)} x, & f \geq f_c^{(m)} \end{cases}} \tag{6.105}$$

and

$$\boxed{\widetilde{E}_z^{(m)} \triangleq \begin{cases} 0, & f < f_c^{(m)} \\ j\frac{k_x^{(m)}}{k_z^{(m)}} E_{x0}^{(m)} e^{-jk_z^{(m)}z} \sin k_x^{(m)} x, & f \geq f_c^{(m)} \end{cases}} \tag{6.106}$$

where m enumerates modes ($m = 0, 1, 2, ...$) and

$$\boxed{k_z^{(m)} \triangleq \sqrt{\beta^2 - \left[k_x^{(m)}\right]^2}} \tag{6.107}$$

$$\boxed{k_x^{(m)} \triangleq m\pi/a} \tag{6.108}$$

Finally, the coefficients $E_{x0}^{(m)}$ depend on sources and/or boundary conditions to the left of the region of interest.

> For the scenario depicted in Figure 6.4, the electric field component of the TM solution is given by Equation 6.104 with modal components determined as indicated by Equations 6.103–6.108. This solution presumes all sources lie to the left of the region of interest, with no additional sources or boundary conditions to the right of the region of interest.

The $m = 0$ mode, commonly referred to as the "TM_0" mode, is of particular importance in the analysis of microstrip transmission line, and is addressed in Section 6.6.

6.6 Parallel Plate Waveguide: The TM_0 Mode

[m0220]

In Section 6.2, the parallel plate waveguide (also shown in Figure 6.5) was introduced. At the end of that section we decomposed the problem into its constituent TE and TM fields. In Section 6.5, we determined the electric field component of the TM field, which was found to consist of a set of discrete modes. In this section, we address the lowest-order ($m = 0$) mode of the TM field, which has special relevance in a number of applications including microstrip transmission lines. This mode is commonly referred to as the "TM_0" mode.

The TM electric field intensity in the waveguide is given by Equation 6.104 with modal components determined as indicated by Equations 6.103–6.108 (Section 6.5). Recall that the $m = 0$ mode can only exist only in the TM case, and does not exist in the TE case. We also noted that the cutoff frequency for this mode is zero, so it may exist at any frequency, and within any non-zero plate separation a. For this mode $k_x^{(0)} = 0$, $k_z^{(0)} = \beta$, and we find

$$\widetilde{\mathbf{E}} = \hat{\mathbf{x}} E_{x0}^{(0)} e^{-j\beta z} \quad (\text{TM}_0 \text{ mode}) \tag{6.109}$$

Remarkably, we find that this mode has the form of a uniform plane wave which propagates in the $+\hat{\mathbf{z}}$ direction; i.e., squarely between the plates. The phase and group velocities of this wave are equal to each other and ω/β, precisely as expected for a uniform

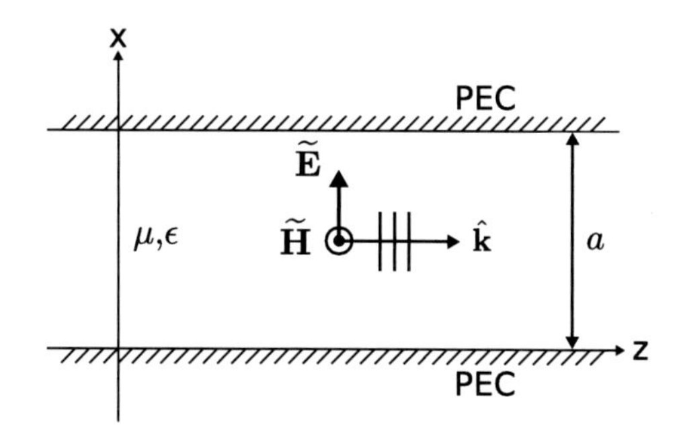

© C. Wang CC BY-SA 4.0 (modified)

Figure 6.5: TM_0 mode in a parallel plate waveguide.

plane wave in unbounded media; i.e., as if the plates did not exist. This observation allows us to easily determine the associated *magnetic* field: Using the plane wave relationship,

$$\widetilde{\mathbf{H}} = \frac{1}{\eta}\hat{\mathbf{k}} \times \widetilde{\mathbf{E}} \tag{6.110}$$

$$= \frac{1}{\eta}\hat{\mathbf{z}} \times \left(\hat{\mathbf{x}} E_{x0}^{(0)} e^{-j\beta z}\right) \tag{6.111}$$

$$= \hat{\mathbf{y}} \frac{E_{x0}^{(0)}}{\eta} e^{-j\beta z} \quad (\text{TM}_0 \text{ mode}) \tag{6.112}$$

Example 6.3. Guided waves in a printed circuit board (PCB).

A very common form of PCB consists of a 1.575 mm-thick slab of low-loss dielectric having relative permittivity ≈ 4.5 sandwiched between two copper planes. Characterize the electromagnetic field in a long strip of this material. Assume a single source exists at one end of the strip, and operates at frequencies below 10 GHz.

Solution. Let us assume that the copper planes exhibit conductivity that is sufficiently high that the inward-facing surfaces may be viewed as perfectly-conducting. Also, let us limit scope to the field deep within the "sandwich," and neglect the region near the edges of the PCB. Under these conditions, the PCB is well-modeled as a parallel-plate waveguide. Thus, the electromagnetic field consists of a combination of TE and TM modes. The active (non-zero) modes depend on the source (a mode must be "stimulated" by the source in order to propagate) and modal cutoff frequencies. The cutoff frequency for mode m is

$$f_c^{(m)} = \frac{m}{2a\sqrt{\mu\epsilon}} \tag{6.113}$$

In this case, $a = 1.575$ mm, $\mu \approx \mu_0$, and $\epsilon \approx 4.5\epsilon_0$. Therefore:

$$f_c^{(m)} \approx (44.9 \text{ GHz})\, m \tag{6.114}$$

Since the cutoff frequency for $m = 1$ is much greater than 10 GHz, we may rest assured that the only mode that can propagate inside the PCB is TM_0. Therefore, the field deep inside the PCB may be interpreted as a single plane wave having the TM_0 structure shown in Figure 6.5, propagating away from the source end of the PCB. The phase velocity is simply that of the apparent plane wave:

$$v_p = \frac{1}{\sqrt{\mu\epsilon}} \approx 1.41 \times 10^8 \text{ m/s} \approx 0.47c \quad (6.115)$$

The scenario described in this example is essentially a very rudimentary form of microstrip transmission line.

6.7 General Relationships for Unidirectional Waves

[m0222]

Analysis of electromagnetic waves in enclosed spaces – and in waveguides in particular – is quite difficult. The task is dramatically simplified if it can be assumed that the wave propagates in a single direction; i.e., is unidirectional. This does not necessarily entail loss of generality. For example: Within a straight waveguide, waves can travel either "forward" or "backward." The principle of superposition allows one to consider these two unidirectional cases separately, and then to simply sum the results.

In this section, the equations that relate the various components of a unidirectional wave are derived. The equations will be derived in Cartesian coordinates, anticipating application to rectangular waveguides. However, the underlying strategy is generally applicable.

We begin with Maxwell's curl equations:

$$\nabla \times \widetilde{\mathbf{E}} = -j\omega\mu\widetilde{\mathbf{H}} \quad (6.116)$$

$$\nabla \times \widetilde{\mathbf{H}} = +j\omega\epsilon\widetilde{\mathbf{E}} \quad (6.117)$$

Let us consider Equation 6.117 first. Solving for $\widetilde{\mathbf{E}}$, we have:

$$\widetilde{\mathbf{E}} = \frac{1}{j\omega\epsilon}\nabla \times \widetilde{\mathbf{H}} \quad (6.118)$$

This is actually three equations; that is, one each for the $\hat{\mathbf{x}}$, $\hat{\mathbf{y}}$, and $\hat{\mathbf{z}}$ components of $\widetilde{\mathbf{E}}$, respectively. To extract these equations, let us define the components as follows:

$$\widetilde{\mathbf{E}} = \hat{\mathbf{x}}\widetilde{E}_x + \hat{\mathbf{y}}\widetilde{E}_y + \hat{\mathbf{z}}\widetilde{E}_z \quad (6.119)$$

$$\widetilde{\mathbf{H}} = \hat{\mathbf{x}}\widetilde{H}_x + \hat{\mathbf{y}}\widetilde{H}_y + \hat{\mathbf{z}}\widetilde{H}_z \quad (6.120)$$

Now applying the equation for curl in Cartesian coordinates (Equation B.16 in Appendix B.2), we find:

$$\widetilde{E}_x = \frac{1}{j\omega\epsilon}\left(\frac{\partial \widetilde{H}_z}{\partial y} - \frac{\partial \widetilde{H}_y}{\partial z}\right) \quad (6.121)$$

$$\widetilde{E}_y = \frac{1}{j\omega\epsilon}\left(\frac{\partial \widetilde{H}_x}{\partial z} - \frac{\partial \widetilde{H}_z}{\partial x}\right) \quad (6.122)$$

$$\widetilde{E}_z = \frac{1}{j\omega\epsilon}\left(\frac{\partial \widetilde{H}_y}{\partial x} - \frac{\partial \widetilde{H}_x}{\partial y}\right) \quad (6.123)$$

Without loss of generality, we may assume that the single direction in which the wave is traveling is in the $+\hat{\mathbf{z}}$ direction. If this is the case, then $\widetilde{\mathbf{H}}$, and subsequently each component of $\widetilde{\mathbf{H}}$, contains a factor of $e^{-jk_z z}$ where k_z is the phase propagation constant in the direction of travel. The remaining factors are independent of z; i.e., depend only on x and y. With this in mind, we further decompose components of $\widetilde{\mathbf{H}}$ as follows:

$$\widetilde{H}_x = \widetilde{h}_x(x,y)e^{-jk_z z} \quad (6.124)$$

$$\widetilde{H}_y = \widetilde{h}_y(x,y)e^{-jk_z z} \quad (6.125)$$

$$\widetilde{H}_z = \widetilde{h}_z(x,y)e^{-jk_z z} \quad (6.126)$$

where $\widetilde{h}_x(x,y)$, $\widetilde{h}_y(x,y)$, and $\widetilde{h}_z(x,y)$ represent the remaining factors. One advantage of this decomposition is that partial derivatives with respect to z reduce to algebraic operations; i.e.:

$$\frac{\partial \widetilde{H}_x}{\partial z} = -jk_z\widetilde{h}_x(x,y)e^{-jk_z z} = -jk_z\widetilde{H}_x \quad (6.127)$$

$$\frac{\partial \widetilde{H}_y}{\partial z} = -jk_z\widetilde{h}_y(x,y)e^{-jk_z z} = -jk_z\widetilde{H}_y \quad (6.128)$$

$$\frac{\partial \widetilde{H}_z}{\partial z} = -jk_z\widetilde{h}_z(x,y)e^{-jk_z z} = -jk_z\widetilde{H}_z \quad (6.129)$$

We now substitute Equations 6.124–6.126 into Equations 6.121–6.123 and then use Equations 6.127–6.129 to eliminate partial derivatives with respect to z. This yields:

$$\widetilde{E}_x = \frac{1}{j\omega\epsilon}\left(\frac{\partial \widetilde{H}_z}{\partial y} + jk_z\widetilde{H}_y\right) \quad (6.130)$$

$$\widetilde{E}_y = \frac{1}{j\omega\epsilon}\left(-jk_z\widetilde{H}_x - \frac{\partial \widetilde{H}_z}{\partial x}\right) \quad (6.131)$$

$$\widetilde{E}_z = \frac{1}{j\omega\epsilon}\left(\frac{\partial \widetilde{H}_y}{\partial x} - \frac{\partial \widetilde{H}_x}{\partial y}\right) \quad (6.132)$$

Applying the same procedure to the curl equation for $\widetilde{\mathbf{H}}$ (Equation 6.116), one obtains:

$$\widetilde{H}_x = \frac{1}{-j\omega\mu}\left(\frac{\partial \widetilde{E}_z}{\partial y} + jk_z\widetilde{E}_y\right) \quad (6.133)$$

$$\widetilde{H}_y = \frac{1}{-j\omega\mu}\left(-jk_z\widetilde{E}_x - \frac{\partial \widetilde{E}_z}{\partial x}\right) \quad (6.134)$$

$$\widetilde{H}_z = \frac{1}{-j\omega\mu}\left(\frac{\partial \widetilde{E}_y}{\partial x} - \frac{\partial \widetilde{E}_x}{\partial y}\right) \quad (6.135)$$

Equations 6.130–6.135 constitute a set of simultaneous equations that represent Maxwell's curl equations in the special case of a unidirectional (specifically, a $+\hat{\mathbf{z}}$-traveling) wave. With just a little bit of algebraic manipulation of these equations, it is possible to obtain expressions for the $\hat{\mathbf{x}}$ and $\hat{\mathbf{y}}$ components of $\widetilde{\mathbf{E}}$ and $\widetilde{\mathbf{H}}$ which depend only on the $\hat{\mathbf{z}}$ components of $\widetilde{\mathbf{E}}$ and $\widetilde{\mathbf{H}}$. Here they are:[3]

$$\widetilde{E}_x = \frac{-j}{k_\rho^2}\left(+k_z\frac{\partial \widetilde{E}_z}{\partial x} + \omega\mu\frac{\partial \widetilde{H}_z}{\partial y}\right) \quad (6.136)$$

$$\widetilde{E}_y = \frac{+j}{k_\rho^2}\left(-k_z\frac{\partial \widetilde{E}_z}{\partial y} + \omega\mu\frac{\partial \widetilde{H}_z}{\partial x}\right) \quad (6.137)$$

$$\widetilde{H}_x = \frac{+j}{k_\rho^2}\left(\omega\epsilon\frac{\partial \widetilde{E}_z}{\partial y} - k_z\frac{\partial \widetilde{H}_z}{\partial x}\right) \quad (6.138)$$

$$\widetilde{H}_y = \frac{-j}{k_\rho^2}\left(\omega\epsilon\frac{\partial \widetilde{E}_z}{\partial x} + k_z\frac{\partial \widetilde{H}_z}{\partial y}\right) \quad (6.139)$$

where

$$k_\rho^2 \triangleq \beta^2 - k_z^2 \quad (6.140)$$

Why define a parameter called "k_ρ"? Note from the definition that $\beta^2 = k_\rho^2 + k_z^2$. Further, note that this equation is an expression of the Pythagorean theorem, which relates the lengths of the sides of a right triangle. Since β is the "overall" phase propagation constant, and k_z is the phase propagation constant for propagation in the $\hat{\mathbf{z}}$ direction in the waveguide, k_ρ must be associated with variation in fields in directions perpendicular to $\hat{\mathbf{z}}$. In the cylindrical coordinate system, this is the $\hat{\rho}$ direction, hence the subscript "ρ." We shall see later that k_ρ plays a special

[3] Students are encouraged to derive these for themselves – only algebra is required. Tip to get started: To get $\widetilde{E}_x$, begin with Equation 6.130, eliminate $\widetilde{H}_y$ using Equation 6.134, and then solve for $\widetilde{E}_x$.

role in determining the structure of fields within the waveguide, and this provides additional motivation to identify this quantity explicitly in the field equations.

Summarizing: If you know the wave is unidirectional, then knowledge of the components of $\widetilde{\mathbf{E}}$ and $\widetilde{\mathbf{H}}$ in the direction of propagation is sufficient to determine each of the remaining components of $\widetilde{\mathbf{E}}$ and $\widetilde{\mathbf{H}}$. There is one catch, however: For this to yield sensible results, k_ρ may not be zero. So, ironically, these expressions don't work in the case of a uniform plane wave, since such a wave would have $\widetilde{E}_z = \widetilde{H}_z = 0$ and $k_z = \beta$ (so $k_\rho = 0$), yielding values of zero divided by zero for each remaining field component. The same issue arises for any other transverse electromagnetic (TEM) wave. For non-TEM waves – and, in particular, unidirectional waves in waveguides – either $\widetilde{E}_z$ or $\widetilde{H}_z$ must be non-zero and k_ρ will be non-zero. In this case, Equations 6.136–6.139 are both usable and useful since they allow determination of all field components given just the $\mathbf{z}$ components.

In fact, we may further exploit this simplicity by taking one additional step: Decomposition of the unidirectional wave into transverse electric (TE) and transverse magnetic (TM) components. In this case, TE means simply that $\widetilde{E}_z = 0$, and TM means simply that $\widetilde{H}_z = 0$. For a wave which is either TE or TM, Equations 6.136–6.139 reduce to one term each.

6.8 Rectangular Waveguide: TM Modes

[m0223]

A rectangular waveguide is a conducting cylinder of rectangular cross section used to guide the propagation of waves. Rectangular waveguide is commonly used for the transport of radio frequency signals at frequencies in the SHF band (3–30 GHz) and higher. The fields in a rectangular waveguide consist of a number of propagating modes which depends on the electrical dimensions of the waveguide. These modes are broadly classified as either transverse magnetic (TM) or transverse electric (TE). In this section, we consider the TM modes.

Figure 6.6 shows the geometry of interest. Here the walls are located at $x = 0$, $x = a$, $y = 0$, and $y = b$; thus, the cross-sectional dimensions of the waveguide are a and b. The interior of the waveguide is presumed to consist of a lossless material exhibiting real-valued permeability μ and real-valued permittivity ϵ, and the walls are assumed to be perfectly-conducting.

Let us limit our attention to a region within the waveguide which is free of sources. Expressed in phasor form, the electric field intensity within the waveguide is governed by the wave equation

$$\nabla^2 \widetilde{\mathbf{E}} + \beta^2 \widetilde{\mathbf{E}} = 0 \qquad (6.141)$$

where

$$\beta = \omega\sqrt{\mu\epsilon} \qquad (6.142)$$

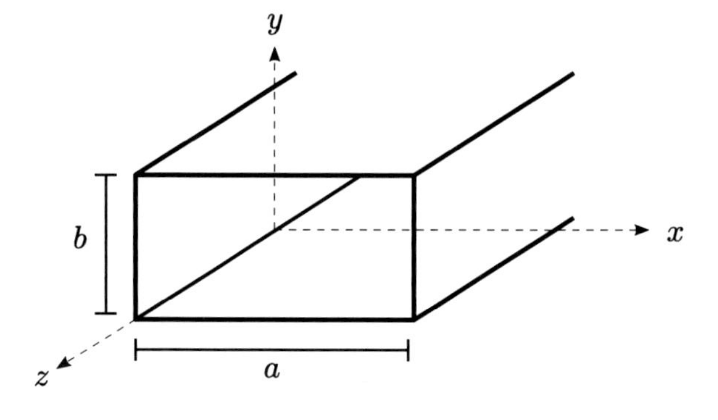

Figure 6.6: Geometry for analysis of fields in a rectangular waveguide.

Equation 6.141 is a partial differential equation. This equation, combined with boundary conditions imposed by the perfectly-conducting plates, is sufficient to determine a unique solution. This solution is most easily determined in Cartesian coordinates, as we shall now demonstrate. First we express $\widetilde{\mathbf{E}}$ in Cartesian coordinates:

$$\widetilde{\mathbf{E}} = \hat{\mathbf{x}}\widetilde{E}_x + \hat{\mathbf{y}}\widetilde{E}_y + \hat{\mathbf{z}}\widetilde{E}_z \tag{6.143}$$

This facilitates the decomposition of Equation 6.141 into separate equations governing the $\hat{\mathbf{x}}$, $\hat{\mathbf{y}}$, and $\hat{\mathbf{z}}$ components of $\widetilde{\mathbf{E}}$:

$$\nabla^2\widetilde{E}_x + \beta^2\widetilde{E}_x = 0 \tag{6.144}$$

$$\nabla^2\widetilde{E}_y + \beta^2\widetilde{E}_y = 0 \tag{6.145}$$

$$\nabla^2\widetilde{E}_z + \beta^2\widetilde{E}_z = 0 \tag{6.146}$$

Next we observe that the operator ∇^2 may be expressed in Cartesian coordinates as follows:

$$\nabla^2 = \frac{\partial^2}{\partial x^2} + \frac{\partial^2}{\partial y^2} + \frac{\partial^2}{\partial z^2} \tag{6.147}$$

so the equations governing the Cartesian components of $\widetilde{\mathbf{E}}$ may be written as follows:

$$\frac{\partial^2}{\partial x^2}\widetilde{E}_x + \frac{\partial^2}{\partial y^2}\widetilde{E}_x + \frac{\partial^2}{\partial z^2}\widetilde{E}_x + \beta^2\widetilde{E}_x = 0 \tag{6.148}$$

$$\frac{\partial^2}{\partial x^2}\widetilde{E}_y + \frac{\partial^2}{\partial y^2}\widetilde{E}_y + \frac{\partial^2}{\partial z^2}\widetilde{E}_y + \beta^2\widetilde{E}_y = 0 \tag{6.149}$$

$$\frac{\partial^2}{\partial x^2}\widetilde{E}_z + \frac{\partial^2}{\partial y^2}\widetilde{E}_z + \frac{\partial^2}{\partial z^2}\widetilde{E}_z + \beta^2\widetilde{E}_z = 0 \tag{6.150}$$

In general, we expect the total field in the waveguide to consist of unidirectional waves propagating in the $+\hat{\mathbf{z}}$ and $-\hat{\mathbf{z}}$ directions. We may analyze either of these waves; then the other wave is easily derived via symmetry, and the total field is simply a linear combination (superposition) of these waves. With this in mind, we limit our focus to the wave propagating in the $+\hat{\mathbf{z}}$ direction.

In Section 6.7, it is shown that all components of the electric and magnetic fields can be easily calculated once $\widetilde{E}_z$ and $\widetilde{H}_z$ are known. The problem is further simplified by decomposing the unidirectional wave into TM and TE components. In this decomposition, the TM component is defined by the property that $\widetilde{H}_z = 0$; i.e., is transverse (perpendicular) to the direction of propagation. Thus, the TM component is completely determined by $\widetilde{E}_z$.

Equations 6.136–6.139 simplify to become:

$$\widetilde{E}_x = -j\frac{k_z}{k_\rho^2}\frac{\partial\widetilde{E}_z}{\partial x} \tag{6.151}$$

$$\widetilde{E}_y = -j\frac{k_z}{k_\rho^2}\frac{\partial\widetilde{E}_z}{\partial y} \tag{6.152}$$

$$\widetilde{H}_x = +j\frac{\omega\mu}{k_\rho^2}\frac{\partial\widetilde{E}_z}{\partial y} \tag{6.153}$$

$$\widetilde{H}_y = -j\frac{\omega\mu}{k_\rho^2}\frac{\partial\widetilde{E}_z}{\partial x} \tag{6.154}$$

where

$$k_\rho^2 \triangleq \beta^2 - k_z^2 \tag{6.155}$$

and k_z is the phase propagation constant; i.e., the wave is assumed to propagate according to $e^{-jk_z z}$.

Now let us address the problem of finding $\widetilde{E}_z$, which will then completely determine the TM field. As in Section 6.7, we recognize that $\widetilde{E}_z$ can be represented as the propagation factor $e^{-jk_z z}$ times a factor that describes variation with respect to the remaining spatial dimensions x and y:

$$\widetilde{E}_z = \widetilde{e}_z(x,y)e^{-jk_z z} \tag{6.156}$$

Substitution of this expression into Equation 6.150 and dividing out the common factor of $e^{-jk_z z}$ yields:

$$\frac{\partial^2}{\partial x^2}\widetilde{e}_z + \frac{\partial^2}{\partial y^2}\widetilde{e}_z - k_z^2\widetilde{e}_z + \beta^2\widetilde{e}_z = 0 \tag{6.157}$$

The last two terms may be combined using Equation 6.155, yielding:

$$\frac{\partial^2}{\partial x^2}\widetilde{e}_z + \frac{\partial^2}{\partial y^2}\widetilde{e}_z + k_\rho^2\widetilde{e}_z = 0 \tag{6.158}$$

This is a partial differential equation for $\widetilde{e}_z$ in the variables x and y. This equation may be solved using the technique of *separation of variables*. In this technique, we recognize that $\widetilde{e}_z(x,y)$ can be written as the product of a function $X(x)$ which depends only on x, and a function $Y(y)$ that depends only on y. That is,

$$\widetilde{e}_z(x,y) = X(x)Y(y) \tag{6.159}$$

Substituting this expression into Equation 6.158, we obtain:

$$Y \frac{\partial^2}{\partial x^2} X + X \frac{\partial^2}{\partial y^2} Y + k_\rho^2 XY = 0 \tag{6.160}$$

Next dividing through by XY, we obtain:

$$\frac{1}{X} \frac{\partial^2}{\partial x^2} X + \frac{1}{Y} \frac{\partial^2}{\partial y^2} Y + k_\rho^2 = 0 \tag{6.161}$$

Note that the first term depends only on x, the second term depends only on y, and the remaining term is a constant. Therefore, the sum of the first and second terms is a constant; namely $-k_\rho^2$. Since these terms depend on either x or y, and not both, the first term must equal some constant, the second term must equal some constant, and these constants must sum to $-k_\rho^2$. Therefore, we are justified in separating the equation into two equations as follows:

$$\frac{1}{X} \frac{\partial^2}{\partial x^2} X + k_x^2 = 0 \tag{6.162}$$

$$\frac{1}{Y} \frac{\partial^2}{\partial y^2} Y + k_y^2 = 0 \tag{6.163}$$

where the new constants k_x^2 and k_y^2 must satisfy

$$k_x^2 + k_y^2 = k_\rho^2 \tag{6.164}$$

Now multiplying Equations 6.162 and 6.163 by X and Y, respectively, we find:

$$\frac{\partial^2}{\partial x^2} X + k_x^2 X = 0 \tag{6.165}$$

$$\frac{\partial^2}{\partial y^2} Y + k_y^2 Y = 0 \tag{6.166}$$

These are familiar one-dimensional differential equations. The solutions are:[4]

$$X = A \cos(k_x x) + B \sin(k_x x) \tag{6.167}$$

$$Y = C \cos(k_y y) + D \sin(k_y y) \tag{6.168}$$

where A, B, C, and D – like k_x and k_y – are constants to be determined. At this point, we observe that the wave we seek can be expressed as follows:

$$\begin{aligned} \widetilde{E}_z &= \widetilde{e}_z(x,y) e^{-jk_z z} \\ &= X(x)\, Y(y)\, e^{-jk_z z} \end{aligned} \tag{6.169}$$

[4]Students are encouraged to confirm that these are correct by confirming that they are solutions to Equations 6.165 and 6.165, respectively.

The solution is essentially complete except for the values of the constants A, B, C, D, k_x, and k_y. The values of these constants are determined by applying the relevant electromagnetic boundary condition. In this case, it is required that the component of $\widetilde{\mathbf{E}}$ that is tangent to a perfectly-conducting wall must be zero. Note that the $\hat{\mathbf{z}}$ component of $\widetilde{\mathbf{E}}$ is tangent to all four walls; therefore:

$$\widetilde{E}_z\,(x = 0) = 0 \tag{6.170}$$

$$\widetilde{E}_z\,(x = a) = 0 \tag{6.171}$$

$$\widetilde{E}_z\,(y = 0) = 0 \tag{6.172}$$

$$\widetilde{E}_z\,(y = b) = 0 \tag{6.173}$$

Referring to Equation 6.169, these boundary conditions in turn require:

$$X\,(x = 0) = 0 \tag{6.174}$$

$$X\,(x = a) = 0 \tag{6.175}$$

$$Y\,(y = 0) = 0 \tag{6.176}$$

$$Y\,(y = b) = 0 \tag{6.177}$$

Evaluating these conditions using Equations 6.167 and 6.168 yields:

$$A \cdot 1 + B \cdot 0 = 0 \tag{6.178}$$

$$A \cos(k_x a) + B \sin(k_x a) = 0 \tag{6.179}$$

$$C \cdot 1 + D \cdot 0 = 0 \tag{6.180}$$

$$C \cos(k_y b) + D \sin(k_y b) = 0 \tag{6.181}$$

Equations 6.178 and 6.180 can be satisfied only if $A = 0$ and $C = 0$, respectively. Subsequently, Equations 6.179 and 6.181 reduce to:

$$\sin(k_x a) = 0 \tag{6.182}$$

$$\sin(k_y b) = 0 \tag{6.183}$$

This in turn requires:

$$k_x = \frac{m\pi}{a}, \quad m = 0, 1, 2... \tag{6.184}$$

$$k_y = \frac{n\pi}{b}, \quad n = 0, 1, 2... \tag{6.185}$$

Each positive integer value of m and n leads to a valid expression for $\widetilde{E}_z$ known as a *mode*. Solutions for which $m = 0$ or $n = 0$ yield $k_x = 0$ or $k_y = 0$, respectively. These correspond to zero-valued fields, and therefore are not of interest. The most general expression for $\widetilde{E}_z$ must account for all non-trivial modes. Summarizing:

$$\widetilde{E}_z = \sum_{m=1}^{\infty}\sum_{n=1}^{\infty} \widetilde{E}_z^{(m,n)} \tag{6.186}$$

where

$$\widetilde{E}_z^{(m,n)} \triangleq E_0^{(m,n)} \sin\left(\frac{m\pi}{a}x\right) \sin\left(\frac{n\pi}{b}y\right) e^{-jk_z^{(m,n)}z} \tag{6.187}$$

where $E_0^{(m,n)}$ is an arbitrary constant (consolidating the constants B and D), and, since $k_x^2 + k_y^2 = k_\rho^2 \triangleq \beta^2 - k_z^2$:

$$k_z^{(m,n)} = \sqrt{\omega^2\mu\epsilon - \left(\frac{m\pi}{a}\right)^2 - \left(\frac{n\pi}{b}\right)^2} \tag{6.188}$$

Summarizing:

> The TM ($\widetilde{H}_z = 0$) component of the unidirectional ($+\hat{\mathbf{z}}$-traveling) wave in a rectangular waveguide is completely determined by Equation 6.186, and consists of modes as defined by Equations 6.187, 6.188, 6.184, and 6.185. The remaining non-zero field components can be determined using Equations 6.151–6.154.

It is customary and convenient to refer to the TM modes in a rectangular waveguide using the notation "TM_{mn}." For example, the mode TM_{12} is given by Equation 6.187 with $m = 1$ and $n = 2$.

Finally, note that values of $k_z^{(m,n)}$ obtained from Equation 6.188 are not necessarily real-valued. It is apparent that for any given value of m, $k_z^{(m,n)}$ will be imaginary-valued for all values of n greater than some value. Similarly, it is apparent that for any given value of n, $k_z^{(m,n)}$ will be imaginary-valued for all values of m greater than some value. This phenomenon is common to both TM and TE components, and so is addressed in a separate section (Section 6.10).

Additional Reading:

- "Waveguide (radio frequency)" on Wikipedia.
- "Separation of variables" on Wikipedia.

6.9 Rectangular Waveguide: TE Modes

[m0225]

A rectangular waveguide is a conducting cylinder of rectangular cross section used to guide the propagation of waves. Rectangular waveguide is commonly used for the transport of radio frequency signals at frequencies in the SHF band (3–30 GHz) and higher. The fields in a rectangular waveguide consist of a number of propagating modes which depends on the electrical dimensions of the waveguide. These modes are broadly classified as either transverse magnetic (TM) or transverse electric (TE). In this section, we consider the TE modes.

Figure 6.7 shows the geometry of interest. Here the walls are located at $x = 0$, $x = a$, $y = 0$, and $y = b$; thus, the cross-sectional dimensions of the waveguide are a and b. The interior of the waveguide is presumed to consist of a lossless material exhibiting real-valued permeability μ and real-valued permittivity ϵ, and the walls are assumed to be perfectly-conducting.

Let us limit our attention to a region within the waveguide which is free of sources. Expressed in phasor form, the magnetic field intensity within the waveguide is governed by the wave equation:

$$\nabla^2\widetilde{\mathbf{H}} + \beta^2\widetilde{\mathbf{H}} = 0 \tag{6.189}$$

where

$$\beta = \omega\sqrt{\mu\epsilon} \tag{6.190}$$

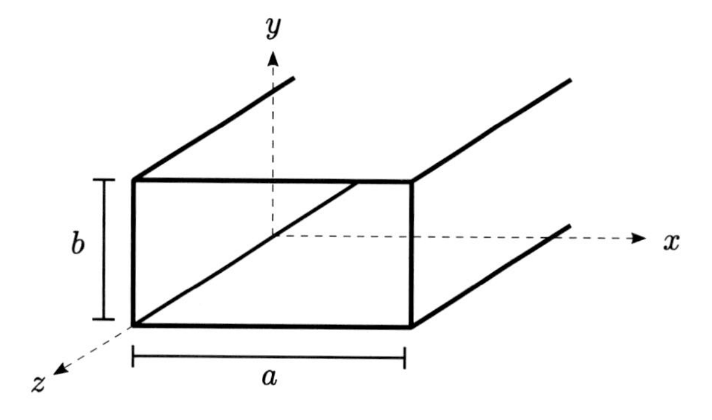

Figure 6.7: Geometry for analysis of fields in a rectangular waveguide.

Equation 6.189 is a partial differential equation. This equation, combined with boundary conditions imposed by the perfectly-conducting plates, is sufficient to determine a unique solution. This solution is most easily determined in Cartesian coordinates, as we shall now demonstrate. First we express $\widetilde{\mathbf{H}}$ in Cartesian coordinates:

$$\widetilde{\mathbf{H}} = \hat{\mathbf{x}}\widetilde{H}_x + \hat{\mathbf{y}}\widetilde{H}_y + \hat{\mathbf{z}}\widetilde{H}_z \tag{6.191}$$

This facilitates the decomposition of Equation 6.189 into separate equations governing the $\hat{\mathbf{x}}$, $\hat{\mathbf{y}}$, and $\hat{\mathbf{z}}$ components of $\widetilde{\mathbf{H}}$:

$$\nabla^2\widetilde{H}_x + \beta^2\widetilde{H}_x = 0 \tag{6.192}$$

$$\nabla^2\widetilde{H}_y + \beta^2\widetilde{H}_y = 0 \tag{6.193}$$

$$\nabla^2\widetilde{H}_z + \beta^2\widetilde{H}_z = 0 \tag{6.194}$$

Next we observe that the operator ∇^2 may be expressed in Cartesian coordinates as follows:

$$\nabla^2 = \frac{\partial^2}{\partial x^2} + \frac{\partial^2}{\partial y^2} + \frac{\partial^2}{\partial z^2} \tag{6.195}$$

so the equations governing the Cartesian components of $\widetilde{\mathbf{H}}$ may be written as follows:

$$\frac{\partial^2}{\partial x^2}\widetilde{H}_x + \frac{\partial^2}{\partial y^2}\widetilde{H}_x + \frac{\partial^2}{\partial z^2}\widetilde{H}_x + \beta^2\widetilde{H}_x = 0 \tag{6.196}$$

$$\frac{\partial^2}{\partial x^2}\widetilde{H}_y + \frac{\partial^2}{\partial y^2}\widetilde{H}_y + \frac{\partial^2}{\partial z^2}\widetilde{H}_y + \beta^2\widetilde{H}_y = 0 \tag{6.197}$$

$$\frac{\partial^2}{\partial x^2}\widetilde{H}_z + \frac{\partial^2}{\partial y^2}\widetilde{H}_z + \frac{\partial^2}{\partial z^2}\widetilde{H}_z + \beta^2\widetilde{H}_z = 0 \tag{6.198}$$

In general, we expect the total field in the waveguide to consist of unidirectional waves propagating in the $+\hat{\mathbf{z}}$ and $-\hat{\mathbf{z}}$ directions. We may analyze either of these waves; then the other wave is easily derived via symmetry, and the total field is simply a linear combination (superposition) of these waves. With this in mind, we limit our focus to the wave propagating in the $+\hat{\mathbf{z}}$ direction.

In Section 6.7, it is shown that all components of the electric and magnetic fields can be easily calculated once $\widetilde{E}_z$ and $\widetilde{H}_z$ are known. The problem is further simplified by decomposing the unidirectional wave into TM and TE components. In this decomposition, the TE component is defined by the property that $\widetilde{E}_z = 0$; i.e., is transverse (perpendicular) to the direction of propagation. Thus, the TE component is completely determined by $\widetilde{H}_z$.
Equations 6.136–6.139 simplify to become:

$$\widetilde{E}_x = -j\frac{\omega\mu}{k_\rho^2}\frac{\partial\widetilde{H}_z}{\partial y} \tag{6.199}$$

$$\widetilde{E}_y = +j\frac{\omega\mu}{k_\rho^2}\frac{\partial\widetilde{H}_z}{\partial x} \tag{6.200}$$

$$\widetilde{H}_x = -j\frac{k_z}{k_\rho^2}\frac{\partial\widetilde{H}_z}{\partial x} \tag{6.201}$$

$$\widetilde{H}_y = -j\frac{k_z}{k_\rho^2}\frac{\partial\widetilde{H}_z}{\partial y} \tag{6.202}$$

where

$$k_\rho^2 \triangleq \beta^2 - k_z^2 \tag{6.203}$$

and k_z is the phase propagation constant; i.e., the wave is assumed to propagate according to $e^{-jk_z z}$.

Now let us address the problem of finding $\widetilde{H}_z$, which will then completely determine the TE field. As in Section 6.7, we recognize that $\widetilde{H}_z$ can be represented as the propagation factor $e^{-jk_z z}$ times a factor that describes variation with respect to the remaining spatial dimensions x and y:

$$\widetilde{H}_z = \widetilde{h}_z(x,y)e^{-jk_z z} \tag{6.204}$$

Substitution of this expression into Equation 6.198 and dividing out the common factor of $e^{-jk_z z}$ yields:

$$\frac{\partial^2}{\partial x^2}\widetilde{h}_z + \frac{\partial^2}{\partial y^2}\widetilde{h}_z - k_z^2\widetilde{h}_z + \beta^2\widetilde{h}_z = 0 \tag{6.205}$$

The last two terms may be combined using Equation 6.203, yielding:

$$\frac{\partial^2}{\partial x^2}\widetilde{h}_z + \frac{\partial^2}{\partial y^2}\widetilde{h}_z + k_\rho^2\widetilde{h}_z = 0 \tag{6.206}$$

This is a partial differential equation for $\widetilde{h}_z$ in the variables x and y. This equation may be solved using the technique of *separation of variables*. In this technique, we recognize that $\widetilde{h}_z(x,y)$ can be written as the product of a function $X(x)$ which depends only on x, and a function $Y(y)$ that depends only on y. That is,

$$\widetilde{h}_z(x,y) = X(x)Y(y) \tag{6.207}$$

Substituting this expression into Equation 6.206, we obtain:

$$Y\frac{\partial^2}{\partial x^2}X + X\frac{\partial^2}{\partial y^2}Y + k_\rho^2 XY = 0 \tag{6.208}$$

Next dividing through by XY, we obtain:

$$\frac{1}{X}\frac{\partial^2}{\partial x^2}X + \frac{1}{Y}\frac{\partial^2}{\partial y^2}Y + k_\rho^2 = 0 \tag{6.209}$$

Note that the first term depends only on x, the second term depends only on y, and the remaining term is a constant. Therefore, the sum of the first and second terms is a constant; namely $-k_\rho^2$. Since these terms depend on either x or y, and not both, the first term must equal some constant, the second term must equal some constant, and these constants must sum to $-k_\rho^2$. Therefore, we are justified in separating the equation into two equations as follows:

$$\frac{1}{X}\frac{\partial^2}{\partial x^2}X + k_x^2 = 0 \tag{6.210}$$

$$\frac{1}{Y}\frac{\partial^2}{\partial y^2}Y + k_y^2 = 0 \tag{6.211}$$

where the new constants k_x^2 and k_y^2 must satisfy

$$k_x^2 + k_y^2 = k_\rho^2 \tag{6.212}$$

Now multiplying Equations 6.210 and 6.211 by X and Y, respectively, we find:

$$\frac{\partial^2}{\partial x^2}X + k_x^2 X = 0 \tag{6.213}$$

$$\frac{\partial^2}{\partial y^2}Y + k_y^2 Y = 0 \tag{6.214}$$

These are familiar one-dimensional differential equations. The solutions are:[5]

$$X = A\cos(k_x x) + B\sin(k_x x) \tag{6.215}$$

$$Y = C\cos(k_y y) + D\sin(k_y y) \tag{6.216}$$

where A, B, C, and D – like k_x and k_y – are constants to be determined. At this point, we observe that the wave we seek can be expressed as follows:

$$\widetilde{H}_z = \widetilde{h}_z(x,y)e^{-jk_z z}$$

$$= X(x)\,Y(y)\,e^{-jk_z z} \tag{6.217}$$

[5]Students are encouraged to confirm that these are correct by confirming that they are solutions to Equations 6.213 and 6.213, respectively.

The solution is essentially complete except for the values of the constants A, B, C, D, k_x, and k_y. The values of these constants are determined by applying the relevant electromagnetic boundary condition. In this case, it is required that any component of $\widetilde{\mathbf{E}}$ that is tangent to a perfectly-conducting wall must be zero. Therefore:

$$\widetilde{E}_y(x=0) = 0 \tag{6.218}$$

$$\widetilde{E}_y(x=a) = 0 \tag{6.219}$$

$$\widetilde{E}_x(y=0) = 0 \tag{6.220}$$

$$\widetilde{E}_x(y=b) = 0 \tag{6.221}$$

Referring to Equation 6.217 and employing Equations 6.199–6.202, we obtain:

$$\frac{\partial}{\partial x}X(x=0) = 0 \tag{6.222}$$

$$\frac{\partial}{\partial x}X(x=a) = 0 \tag{6.223}$$

$$\frac{\partial}{\partial y}Y(y=0) = 0 \tag{6.224}$$

$$\frac{\partial}{\partial y}Y(y=b) = 0 \tag{6.225}$$

Evaluating the partial derivatives and dividing out common factors of k_x and k_y, we find:

$$-A\sin(k_x\cdot 0) + B\cos(k_x\cdot 0) = 0 \tag{6.226}$$

$$-A\sin(k_x\cdot a) + B\cos(k_x\cdot a) = 0 \tag{6.227}$$

$$-C\sin(k_y\cdot 0) + D\cos(k_y\cdot 0) = 0 \tag{6.228}$$

$$-C\sin(k_y\cdot b) + D\cos(k_y\cdot b) = 0 \tag{6.229}$$

Evaluating:

$$-A\cdot 0 + B\cdot 1 = 0 \tag{6.230}$$

$$-A\sin(k_x a) + B\cos(k_x a) = 0 \tag{6.231}$$

$$-C\cdot 0 + D\cdot 1 = 0 \tag{6.232}$$

$$-C\sin(k_y b) + D\cos(k_y b) = 0 \tag{6.233}$$

Equations 6.230 and 6.232 can be satisfied only if $B = 0$ and $D = 0$, respectively. Subsequently, Equations 6.231 and 6.233 reduce to:

$$\sin(k_x a) = 0 \tag{6.234}$$

$$\sin(k_y b) = 0 \tag{6.235}$$

This in turn requires:

$$k_x = \frac{m\pi}{a}, \quad m = 0,1,2... \tag{6.236}$$

$$k_y = \frac{n\pi}{b}, \quad n = 0,1,2... \tag{6.237}$$

Each positive integer value of m and n leads to a valid expression for $\widetilde{H}_z$ known as a *mode*. Summarizing:

$$\widetilde{H}_z = \sum_{m=0}^{\infty} \sum_{n=0}^{\infty} \widetilde{H}_z^{(m,n)} \quad (6.238)$$

where

$$\widetilde{H}_z^{(m,n)} \triangleq H_0^{(m,n)} \cos\left(\frac{m\pi}{a}x\right) \cos\left(\frac{n\pi}{b}y\right) e^{-jk_z^{(m,n)}z} \quad (6.239)$$

where $H_0^{(m,n)}$ is an arbitrary constant (consolidating the constants A and C), and, since $k_x^2 + k_y^2 = k_\rho^2 \triangleq \beta^2 - k_z^2$:

$$k_z^{(m,n)} = \sqrt{\omega^2\mu\epsilon - \left(\frac{m\pi}{a}\right)^2 - \left(\frac{n\pi}{b}\right)^2} \quad (6.240)$$

Summarizing:

> The TE ($\widetilde{E}_z = 0$) component of the unidirectional ($+\hat{\mathbf{z}}$-traveling) wave in a rectangular waveguide is completely determined by Equation 6.238, and consists of modes as defined by Equations 6.239, 6.240, 6.236, and 6.237. The remaining non-zero field components can be determined using Equations 6.199–6.202.

It is customary and convenient to refer to the TE modes in a rectangular waveguide using the notation "TE$_{mn}$." For example, the mode TE$_{12}$ is given by Equation 6.239 with $m = 1$ and $n = 2$.

Although Equation 6.238 implies the existence of a TE$_{00}$ mode, it should be noted that this wave has no non-zero electric field components. This can be determined mathematically by following the procedure outlined above. However, this is also readily confirmed as follows: $\widetilde{E}_x$ is constant for the TE$_{00}$ mode because $k_\rho = 0$ for this mode, however, $\widetilde{E}_x$ must be zero to meet the boundary conditions on the walls at $y = 0$ and $y = b$. Similarly, $\widetilde{E}_y$ is constant for the TE$_{00}$ mode, however, $\widetilde{E}_y$ must be zero to meet the boundary conditions on the walls at $x = 0$ and $x = b$.

Finally, note that values of $k_z^{(m,n)}$ obtained from Equation 6.240 are not necessarily real-valued. It is apparent that for any given value of m, $k_z^{(m,n)}$ will be imaginary-valued for all values of n greater than some value. Similarly, it is apparent that for any given value of n, $k_z^{(m,n)}$ will be imaginary-valued for all values of m greater than some value. This phenomenon is common to both TE and TM components, and so is addressed in a separate section (Section 6.10).

Additional Reading:

- "Waveguide (radio frequency)" on Wikipedia.
- "Separation of variables" on Wikipedia.

6.10 Rectangular Waveguide: Propagation Characteristics

[m0224]

In this section, we consider the propagation characteristics of TE and TM modes in rectangular waveguides. Because these modes exhibit the same phase dependence on z, findings of this section apply equally to both sets of modes. Recall that the TM modes in a rectangular waveguide are given by:

$$\widetilde{E}_z^{(m,n)} = E_0^{(m,n)} \sin\left(\frac{m\pi}{a}x\right) \sin\left(\frac{n\pi}{b}y\right) e^{-jk_z^{(m,n)}z} \tag{6.241}$$

where $E_0^{(m,n)}$ is an arbitrary constant (determined in part by sources), and:

$$k_z^{(m,n)} = \sqrt{\omega^2\mu\epsilon - \left(\frac{m\pi}{a}\right)^2 - \left(\frac{n\pi}{b}\right)^2} \tag{6.242}$$

The TE modes in a rectangular waveguide are:

$$\widetilde{H}_z^{(m,n)} = H_0^{(m,n)} \cos\left(\frac{m\pi}{a}x\right) \cos\left(\frac{n\pi}{b}y\right) e^{-jk_z^{(m,n)}z} \tag{6.243}$$

where $H_0^{(m,n)}$ is an arbitrary constant (determined in part by sources).

Cutoff frequency. First, observe that values of $k_z^{(m,n)}$ obtained from Equation 6.242 are not necessarily real-valued. For any given value of m, $(k_z^{(m,n)})^2$ will be negative for all values of n greater than some value. Similarly, for any given value of n, $(k_z^{(m,n)})^2$ will be negative for all values of m greater than some value. Should either of these conditions occur, we find:

$$\begin{aligned}\left(k_z^{(m,n)}\right)^2 &= \omega^2\mu\epsilon - \left(\frac{m\pi}{a}\right)^2 - \left(\frac{n\pi}{b}\right)^2 < 0 \\ &= -\left|\omega^2\mu\epsilon - \left(\frac{m\pi}{a}\right)^2 - \left(\frac{n\pi}{b}\right)^2\right| \\ &= -\alpha^2\end{aligned} \tag{6.244}$$

where α is a positive real-valued constant. So:

$$k_z^{(m,n)} = \pm j\alpha \tag{6.245}$$

Subsequently:

$$\begin{aligned}e^{-jk_z^{(m,n)}z} &= e^{-j(\pm j\alpha)z} \\ &= e^{\pm\alpha z}\end{aligned} \tag{6.246}$$

The "+" sign option corresponds to a wave that grows exponentially in magnitude with increasing z, which is non-physical behavior. Therefore:

$$e^{-jk_z^{(m,n)}z} = e^{-\alpha z} \tag{6.247}$$

Summarizing: When values of m or n are such that $(k_z^{(m,n)})^2 < 0$, the magnitude of the associated wave is no longer constant with z. Instead, the magnitude of the wave decreases exponentially with increasing z. Such a wave does not effectively convey power through the waveguide, and is said to be *cut off*.

Since waveguides are normally intended for the efficient transfer of power, it is important to know the criteria for a mode to be cut off. Since cutoff occurs when $(k_z^{(m,n)})^2 < 0$, cutoff occurs when:

$$\omega^2\mu\epsilon > \left(\frac{m\pi}{a}\right)^2 + \left(\frac{n\pi}{b}\right)^2 \tag{6.248}$$

Since $\omega = 2\pi f$:

$$f > \frac{1}{2\pi\sqrt{\mu\epsilon}}\sqrt{\left(\frac{m\pi}{a}\right)^2 + \left(\frac{n\pi}{b}\right)^2} \tag{6.249}$$

$$= \frac{1}{2\sqrt{\mu\epsilon}}\sqrt{\left(\frac{m}{a}\right)^2 + \left(\frac{n}{b}\right)^2} \tag{6.250}$$

Note that $1/\sqrt{\mu\epsilon}$ is the phase velocity v_p for the medium used in the waveguide. With this in mind, let us define:

$$v_{pu} \triangleq \frac{1}{\sqrt{\mu\epsilon}} \tag{6.251}$$

This is the phase velocity in an unbounded medium having the same permeability and permittivity as the interior of the waveguide. Thus:

$$f > \frac{v_{pu}}{2}\sqrt{\left(\frac{m}{a}\right)^2 + \left(\frac{n}{b}\right)^2} \tag{6.252}$$

In other words, the mode (m, n) avoids being cut off if the frequency is high enough to meet this criterion. Thus, it is useful to make the following definition:

$$f_{mn} \triangleq \frac{v_{pu}}{2}\sqrt{\left(\frac{m}{a}\right)^2 + \left(\frac{n}{b}\right)^2} \tag{6.253}$$

The *cutoff frequency* f_{mn} (Equation 6.253) is the lowest frequency for which the mode (m, n) is able to propagate (i.e., not cut off).

Example 6.4. Cutoff frequencies for WR-90.

WR-90 is a popular implementation of rectangular waveguide. WR-90 is air-filled with dimensions $a = 22.86$ mm and $b = 10.16$ mm. Determine cutoff frequencies and, in particular, the lowest frequency at which WR-90 can be used.

Solution. Since WR-90 is air-filled, $\mu \approx \mu_0$, $\epsilon \approx \epsilon_0$, and $v_{pu} \approx 1\sqrt{\mu_0\epsilon_0} \cong 3.00 \times 10^8$ m/s. Cutoff frequencies are given by Equation 6.253. Recall that there are no non-zero TE or TM modes with $m = 0$ and $n = 0$. Since $a > b$, the lowest non-zero cutoff frequency is achieved when $m = 1$ and $n = 0$. In this case, Equation 6.253 yields $f_{10} = \underline{6.557 \text{ GHz}}$; this is the lowest frequency that is able to propagate efficiently in the waveguide. The next lowest cutoff frequency is $f_{20} = 13.114$ GHz. The third lowest cutoff frequency is $f_{01} = 14.754$ GHz. The lowest-order TM mode that is non-zero and not cut off is TM_{11} ($f_{11} = 16.145$ GHz).

Phase velocity. The phase velocity for a wave propagating within a rectangular waveguide is greater than that of electromagnetic radiation in unbounded space. For example, the phase velocity of any propagating mode in a vacuum-filled waveguide is greater than c, the speed of light in free space. This is a surprising result. Let us first derive this result and then attempt to make sense of it.

Phase velocity v_p in the rectangular waveguide is given by

$$v_p \triangleq \frac{\omega}{k_z^{(m,n)}} \tag{6.254}$$

$$= \frac{\omega}{\sqrt{\omega^2\mu\epsilon - (m\pi/a)^2 - (n\pi/b)^2}} \tag{6.255}$$

Immediately we observe that phase velocity seems to be different for different modes. Dividing the numerator and denominator by $\beta = \omega\sqrt{\mu\epsilon}$, we obtain:

$$v_p = \frac{1}{\sqrt{\mu\epsilon}} \frac{1}{\sqrt{1 - (\omega^2\mu\epsilon)^{-1}\left[(m\pi/a)^2 + (n\pi/b)^2\right]}} \tag{6.256}$$

Note that $1/\sqrt{\mu\epsilon}$ is v_{pu}, as defined earlier. Employing Equation 6.253 and also noting that $\omega = 2\pi f$, Equation 6.256 may be rewritten in the following form:

$$v_p = \frac{v_{pu}}{\sqrt{1 - (f_{mn}/f)^2}} \tag{6.257}$$

For any propagating mode, $f > f_{mn}$; subsequently, $v_p > v_{pu}$. In particular, $v_p > c$ for a vacuum-filled waveguide.

How can this not be a violation of fundamental physics? As noted in Section 6.1, phase velocity is *not* necessarily the speed at which information travels, but is merely the speed at which a point of constant phase travels. To send information, we must create a disturbance in the otherwise sinusoidal excitation presumed in the analysis so far. The complex field structure creates points of constant phase that travel faster than the disturbance is able to convey information, so there is no violation of physical principles.

Group velocity. As noted in Section 6.1, the speed at which information travels is given by the group velocity v_g. In unbounded space, $v_g = v_p$, so the speed of information is equal to the phase velocity in that case. In a rectangular waveguide, the situation is different. We find:

$$v_g = \left(\frac{\partial k_z^{(m,n)}}{\partial \omega}\right)^{-1} \tag{6.258}$$

$$= v_{pu}\sqrt{1 - (f_{mn}/f)^2} \tag{6.259}$$

which is always *less* than v_{pu} for a propagating mode.

Note that group velocity in the waveguide depends on frequency in two ways. First, because f_{mn} takes on different values for different modes, group velocity is different for different modes. Specifically, higher-order modes propagate more slowly than lower-order modes having the same frequency. This is known as *modal dispersion*. Secondly, note that the group velocity of any given mode depends on frequency. This is known as *chromatic dispersion*.

The speed of a signal within a rectangular waveguide is given by the group velocity of the associated mode (Equation 6.259). This speed is less than the speed of propagation in unbounded media having the same permittivity and permeability. Speed depends on the ratio f_{mn}/f, and generally decreases with increasing frequency for any given mode.

[m0212]

Example 6.5. Speed of propagating in WR-90.

Revisiting WR-90 waveguide from Example 6.4: What is the speed of propagation for a narrowband signal at 10 GHz?

Solution. Let us assume that "narrowband" here means that the bandwidth is negligible relative to the center frequency, so that we need only consider the center frequency. As previously determined, the lowest-order propagating mode is TE_{10}, for which $f_{10} = 6.557$ GHz. The next-lowest cutoff frequency is $f_{20} = 13.114$ GHz. Therefore, only the TE_{10} mode is available for this signal. The group velocity for this mode at the frequency of interest is given by Equation 6.259. Using this equation, the speed of propagation is found to be $\cong 2.26 \times 10^8$ m/s, which is about 75.5% of c.

Image Credits

Fig. 6.1: © Sevenchw (C. Wang),
https://commons.wikimedia.org/wiki/File:Geometry_for_analysis_of_fields_in_parallel_plate_waveguide.svg,
CC BY-SA 4.0 (https://creativecommons.org/licenses/by-sa/4.0/), modified.

Fig. 6.2: © Sevenchw (C. Wang),
https://commons.wikimedia.org/wiki/File:TE_component_of_electric_field_in_parallel_plate_waveguide.svg,
CC BY-SA 4.0 (https://creativecommons.org/licenses/by-sa/4.0/).

Fig. 6.3: © Sevenchw (C. Wang),
https://commons.wikimedia.org/wiki/File:Magnitude_of_the_two_lowest-order_TE_modes_in_parallel_plate
_waveguide.svg,
CC BY-SA 4.0 (https://creativecommons.org/licenses/by-sa/4.0/).

Fig. 6.4: © Sevenchw (C. Wang),
https://commons.wikimedia.org/wiki/File:TM_component_of_electric_field_in_parallel_plate_waveguide.svg,
CC BY-SA 4.0 (https://creativecommons.org/licenses/by-sa/4.0/).

Fig. 6.5: © Sevenchw (C. Wang),
https://commons.wikimedia.org/wiki/File:TM_component_of_electric_field_in_parallel_plate_waveguide.svg,
CC BY-SA 4.0 (https://creativecommons.org/licenses/by-sa/4.0/), modified.

Chapter 7

Transmission Lines Redux

7.1 Parallel Wire Transmission Line

[m0188]

A parallel wire transmission line consists of wires separated by a dielectric spacer. Figure 7.1 shows a common implementation, commonly known as "twin lead." The wires in twin lead line are held in place by a mechanical spacer comprised of the same low-loss dielectric material that forms the jacket of each wire. Very little of the total energy associated with the electric and magnetic fields lies inside this material, so the jacket and spacer can usually be neglected for the purposes of analysis and electrical design.

Parallel wire transmission line is often employed in radio applications up to about 100 MHz as an alternative to coaxial line. Parallel wire line has the advantages of lower cost and lower loss than coaxial line in this frequency range. However, parallel wire line lacks the self-shielding property of coaxial cable; i.e., the electromagnetic fields of coaxial line are isolated by the outer conductor, whereas those of parallel wire line are exposed and prone to interaction with nearby structures and devices. This prevents the use of parallel wire line in many applications.

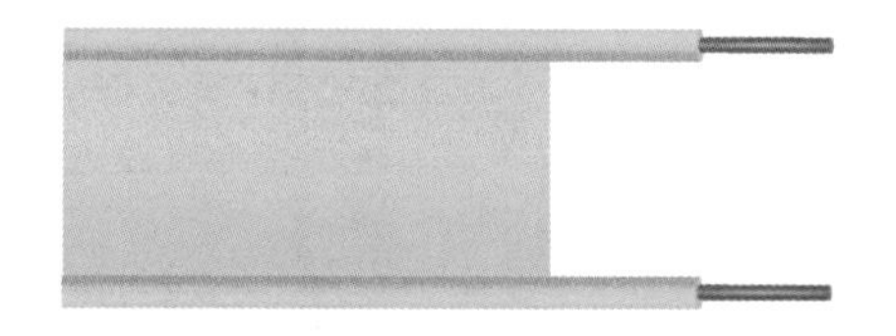

© SpinningSpark, Inductiveload CC BY SA 3.0 (modified)

Figure 7.1: Twin lead, a commonly-encountered form of parallel wire transmission line.

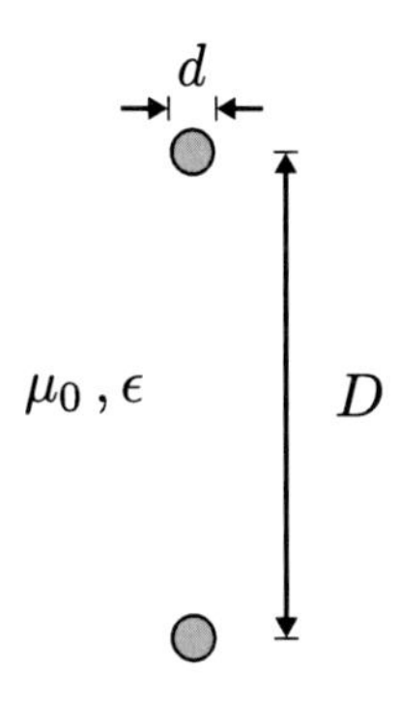

© C. Wang CC BY SA 4.0

Figure 7.2: Parallel wire transmission line structure and design parameters.

Another discriminator between parallel wire line and coaxial line is that parallel wire line is differential.[1] The conductor geometry is symmetric and neither conductor is favored as a signal datum ("ground"). Thus, parallel wire line is commonly used in applications where the signal sources and/or loads are also differential; common examples are the dipole antenna and differential amplifiers.[2]

Figure 7.2 shows a cross-section of parallel wire line. Relevant parameters include the wire diameter, d; and the center-to-center spacing, D.

[1] The references in "Additional Reading" at the end of this section may be helpful if you are not familiar with this concept.

[2] This is in contrast to "single-ended" line such as coaxial line, which has conductors of different cross-sections and the outer conductor is favored as the datum.

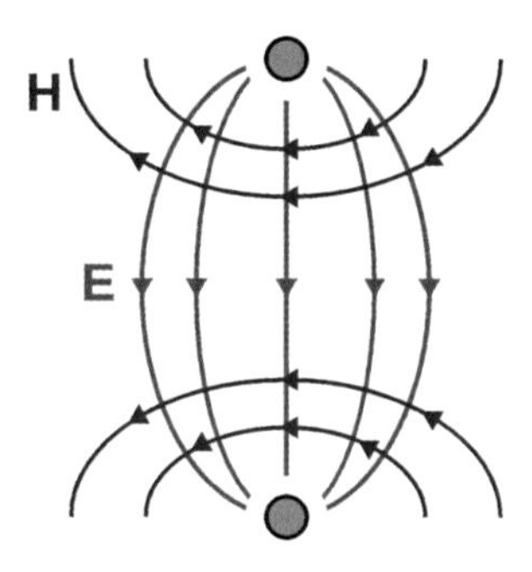

© S. Lally CC BY SA 4.0

Figure 7.3: Structure of the electric and magnetic fields for a cross-section of parallel wire line. In this case, the wave is propagating away from the viewer.

The associated field structure is transverse electromagnetic (TEM) and is therefore completely described by a single cross-section along the line, as shown in Figure 7.3. Expressions for these fields exist, but are complex and not particularly useful except as a means to calculate other parameters of interest. One of these parameters is, of course, the characteristic impedance since this parameter plays an important role in the analysis and design of systems employing transmission lines. The characteristic impedance may be determined using the "lumped element" transmission line model using the following expression:

$$Z_0 = \sqrt{\frac{R' + j\omega L'}{G' + j\omega C'}} \tag{7.1}$$

where R', G', C', and L' are the resistance, conductance, capacitance, and inductance per unit length, respectively. This analysis is considerably simplified by neglecting loss; therefore, let us assume the "low-loss" conditions $R' \ll \omega L'$ and $G' \ll \omega C'$. Then we find:

$$Z_0 \approx \sqrt{\frac{L'}{C'}} \quad \text{(low loss)} \tag{7.2}$$

and the problem is reduced to determining inductance and capacitance of the transmission line. These are

$$L' = \frac{\mu_0}{\pi} \ln\left[(D/d) + \sqrt{(D/d)^2 - 1}\right] \tag{7.3}$$

$$C' = \frac{\pi\epsilon}{\ln\left[(D/d) + \sqrt{(D/d)^2 - 1}\right]} \tag{7.4}$$

Because the wire separation D is typically much greater than the wire diameter d, $D/d \gg 1$ and so $\sqrt{(D/d)^2 - 1} \approx D/d$. This leads to the simplified expressions

$$L' \approx \frac{\mu_0}{\pi} \ln(2D/d) \quad (D \gg d) \tag{7.5}$$

$$C' \approx \frac{\pi\epsilon}{\ln(2D/d)} \quad (D \gg d) \tag{7.6}$$

Now returning to Equation 7.2:

$$Z_0 \approx \frac{1}{\pi}\sqrt{\frac{\mu_0}{\epsilon}} \ln(2D/d) \tag{7.7}$$

Noting that $\epsilon = \epsilon_r\epsilon_0$ and $\sqrt{\mu_0/\epsilon_0} \triangleq \eta_0$, we obtain

$$\boxed{Z_0 \approx \frac{1}{\pi}\frac{\eta_0}{\sqrt{\epsilon_r}} \ln(2D/d)} \tag{7.8}$$

The characteristic impedance of parallel wire line, assuming low-loss conditions and wire spacing much greater than wire diameter, is given by Equation 7.8.

Observe that the characteristic impedance of parallel wire line increases with increasing D/d. Since this ratio is large, the characteristic impedance of parallel wire line tends to be large relative to common values of other kinds of TEM transmission line, such as coaxial line and microstrip line. An example follows.

Example 7.1. 300 Ω twin-lead.

A commonly-encountered form of parallel wire transmission line is 300 Ω twin-lead. Although implementations vary, the wire diameter is usually about 1 mm and and the wire spacing is usually about 6 mm. The relative permittivity of the medium $\epsilon_r \approx 1$ for the purposes of calculating transmission line parameters, since the jacket and spacer have only a small effect on the fields. For these values, Equation 7.8 gives $Z_0 \approx 298\ \Omega$, as expected.

Under the assumption that the wire jacket/spacer material has a negligible effect on the electromagnetic fields, and that the line is suspended in air so that $\epsilon_r \approx 1$, the phase velocity v_p for a parallel wire line is approximately that of any electromagnetic wave in free space; i.e., c. In practical twin-lead, the effect of a plastic jacket/spacer material is to reduce the phase velocity by a few percent up to about 20%, depending on the materials and details of construction. So in practice $v_p \approx 0.8c$ to $0.9c$ for twin-lead line.

Additional Reading:

- "Twin-lead" on Wikipedia.
- "Differential signaling" on Wikipedia.
- Sec. 8.7 ("Differential Circuits") in S.W. Ellingson, *Radio Systems Engineering*, Cambridge Univ. Press, 2016.

7.2 Microstrip Line Redux

[m0186]

A microstrip transmission line consists of a narrow metallic trace separated from a metallic ground plane by a slab of dielectric material, as shown in Figure 7.4. This is a natural way to implement a transmission line on a printed circuit board, and so accounts for an important and expansive range of applications. The reader should be aware that microstrip is distinct from *stripline*, which is a distinct type of transmission line; see "Additional Reading" at the end of this section for disambiguation of these terms.

A microstrip line is single-ended[3] in the sense that the conductor geometry is asymmetric and the one conductor – namely, the ground plane – also normally serves as ground for the source and load.

The spacer material is typically a low-loss dielectric material having permeability approximately equal to that of free space ($\mu \approx \mu_0$) and relative permittivity ϵ_r in the range of 2 to about 10 or so.

The structure of a microstrip line is similar to that of a parallel plate waveguide (Section 6.6), with the obvious difference that one of the "plates" has finite length in the direction perpendicular to the direction of propagation. Despite this difference, the parallel plate waveguide provides some useful insight into the operation of the microstrip line. Microstrip line is nearly always operated below the cutoff frequency of

[3]The reference in "Additional Reading" at the end of this section may be helpful if you are not familiar with this concept.

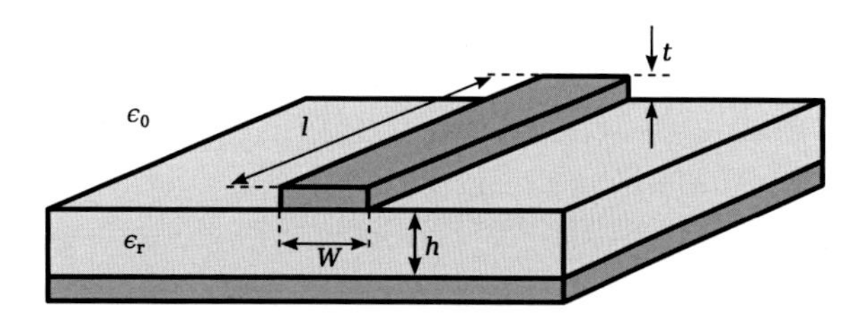

© 7head7metal7 CC BY SA 3.0 (modified)

Figure 7.4: Microstrip transmission line structure and design parameters.

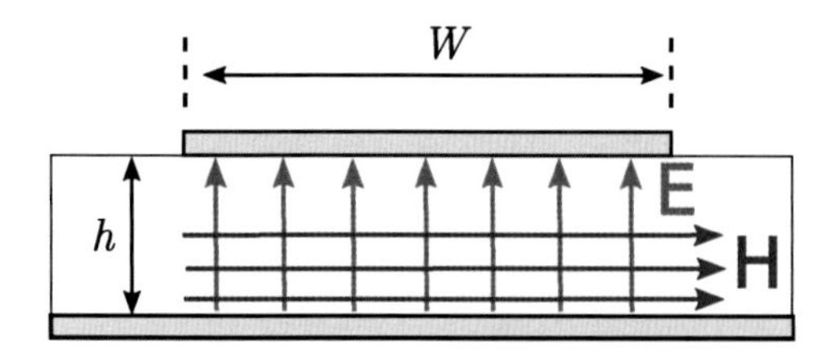

Figure 7.5: *Approximate* structure of the electric and magnetic fields within microstrip line, assuming TM_0 operation. The fields *outside* the line are possibly significant, complicated, and not shown. In this case, the wave is propagating away from the viewer.

all but the TM_0 mode, whose cutoff frequency is zero. This guarantees that only the TM_0 mode can propagate. The TM_0 mode has the form of a uniform plane wave, as shown in Figure 7.5. The electric field is oriented in the direction perpendicular to the plates, and magnetic field is oriented in the direction parallel to the plates. The direction of propagation $\mathbf{E} \times \mathbf{H}$ for the TM_0 mode always points in the same direction; namely, along the axis of the transmission line. Therefore, microstrip lines nominally exhibit transverse electromagnetic (TEM) field structure.

The limited width W of the trace results in a "fringing field" – i.e., significant deviations from TM_0 field structure in the dielectric beyond the edges of the trace and above the trace. The fringing fields may play a significant role in determining the characteristic impedance Z_0. Since Z_0 is an important parameter in the analysis and design of systems using transmission lines, we are motivated to not only determine Z_0 for the microstrip line, but also to understand how variation in W affects Z_0. Let us address this issue by considering the following three special cases, in order:

- $W \gg h$, which we shall refer to as the "wide" case.
- $W \ll h$, which we shall refer to as the "narrow" case.
- $W \sim h$; i.e., the intermediate case in which h and W equal to within an order of magnitude or so.

Wide case. If $W \gg h$, most of the energy associated with propagating waves lies directly underneath the trace, and Figure 7.5 provides a relatively accurate impression of the fields in this region. The characteristic impedance Z_0 may be determined using the "lumped element" transmission line model using the following expression:

$$Z_0 = \sqrt{\frac{R' + j\omega L'}{G' + j\omega C'}} \tag{7.9}$$

where R', G', C', and L' are the resistance, conductance, capacitance, and inductance per unit length, respectively. For the present analysis, nothing is lost by assuming loss is negligible; therefore, let us assume $R' \ll \omega L'$ and $G' \ll \omega G'$, yielding

$$Z_0 \approx \sqrt{\frac{L'}{C'}} \tag{7.10}$$

Thus the problem is reduced to determining capacitance and inductance of the transmission line.

Wide microstrip line resembles a parallel-plate capacitor whose plate spacing d is very small compared to the plate area A. In this case, fringing fields may be considered negligible and one finds that the capacitance C is given by

$$C \approx \frac{\epsilon A}{d} \quad \text{(parallel plate capacitor)} \tag{7.11}$$

In terms of wide microstrip line, $A = Wl$ where l is length, and $d = h$. Therefore:

$$C' \triangleq \frac{C}{l} \approx \frac{\epsilon W}{h} \quad (W \gg h) \tag{7.12}$$

To determine L', consider the view of the microstrip line shown in Figure 7.6. Here a current source applies a steady current I on the left, and a resistive load closes the current loop on the right. Ampere's law for magnetostatics and the associated "right hand rule" require that $\mathbf{H}$ is directed into the page and is approximately uniform. The magnetic flux between the trace and the ground plane is

$$\Phi = \int_{\mathcal{S}} \mathbf{B} \cdot d\mathbf{s} \tag{7.13}$$

where $\mathcal{S}$ is the surface bounded by the current loop and $\mathbf{B} = \mu_0 \mathbf{H}$. In the present problem, the area of $\mathcal{S}$ is hl and $\mathbf{H}$ is approximately constant over $\mathcal{S}$, so:

$$\Phi \approx \mu_0 H hl \tag{7.14}$$

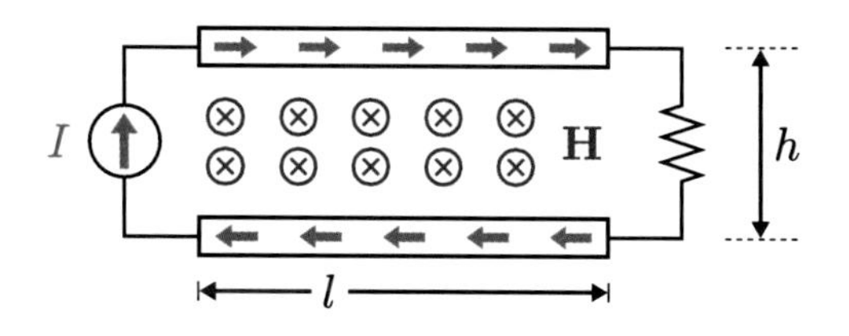

© C. Wang CC BY SA 4.0

Figure 7.6: View from the side of a microstrip line, used to determine L'.

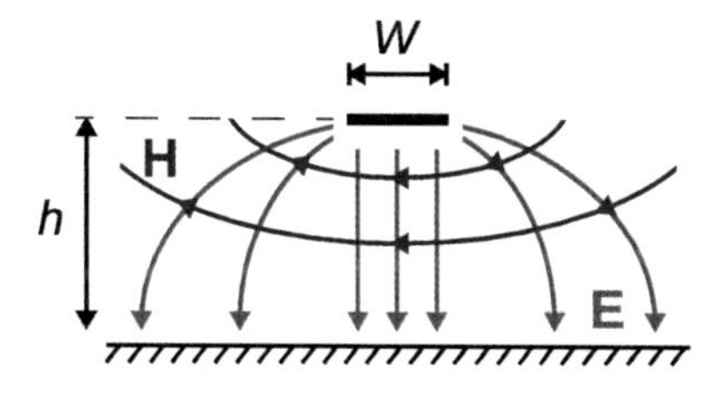

© S. Lally CC BY SA 4.0

Figure 7.7: Electric and magnetic fields lines for narrow ($W \ll h$) microstrip line.

where H is the magnitude of $\mathbf{H}$. Next, recall that:

$$L \triangleq \frac{\Phi}{I} \tag{7.15}$$

So, we may determine L if we are able to obtain an expression for I in terms of H. This can be done as follows. First, note that we can express I in terms of the current density on the trace; i.e.,

$$I = J_s W \tag{7.16}$$

where J_s is the current density (SI base units of A/m) on the trace. Next, we note that the boundary condition for $\mathbf{H}$ on the trace requires that the discontinuity in the tangent component of $\mathbf{H}$ going from the trace (where the magnetic field intensity is H) to beyond the trace (i.e., outside the transmission line, where the magnetic field intensity is approximately zero) be equal to the surface current. Thus, $J_s \approx H$ and

$$I = J_s W \approx HW \tag{7.17}$$

Returning to Equation 7.15, we find:

$$L \triangleq \frac{\Phi}{I} \approx \frac{\mu_0 H h l}{HW} = \frac{\mu_0 h l}{W} \tag{7.18}$$

Subsequently,

$$L' \triangleq \frac{L}{l} \approx \frac{\mu_0 h}{W} \quad (W \gg h) \tag{7.19}$$

Now the characteristic impedance is found to be

$$Z_0 \approx \sqrt{\frac{L'}{C'}} \approx \sqrt{\frac{\mu_0 h/W}{\epsilon W/h}} = \sqrt{\frac{\mu_0}{\epsilon}}\frac{h}{W} \tag{7.20}$$

The factor $\sqrt{\mu_0/\epsilon}$ is recognized as the wave impedance η. It is convenient to express this in terms of the free space wave impedance $\eta_0 \triangleq \sqrt{\mu_0/\epsilon_0}$, leading to the expression we seek:

$$\boxed{Z_0 \approx \frac{\eta_0}{\sqrt{\epsilon_r}}\frac{h}{W} \quad (W \gg h)} \tag{7.21}$$

> The characteristic impedance of "wide" ($W \gg h$) microstrip line is given approximately by Equation 7.21.

It is worth noting that the characteristic impedance of wide transmission line is proportional to h/W. The factor h/W figures prominently in the narrow- and intermediate-width cases as well, as we shall soon see.

Narrow case. Figure 7.5 does not accurately depict the fields in the case that $W \ll h$. Instead, much of the energy associated with the electric and magnetic fields lies beyond and above the trace. Although these fields are relatively complex, we can develop a rudimentary model of the field structure by considering the relevant boundary conditions. In particular, the tangential component of $\mathbf{E}$ must be zero on the surfaces of the trace and ground plane. Also, we expect magnetic field lines to be perpendicular to the electric field lines so that the direction of propagation is along the axis of the line. These insights lead to Figure 7.7.

Note that the field lines shown in Figure 7.7 are quite similar to those for parallel wire line (Section 7.1). If we choose diameter $d = W$ and wire spacing $D = 2h$, then the fields of the microstrip line in the dielectric spacer must be similar to those of the parallel wire line between the lines. This is shown in

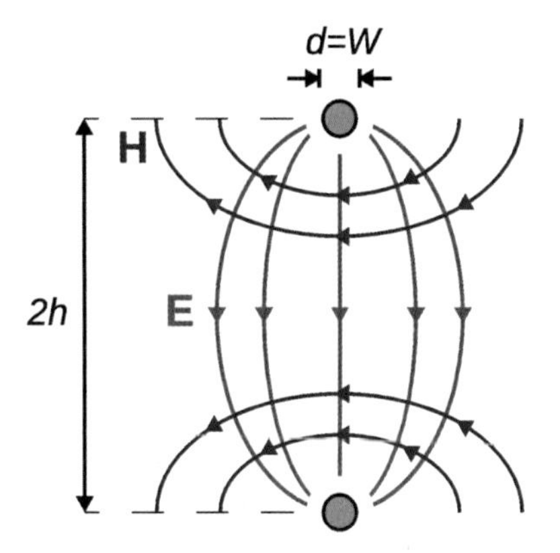

Figure 7.8: Noting the similarity of the fields in narrow microstrip line to those in a parallel wire line.

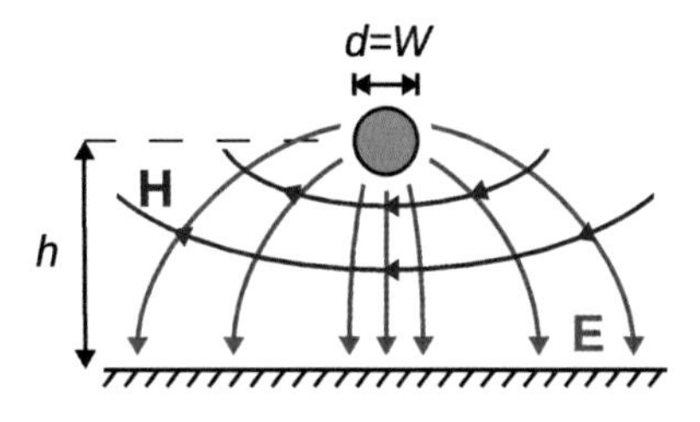

Figure 7.9: Modeling the fields in narrow microstrip line as those of a parallel wire line, now introducing the ground plane.

Figure 7.8. Note that the fields above the dielectric spacer in the microstrip line will typically be somewhat different (since the material above the trace is typically different; e.g., air). However, it remains true that we expect most of the energy to be contained in the dielectric, so we shall assume that this difference has a relatively small effect.

Next, we continue to refine the model by introducing the ground plane, as shown in Figure 7.9: The fields in the upper half-space are not perturbed when we do this, since the fields in Figure 7.8 already satisfy the boundary conditions imposed by the new ground plane. Thus, we see that the parallel wire transmission line provides a pretty good guide to the structure of the fields for the narrow transmission line, at least in the dielectric region of the upper half-space.

We are now ready to estimate the characteristic impedance $Z_0 \approx \sqrt{L'/C'}$ of low-loss narrow microstrip line. Neglecting the differences noted above, we estimate that this is roughly equal to the characteristic impedance of the analogous ($d = W$ and $D = 2h$) parallel wire line. Under this assumption, we obtain from Equation 7.8:

$$\boxed{Z_0 \sim \frac{1}{\pi} \frac{\eta_0}{\sqrt{\epsilon_r}} \ln\left(4h/W\right) \quad (W \ll h)} \tag{7.22}$$

This estimate will exhibit only "order of magnitude" accuracy (hence the "$\sim$" symbol), since the contribution from the fields in half of the relevant space is ignored. However we expect that Equation 7.22 will accurately capture the dependence of Z_0 on the parameters ϵ_r and h/W. These properties can be useful for making fine adjustments to a microstrip design.

> The characteristic impedance of "narrow" ($W \ll h$) microstrip line can be roughly approximated by Equation 7.22.

Intermediate case. An expression for Z_0 in the intermediate case – even a rough estimate – is difficult to derive, and beyond the scope of this book. However, we are not completely in the dark, since we can reasonably anticipate that Z_0 in the intermediate case should be intermediate to estimates provided by the wide and narrow cases. This is best demonstrated by example. Figure 7.10 shows estimates of Z_0 using

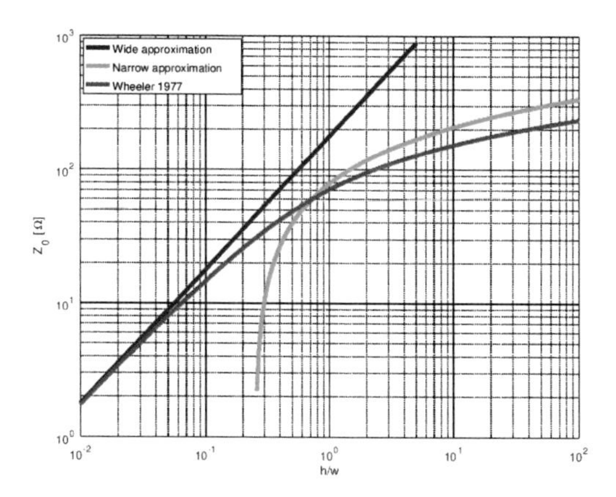

Figure 7.10: Z_0 for FR4 as a function of h/W, as determined by the "wide" and "narrow" approximations, along with the Wheeler 1977 formula. Note that the vertical and horizontal axes of this plot are in log scale.

the wide and narrow expressions (blue and green curves, respectively) for a particular implementation of microstrip line (see Example 7.2 for details). Since Z_0 varies smoothly with h/W, it is reasonable to expect that simply averaging the values generated using the wide and narrow assumptions would give a pretty good estimate when $h/W \sim 1$.

However, it is also possible to obtain an accurate estimate directly. A widely-accepted and broadly-applicable formula is provided in Wheeler 1977 (cited in "Additional Reading" at the end of this section). This expression is valid over the full range of h/W, not merely the intermediate case of $h/W \sim 1$. Here it is:

$$Z_0 \approx \frac{42.4\ \Omega}{\sqrt{\epsilon_r + 1}} \times \ln\left[1 + \frac{4h}{W'}\left(K + \sqrt{K^2 + \frac{1 + 1/\epsilon_r}{2}\pi^2}\right)\right] \tag{7.23}$$

where

$$K \triangleq \frac{14 + 8/\epsilon_r}{11}\left(\frac{4h}{W'}\right) \tag{7.24}$$

and W' is W adjusted to account for the thickness t of the microstrip line. Typically $t \ll W$ and $t \ll h$, for which $W' \approx W$. Although complicated, this formula should not be completely surprising. For example, note the parameters h and W appear in this formula as the factor $4h/W$, which we encountered in the "narrow" approximation. Also, we see that the formula indicates Z_0 increases with increasing h/W and decreasing ϵ_r, as we determined in both the "narrow" and "wide" cases.

The following example provides a demonstration for the very common case of microstrip implementation in FR4 circuit board material.

Example 7.2. Characteristic impedance of microstrip lines in FR4.

FR4 printed circuit boards consist of a substrate having $h \cong 1.575$ mm and $\epsilon_r \approx 4.5$. Figure 7.10 shows Z_0 as a function of h/W, as determined by the wide and narrow approximations, along with the value obtained using the Wheeler 1977 formula. The left side of the plot represents the wide condition, whereas the right side of this plot represents the narrow condition. The Wheeler 1977 formula is an accurate estimate over the entire horizontal span. Note that the wide approximation is accurate only for $h/W < 0.1$ or so, improving with decreasing h/W as expected. The narrow approximation overestimates Z_0 by a factor of about 1.4 (i.e., about 40%). This is consistent with our previous observation that this approximation should yield only about "order of magnitude" accuracy. Nevertheless, the narrow approximation exhibits approximately the same rate of increase with h/W as does the Wheeler 1977 formula.

Also worth noting from Figure 7.10 is the important and commonly-used result that $Z_0 \approx 50\ \Omega$ is obtained for $h/W \approx 0.5$. Thus, a $50\ \Omega$ microstrip line in FR4 has a trace width of about 3 mm.

A useful "take away" from this example is that the wide and narrow approximations serve as useful guides for understanding how Z_0 changes as a function of h/W and ϵ_r. This is useful especially for making adjustments to a microstrip line design once an accurate value of Z_0 is obtained from some other method; e.g., using the Wheeler 1977 formula or from measurements.

FR4 circuit board construction is so common that the result from the previous example deserves to be highlighted:

> In FR4 printed circuit board construction (substrate thickness 1.575 mm, relative permittivity ≈ 4.5, negligible trace thickness), $Z_0 \approx 50\ \Omega$ requires a trace width of about 3 mm. Z_0 scales roughly in proportion to h/W around this value.

Simpler approximations for Z_0 are also commonly employed in the design and analysis of microstrip lines. These expressions are limited in the range of h/W for which they are valid, and can usually be shown to be special cases or approximations of Equation 7.23. Nevertheless, they are sometimes useful for quick "back of the envelope" calculations.

Wavelength in microstrip line. An accurate general formula for wavelength λ in microstrip line is similarly difficult to derive. A useful approximate technique employs a result from the theory of uniform plane waves in unbounded media. For such waves, the phase propagation constant β is given by

$$\beta = \omega\sqrt{\mu\epsilon} \tag{7.25}$$

It turns out that the electromagnetic field structure for the guided wave in a microstrip line is similar in the sense that it exhibits TEM field structure, as does the uniform plane wave. However, the guided wave is different in that it exists in both the dielectric spacer and the air above the spacer. Thus, we presume that β for the guided wave can be approximated as that of a uniform plane wave in unbounded media having the same permeability μ_0 but a different relative permittivity, which we shall assign the symbol $\epsilon_{r,eff}$ (for "*effective* relative permittivity"). Then:

$$\begin{aligned}\beta &\approx \omega\sqrt{\mu_0\ \epsilon_{r,eff}\ \epsilon_0} \quad \text{(low-loss microstrip)} \\ &= \beta_0\sqrt{\epsilon_{r,eff}}\end{aligned} \tag{7.26}$$

In other words, the phase propagation constant in a microstrip line can be approximated as the free-space phase propagation $\beta_0 \triangleq \omega\sqrt{\mu_0\epsilon_0}$ times a correction factor $\sqrt{\epsilon_{r,eff}}$.

Next, $\epsilon_{r,eff}$ is crudely approximated as the average of the relative permittivity of the dielectric slab and the relative permittivity of free space; i.e.,:

$$\epsilon_{r,eff} \approx \frac{\epsilon_r + 1}{2} \tag{7.27}$$

Various refinements exist to improve on this approximation; however, in practice, variations in the value of ϵ_r for the dielectric due to manufacturing processes typically make a more precise estimate irrelevant.

Using this concept, we obtain

$$\lambda = \frac{2\pi}{\beta} = \frac{2\pi}{\beta_0\sqrt{\epsilon_{r,eff}}} = \frac{\lambda_0}{\sqrt{\epsilon_{r,eff}}} \tag{7.28}$$

where λ_0 is the free-space wavelength c/f. Similarly the phase velocity v_p can be estimated using the relationship

$$v_p = \frac{\omega}{\beta} = \frac{c}{\sqrt{\epsilon_{r,eff}}} \tag{7.29}$$

i.e., the phase velocity in microstrip is slower than c by a factor of $\sqrt{\epsilon_{r,eff}}$.

Example 7.3. Wavelength and phase velocity in microstrip in FR4 printed circuit boards.

FR4 is a low-loss fiberglass epoxy dielectric that is commonly used to make printed circuit boards (see "Additional Reading" at the end of this section). For FR4, $\epsilon_r \approx 4.5$. The effective relative permittivity is therefore:

$$\epsilon_{r,eff} \approx (4.5 + 1)/2 = 2.75$$

Thus, we estimate the phase velocity for the wave guided by this line to be about $c/\sqrt{2.75}$; i.e., 60% of c. Similarly, the wavelength of this wave is about 60% of the free space wavelength. In practice, these values are found to be slightly less; typically 50%–55%. The difference is attributable to the crude approximation of Equation 7.27.

Additional Reading:

- "Microstrip" on Wikipedia.

- "Printed circuit board" on Wikipedia.
- "Stripline" on Wikipedia.
- "Single-ended signaling" on Wikipedia.
- Sec. 8.7 ("Differential Circuits") in S.W. Ellingson, *Radio Systems Engineering*, Cambridge Univ. Press, 2016.
- H.A. Wheeler, "Transmission Line Properties of a Strip on a Dielectric Sheet on a Plane," *IEEE Trans. Microwave Theory & Techniques*, Vol. 25, No. 8, Aug 1977, pp. 631–47.
- "FR-4" on Wikipedia.

7.3 Attenuation in Coaxial Cable

[m0189]

In this section, we consider the issue of attenuation in coaxial transmission line. Recall that attenuation can be interpreted in the context of the "lumped element" equivalent circuit transmission line model as the contributions of the resistance per unit length R' and conductance per unit length G'. In this model, R' represents the physical resistance in the inner and outer conductors, whereas G' represents loss due to current flowing directly between the conductors through the spacer material.

The parameters used to describe the relevant features of coaxial cable are shown in Figure 7.11. In this figure, a and b are the radii of the inner and outer conductors, respectively. σ_{ic} and σ_{oc} are the conductivities (SI base units of S/m) of the inner and outer conductors, respectively. Conductors are assumed to be non-magnetic; i.e., having permeability μ equal to the free space value μ_0. The spacer material is assumed to be a lossy dielectric having relative permittivity ϵ_r and conductivity σ_s.

Resistance per unit length. The resistance per unit length is the sum of the resistances of the inner and outer conductor per unit length. The resistance per unit length of the inner conductor is determined by σ_{ic} and the effective cross-sectional area through which the current flows. The latter is equal to the circumference $2\pi a$ times the skin depth δ_{ic} of the

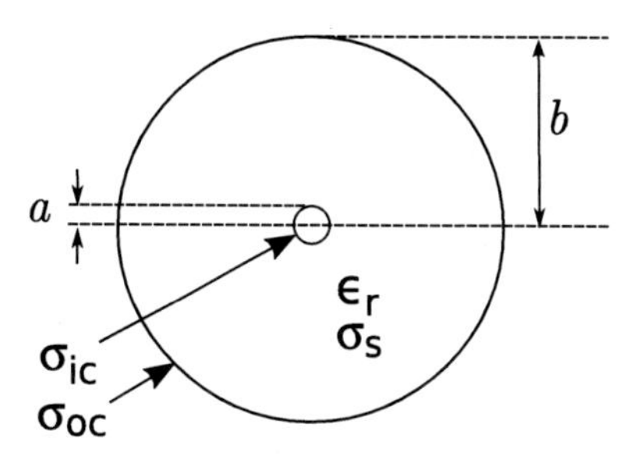

Figure 7.11: Parameters defining the design of a coaxial cable.

inner conductor, so:

$$R'_{ic} \approx \frac{1}{(2\pi a \cdot \delta_{ic})\,\sigma_{ic}} \quad \text{for } \delta_{ic} \ll a \tag{7.30}$$

This expression is only valid for $\delta_{ic} \ll a$ because otherwise the cross-sectional area through which the current flows is not well-modeled as a thin ring near the surface of the conductor. Similarly, we find the resistance per unit length of the outer conductor is

$$R'_{oc} \approx \frac{1}{(2\pi b \cdot \delta_{oc})\,\sigma_{oc}} \quad \text{for } \delta_{oc} \ll t \tag{7.31}$$

where δ_{oc} is the skin depth of the outer conductor and t is the thickness of the outer conductor. Therefore, the total resistance per unit length is

$$\begin{aligned} R' &= R'_{ic} + R'_{oc} \\ &\approx \frac{1}{(2\pi a \cdot \delta_{ic})\,\sigma_{ic}} + \frac{1}{(2\pi b \cdot \delta_{oc})\,\sigma_{oc}} \end{aligned} \tag{7.32}$$

Recall that skin depth depends on conductivity. Specifically:

$$\delta_{ic} = \sqrt{2/\omega\mu\sigma_{ic}} \tag{7.33}$$

$$\delta_{oc} = \sqrt{2/\omega\mu\sigma_{oc}} \tag{7.34}$$

Expanding Equation 7.32 to show explicitly the dependence on conductivity, we find:

$$R' \approx \frac{1}{2\pi\sqrt{2/\omega\mu_0}}\left[\frac{1}{a\sqrt{\sigma_{ic}}} + \frac{1}{b\sqrt{\sigma_{oc}}}\right] \tag{7.35}$$

At this point it is convenient to identify two particular cases for the design of the cable. In the first case, "Case I," we assume $\sigma_{oc} \gg \sigma_{ic}$. Since $b > a$, we have in this case

$$\begin{aligned} R' &\approx \frac{1}{2\pi\sqrt{2/\omega\mu_0}}\left[\frac{1}{a\sqrt{\sigma_{ic}}}\right] \\ &= \frac{1}{2\pi\delta_{ic}\sigma_{ic}}\,\frac{1}{a} \quad \text{(Case I)} \end{aligned} \tag{7.36}$$

In the second case, "Case II," we assume $\sigma_{oc} = \sigma_{ic}$. In this case, we have

$$\begin{aligned} R' &\approx \frac{1}{2\pi\sqrt{2/\omega\mu_0}}\left[\frac{1}{a\sqrt{\sigma_{ic}}} + \frac{1}{b\sqrt{\sigma_{ic}}}\right] \\ &= \frac{1}{2\pi\delta_{ic}\sigma_{ic}}\left[\frac{1}{a} + \frac{1}{b}\right] \quad \text{(Case II)} \end{aligned} \tag{7.37}$$

A simpler way to deal with these two cases is to represent them both using the single expression

$$R' \approx \frac{1}{2\pi\delta_{ic}\sigma_{ic}}\left[\frac{1}{a} + \frac{C}{b}\right] \tag{7.38}$$

where $C = 0$ in Case I and $C = 1$ in Case II.

Conductance per unit length. The conductance per unit length of coaxial cable is simply that of the associated coaxial structure at DC; i.e.,

$$G' = \frac{2\pi\sigma_s}{\ln(b/a)} \tag{7.39}$$

Unlike resistance, the conductance is independent of frequency, at least to the extent that σ_s is independent of frequency.

Attenuation. The attenuation of voltage and current waves as they propagate along the cable is represented by the factor $e^{-\alpha z}$, where z is distance traversed along the cable. It is possible to find an expression for α in terms of the material and geometry parameters using:

$$\gamma \triangleq \sqrt{(R' + j\omega L')(G' + j\omega C')} = \alpha + j\beta \tag{7.40}$$

where L' and C' are the inductance per unit length and capacitance per unit length, respectively. These are given by

$$L' = \frac{\mu}{2\pi}\ln(b/a) \tag{7.41}$$

and

$$C' = \frac{2\pi\epsilon_0\epsilon_r}{\ln(b/a)} \tag{7.42}$$

In principle we could solve Equation 7.40 for α. However, this course of action is quite tedious, and a simpler approximate approach facilitates some additional insights. In this approach, we define parameters α_R associated with R' and α_G associated with G' such that

$$e^{-\alpha_R z}e^{-\alpha_G z} = e^{-(\alpha_R+\alpha_G)z} = e^{-\alpha z} \tag{7.43}$$

which indicates

$$\alpha = \alpha_R + \alpha_G \tag{7.44}$$

Next we postulate

$$\alpha_R \approx K_R\frac{R'}{Z_0} \tag{7.45}$$

where Z_0 is the characteristic impedance

$$Z_0 \approx \frac{\eta_0}{2\pi}\frac{1}{\sqrt{\epsilon_r}}\ln\frac{b}{a} \quad \text{(low loss)} \tag{7.46}$$

and where K_R is a unitless constant to be determined. The justification for Equation 7.45 is as follows: First, α_R must increase monotonically with increasing R'. Second, R' must be divided by an impedance in order to obtain the correct units of 1/m. Using similar reasoning, we postulate

$$\alpha_G \approx K_G G' Z_0 \tag{7.47}$$

where K_G is a unitless constant to be determined. The following example demonstrates the validity of Equations 7.45 and 7.47, and will reveal the values of K_R and K_G.

Example 7.4. Attenuation constant for RG-59.

RG-59 is a popular form of coaxial cable having the parameters $a \cong 0.292$ mm, $b \cong 1.855$ mm, $\sigma_{ic} \cong 2.28 \times 10^7$ S/m, $\sigma_s \cong 5.9 \times 10^{-5}$ S/m, and $\epsilon_r \cong 2.25$. The conductivity σ_{oc} of the outer conductor is difficult to quantify because it consists of a braid of thin metal strands. However, $\sigma_{oc} \gg \sigma_{ic}$, so we may assume Case I; i.e., $\sigma_{oc} \gg \sigma_{ic}$, and subsequently $C = 0$. Figure 7.12 shows the components α_G and α_R computed for the particular choice $K_R = K_G = 1/2$. The figure also shows $\alpha_G + \alpha_R$, along with α computed using Equation 7.40. We find that the agreement between these values is very good, which is compelling evidence that the ansatz is valid and $K_R = K_G = 1/2$.

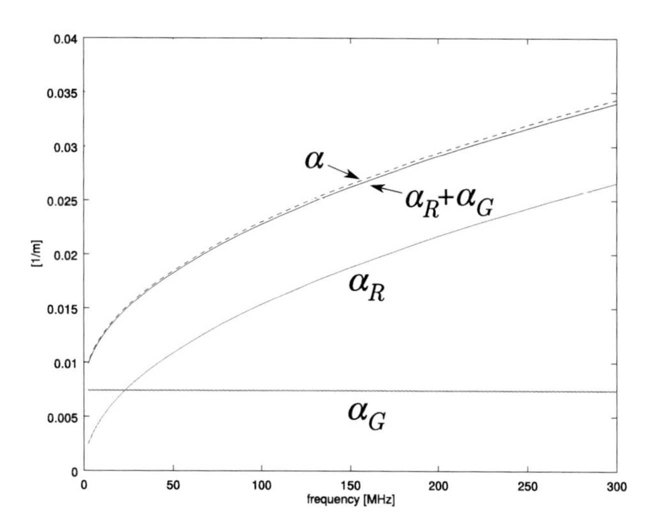

Figure 7.12: Comparison of $\alpha = \text{Re}\{\gamma\}$ to α_R, α_G, and $\alpha_R + \alpha_G$ for $K_R = K_G = 1/2$. The result for α has been multiplied by 1.01; otherwise the curves would be too close to tell apart.

Note that there is nothing to indicate that the results demonstrated in the example are not generally true. Thus, we come to the following conclusion:

The attenuation constant $\alpha \approx \alpha_G + \alpha_R$ where $\alpha_G \triangleq R'/2Z_0$ and $\alpha_R \triangleq G'Z_0/2$.

Minimizing attenuation. Let us now consider if there are design choices which minimize the attenuation of coaxial cable. Since $\alpha = \alpha_R + \alpha_G$, we may consider α_R and α_G independently. Let us first consider α_G:

$$\begin{aligned}\alpha_G &\triangleq \frac{1}{2}G'Z_0 \\ &\approx \frac{1}{2}\cdot\frac{2\pi\sigma_s}{\ln(b/a)}\cdot\frac{1}{2\pi}\frac{\eta_0}{\sqrt{\epsilon_r}}\ln(b/a) \\ &= \frac{\eta_0}{2}\frac{\sigma_s}{\sqrt{\epsilon_r}}\end{aligned} \tag{7.48}$$

It is clear from this result that α_G is minimized by minimizing $\sigma_s/\sqrt{\epsilon_r}$. Interestingly the physical dimensions a and b have no discernible effect on α_G. Now we consider α_R:

$$\begin{aligned}\alpha_R &\triangleq \frac{R'}{2Z_0} \\ &= \frac{1}{2}\frac{(1/2\pi\delta_{ic}\sigma_{ic})\,[1/a + C/b]}{(1/2\pi)\left(\eta_0/\sqrt{\epsilon_r}\right)\ln(b/a)} \\ &= \frac{\sqrt{\epsilon_r}}{2\eta_0\delta_{ic}\sigma_{ic}}\cdot\frac{[1/a + C/b]}{\ln(b/a)}\end{aligned} \tag{7.49}$$

Now making the substitution $\delta_{ic} = \sqrt{2/\omega\mu_0\sigma_{ic}}$ in order to make the dependences on the constitutive parameters explicit, we find:

$$\alpha_R = \frac{1}{2\sqrt{2}\cdot\eta_0}\sqrt{\frac{\omega\mu_0\epsilon_r}{\sigma_{ic}}}\cdot\frac{[1/a + C/b]}{\ln(b/a)} \tag{7.50}$$

Here we see that α_R is minimized by minimizing ϵ_r/σ_{ic}. It's not surprising to see that we should maximize σ_{ic}. However, it's a little surprising that we should minimize ϵ_r. Furthermore, this is in contrast to α_G, which is minimized by *maximizing* ϵ_r. Clearly there is a tradeoff to be made here. To determine the parameters of this tradeoff, first note that the result depends on frequency: Since α_R dominates over α_G at sufficiently high frequency (as demonstrated in Figure 7.12), it seems we should minimize ϵ_r if the intended frequency of operation is sufficiently high; otherwise the optimum value is frequency-dependent. However, σ_s may vary as a function of ϵ_r, so a general conclusion about optimum values of σ_s and ϵ_r is not appropriate.

However, we also see that α_R – unlike α_G – depends on a and b. This implies the existence of a generally-optimum geometry. To find this geometry, we minimize α_R by taking the derivative with respect to a, setting the result equal to zero, and solving for a and/or b. Here we go:

$$\frac{\partial}{\partial a}\alpha_R = \frac{1}{2\sqrt{2}\cdot\eta_0}\sqrt{\frac{\omega\mu_0\epsilon_r}{\sigma_{ic}}}\cdot\frac{\partial}{\partial a}\frac{[1/a+C/b]}{\ln{(b/a)}} \tag{7.51}$$

This derivative is worked out in an addendum at the end of this section. Using the result from the addendum, the right side of Equation 7.51 can be written as follows:

$$\frac{1}{2\sqrt{2}\cdot\eta_0}\sqrt{\frac{\omega\mu_0\epsilon_r}{\sigma_{ic}}}\cdot\left[\frac{-1}{a^2\ln{(b/a)}}+\frac{1/a+C/b}{a\ln^2{(b/a)}}\right] \tag{7.52}$$

In order for $\partial\alpha_R/\partial a=0$, the factor in the square brackets above must be equal to zero. After a few steps of algebra, we find:

$$\ln{(b/a)} = 1+\frac{C}{b/a} \tag{7.53}$$

In Case I ($\sigma_{oc}\gg\sigma_{ic}$), $C=0$ so:

$$b/a = e \cong 2.72 \quad \text{(Case I)} \tag{7.54}$$

In Case II ($\sigma_{oc}=\sigma_{ic}$), $C=1$. The resulting equation can be solved by plotting the function, or by a few iterations of trial and error; either way one quickly finds

$$b/a \cong 3.59 \quad \text{(Case II)} \tag{7.55}$$

Summarizing, we have found that α is minimized by choosing the ratio of the outer and inner radii to be somewhere between 2.72 and 3.59, with the precise value depending on the relative conductivity of the inner and outer conductors.

Substituting these values of b/a into Equation 7.46, we obtain:

$$Z_0 \approx \frac{59.9\ \Omega}{\sqrt{\epsilon_r}} \text{ to } \frac{76.6\ \Omega}{\sqrt{\epsilon_r}} \tag{7.56}$$

as the range of impedances of coaxial cable corresponding to physical designs that minimize attenuation.

> Equation 7.56 gives the range of characteristic impedances that minimize attenuation for coaxial transmission lines. The precise value within this range depends on the ratio of the conductivity of the outer conductor to that of the inner conductor.

Since $\epsilon_r\geq 1$, the impedance that minimizes attenuation is less for dielectric-filled cables than it is for air-filled cables. For example, let us once again consider the RG-59 from Example 7.4. In that case, $\epsilon_r\cong 2.25$ and $C=0$, indicating $Z_0\approx 39.9\ \Omega$ is optimum for attenuation. The actual characteristic impedance of Z_0 is about 75 Ω, so clearly RG-59 is not optimized for attenuation. This is simply because other considerations apply, including power handling capability (addressed in Section 7.4) and the convenience of standard values (addressed in Section 7.5).

Addendum: Derivative of $a^2\ln(b/a)$. Evaluation of Equation 7.51 requires finding the derivative of $a^2\ln(b/a)$ with respect to a. Using the chain rule, we find:

$$\frac{\partial}{\partial a}\left[a^2\ln\left(\frac{b}{a}\right)\right] = \left[\frac{\partial}{\partial a}a^2\right]\ln\left(\frac{b}{a}\right) + a^2\left[\frac{\partial}{\partial a}\ln\left(\frac{b}{a}\right)\right] \tag{7.57}$$

Note

$$\frac{\partial}{\partial a}a^2 = 2a \tag{7.58}$$

and

$$\frac{\partial}{\partial a}\ln\left(\frac{b}{a}\right) = \frac{\partial}{\partial a}\left[\ln(b) - \ln(a)\right]$$
$$= -\frac{\partial}{\partial a}\ln(a)$$
$$= -\frac{1}{a} \tag{7.59}$$

So:

$$\frac{\partial}{\partial a}\left[a^2\ln\left(\frac{b}{a}\right)\right] = [2a]\ln\left(\frac{b}{a}\right) + a^2\left[-\frac{1}{a}\right]$$
$$= \boxed{2a\ln\left(\frac{b}{a}\right) - a} \tag{7.60}$$

This result is substituted for $a^2\ln(b/a)$ in Equation 7.51 to obtain Equation 7.52.

7.4 Power Handling Capability of Coaxial Cable

[m0190]

The term "power handling" refers to maximum power that can be safely transferred by a transmission line. This power is limited because when the electric field becomes too large, dielectric breakdown and arcing may occur. This may result in damage to the line and connected devices, and so must be avoided. Let E_{pk} be the maximum safe value of the electric field intensity within the line, and let P_{max} be the power that is being transferred under this condition. This section addresses the following question: How does one design a coaxial cable to maximize P_{max} for a given E_{pk}?

We begin by finding the electric potential V within the cable. This can be done using Laplace's equation:

$$\nabla^2 V = 0 \tag{7.61}$$

Using the cylindrical (ρ, ϕ, z) coordinate system with the z axis along the inner conductor, we have $\partial V/\partial\phi = 0$ due to symmetry. Also we set $\partial V/\partial z = 0$ since the result should not depend on z. Thus, we have:

$$\frac{1}{\rho}\frac{\partial}{\partial\rho}\left(\rho\frac{\partial V}{\partial\rho}\right) = 0 \tag{7.62}$$

Solving for V, we have

$$V(\rho) = A\ln\rho + B \tag{7.63}$$

where A and B are arbitrary constants, presumably determined by boundary conditions. Let us assume a voltage V_0 measured from the inner conductor (serving as the "+" terminal) to the outer conductor (serving as the "−" terminal). For this choice, we have:

$$V(a) = V_0 \quad\rightarrow\quad A\ln a + B = V_0 \tag{7.64}$$
$$V(b) = 0 \quad\rightarrow\quad A\ln b + B = 0 \tag{7.65}$$

Subtracting the second equation from the first and solving for A, we find $A = -V_0/\ln(b/a)$. Subsequently, B is found to be $V_0\ln(b)/\ln(b/a)$, and so

$$V(\rho) = \frac{-V_0}{\ln(b/a)}\ln\rho + \frac{V_0\ln(b)}{\ln(b/a)} \tag{7.66}$$

The electric field intensity is given by:

$$\mathbf{E} = -\nabla V \tag{7.67}$$

Again we have $\partial V/\partial\phi = \partial V/\partial z = 0$, so

$$\mathbf{E} = -\hat{\rho}\frac{\partial}{\partial\rho}V \tag{7.68}$$

$$= -\hat{\rho}\frac{\partial}{\partial\rho}\left[\frac{-V_0}{\ln(b/a)}\ln\rho + \frac{V_0\ln(b)}{\ln(b/a)}\right] \tag{7.69}$$

$$= +\hat{\rho}\frac{V_0}{\rho\ln(b/a)} \tag{7.70}$$

Note that the maximum electric field intensity in the spacer occurs at $\rho = a$; i.e., at the surface of the inner conductor. Therefore:

$$E_{pk} = \frac{V_0}{a\ln(b/a)} \tag{7.71}$$

The power transferred by the line is maximized when the impedances of the source and load are matched to Z_0. In this case, the power transferred is $V_0^2/2Z_0$. Recall that the characteristic impedance Z_0 is given in the "low-loss" case as

$$Z_0 \approx \frac{1}{2\pi}\frac{\eta_0}{\sqrt{\epsilon_r}}\ln\left(\frac{b}{a}\right) \tag{7.72}$$

Therefore, the maximum safe power is

$$P_{max} = \frac{V_0^2}{2Z_0} \tag{7.73}$$

$$\approx \frac{E_{pk}^2\, a^2\ln^2(b/a)}{2\cdot(1/2\pi)\left(\eta_0/\sqrt{\epsilon_r}\right)\ln(b/a)} \tag{7.74}$$

$$= \frac{\pi E_{pk}^2}{\eta_0/\sqrt{\epsilon_r}}\, a^2\ln(b/a) \tag{7.75}$$

Now let us consider if there is a value of a which maximizes P_{max}. We do this by seeing if $\partial P_{max}/\partial a = 0$ for some values of a and b. The derivative is worked out in an addendum at the end of this section. Using the result from the addendum, we find:

$$\frac{\partial}{\partial a}P_{max} = \frac{\pi E_{pk}^2}{\eta_0/\sqrt{\epsilon_r}}\left[2a\ln(b/a) - a\right] \tag{7.76}$$

For the above expression to be zero, it must be true that $2\ln(b/a) - 1 = 0$. Solving for b/a, we obtain:

$$\frac{b}{a} = \sqrt{e} \cong 1.65 \tag{7.77}$$

for optimum power handling. In other words, 1.65 is the ratio of the radii of the outer and inner conductors that maximizes the power that can be safely handled by the cable.

Equation 7.75 suggests that ϵ_r should be maximized in order to maximize power handling, and you wouldn't be wrong for noting that, however, there are some other factors that may indicate otherwise. For example, a material with higher ϵ_r may also have higher σ_s, which means more current flowing through the spacer and thus more ohmic heating. This problem is so severe that cables that handle high RF power often use air as the spacer, even though it has the *lowest* possible value of ϵ_r. Also worth noting is that σ_{ic} and σ_{oc} do not matter according to the analysis we've just done; however, to the extent that limited conductivity results in significant ohmic heating in the conductors – which we have also not considered – there may be something to consider. Suffice it to say, the actionable finding here concerns the ratio of the radii; the other parameters have not been suitably constrained by this analysis.

Substituting $\sqrt{e}$ for b/a in Equation 7.72, we find:

$$Z_0 \approx \frac{30.0\ \Omega}{\sqrt{\epsilon_r}} \tag{7.78}$$

This is the characteristic impedance of coaxial line that optimizes power handling, subject to the caveats identified above. For air-filled cables, we obtain 30 Ω. Since $\epsilon_r \geq 1$, this optimum impedance is less for dielectric-filled cables than it is for air-filled cables.

Summarizing:

> The power handling capability of coaxial transmission line is optimized when the ratio of radii of the outer to inner conductors b/a is about 1.65. For the air-filled cables typically used in high-power applications, this corresponds to a characteristic impedance of about 30 Ω.

Addendum: Derivative of $(1/a + C/b)\,/\ln(b/a)$. Evaluation of Equation 7.75 requires finding the derivative of $(1/a + C/b)\,/\ln(b/a)$ with respect to a.

Using the chain rule, we find:

$$\frac{\partial}{\partial a}\left[\frac{1/a+C/b}{\ln\left(b/a\right)}\right] = \left[\frac{\partial}{\partial a}\left(\frac{1}{a}+\frac{C}{b}\right)\right]\ln^{-1}\left(\frac{b}{a}\right) + \left(\frac{1}{a}+\frac{C}{b}\right)\left[\frac{\partial}{\partial a}\ln^{-1}\left(\frac{b}{a}\right)\right] \tag{7.79}$$

Note

$$\frac{\partial}{\partial a}\left(\frac{1}{a}+\frac{C}{b}\right) = -\frac{1}{a^2} \tag{7.80}$$

To handle the quantity in the second set of square brackets, first define $v = \ln u$, where $u = b/a$. Then:

$$\begin{aligned}\frac{\partial}{\partial a}v^{-1} &= \left[\frac{\partial}{\partial v}v^{-1}\right]\left[\frac{\partial v}{\partial u}\right]\left[\frac{\partial u}{\partial a}\right] \\ &= \left[-v^{-2}\right]\left[\frac{1}{u}\right]\left[-ba^{-2}\right] \\ &= \left[-\ln^{-2}\left(\frac{b}{a}\right)\right]\left[\frac{a}{b}\right]\left[-ba^{-2}\right] \\ &= \frac{1}{a}\ln^{-2}\left(\frac{b}{a}\right)\end{aligned} \tag{7.81}$$

So:

$$\frac{\partial}{\partial a}\left[\frac{1/a+C/b}{\ln\left(b/a\right)}\right] = \left[-\frac{1}{a^2}\right]\ln^{-1}\left(\frac{b}{a}\right) + \left(\frac{1}{a}+\frac{C}{b}\right)\left[\frac{1}{a}\ln^{-2}\left(\frac{b}{a}\right)\right] \tag{7.82}$$

This result is substituted in Equation 7.75 to obtain Equation 7.76.

7.5 Why 50 Ohms?

[m0191]

The quantity 50 Ω appears in a broad range of applications across the field of electrical engineering. In particular, it is a very popular value for the characteristic impedance of transmission line, and is commonly specified as the port impedance for signal sources, amplifiers, filters, antennas, and other RF components. So, what's special about 50 Ω? The short answer is "nothing." In fact, other standard impedances are in common use – prominent among these is 75 Ω. It is shown in this section that a broad range of impedances – on the order of 10s of ohms – emerge as useful values based on technical considerations such as minimizing attenuation, maximizing power handling, and compatibility with common types of antennas. Characteristic impedances up to 300 Ω and beyond are useful in particular applications. However, it is not practical or efficient to manufacture and sell products for every possible impedance in this range. Instead, engineers have settled on 50 Ω as a round number that lies near the middle of this range, and have chosen a few other values to accommodate the smaller number of applications where there may be specific compelling considerations.

So, the question becomes "what makes characteristic impedances in the range of 10s of ohms particularly useful?" One consideration is attenuation in coaxial cable. Coaxial cable is by far the most popular type of transmission line for connecting devices on separate printed circuit boards or in separate enclosures. The attenuation of coaxial cable is addressed in Section 7.3. In that section, it is shown that attenuation is minimized for characteristic impedances in the range $(60~\Omega)/\sqrt{\epsilon_r}$ to $(77~\Omega)/\sqrt{\epsilon_r}$, where ϵ_r is the relative permittivity of the spacer material. So, we find that Z_0 in the range 60 Ω to 77 Ω is optimum for air-filled cable, but more like 40 Ω to 50 Ω for cables using a plastic spacer material having typical $\epsilon_r \approx 2.25$. Thus, 50 Ω is clearly a reasonable choice if a single standard value is to be established for all such cable.

Coaxial cables are often required to carry high power signals. In such applications, power handling capability is also important, and is addressed in Section 7.4. In that section, we find the power handling capability of coaxial cable is optimized when the ratio of radii of the outer to inner conductors b/a is about 1.65. For the air-filled cables typically used in high-power applications, this corresponds to a characteristic impedance of about 30 Ω. This is significantly less than the 60 Ω to 77 Ω that minimizes attenuation in air-filled cables. So, 50 Ω can be viewed as a compromise between minimizing attenuation and maximizing power handling in air-filled coaxial cables.

Although the preceding arguments justify 50 Ω as a standard value, one can also see how one might make a case for 75 Ω as a secondary standard value, especially for applications where attenuation is the primary consideration.

Values of 50 Ω and 75 Ω also offer some convenience when connecting RF devices to antennas. For example, 75 Ω is very close to the impedance of the commonly-encountered half-wave dipole antenna (about $73 + j42$ Ω), which may make impedance matching to that antenna easier. Another commonly-encountered antenna is the quarter-wave monopole, which exhibits an impedance of about $36 + j21$ Ω, which is close to 50 Ω. In fact, we see that if we desire a single characteristic impedance that is equally convenient for applications involving either type of antenna, then 50 Ω is a reasonable choice.

A third commonly-encountered antenna is the *folded* half-wave dipole. This type of antenna is similar to a half-wave dipole but has better bandwidth, and is commonly used in FM and TV systems and land mobile radio (LMR) base stations. A folded half-wave dipole has an impedance of about 300 Ω and is balanced (not single-ended); thus, there is a market for balanced transmission line having $Z_0 = 300$ Ω. However, it is very easy and inexpensive to implement a balun (a device which converts the dipole output from balanced to unbalanced) while simultaneously stepping down impedance by a factor of 4; i.e., to 75 Ω. Thus, we have an additional application for 75 Ω coaxial line.

Finally, note that it is quite simple to implement microstrip transmission line having characteristic impedance in the range 30 Ω to 75 Ω. For example, 50 Ω on commonly-used 1.575 mm FR4 requires a width-to-height ratio of about 2, so the trace is about 3 mm wide. This is a very manageable size and easily implemented in printed circuit board designs.

Additional Reading:

- "Dipole antenna" on Wikipedia.
- "Monopole antenna" on Wikipedia.
- "Balun" on Wikipedia.

[m0187]

Image Credits

Fig. 7.1: © SpinningSpark, Inductiveload,
https://commons.wikimedia.org/wiki/File:Twin-lead_cable_dimension.svg,
CC BY-SA 3.0 (https://creativecommons.org/licenses/by-sa/3.0/).
Minor modifications.

Fig. 7.2: © Sevenchw (C. Wang),
https://commons.wikimedia.org/wiki/File:Parallel_wire_transmission_line_structure_and_design_parameters.svg,
CC BY-SA 4.0 (https://creativecommons.org/licenses/by-sa/4.0/).

Fig. 7.3: © Offaperry (S. Lally),
https://commons.wikimedia.org/wiki/File:Electric_and_Magnetic_Field_of_Wire_Cross-Section.svg,
CC BY-SA 4.0 (https://creativecommons.org/licenses/by-sa/4.0/).

Fig. 7.4: © 7head7metal7, https://commons.wikimedia.org/wiki/File:Microstrip_scheme.svg,
CC BY-SA 3.0 (https://creativecommons.org/licenses/by-sa/3.0/).
Minor modifications from the original.

Fig. 7.6: © Sevenchw (C. Wang),
https://commons.wikimedia.org/wiki/File:View_from_the_side_of_a_microstrip_line.svg,
CC BY-SA 4.0 (https://creativecommons.org/licenses/by-sa/4.0/).

Fig. 7.7: © Offaperry (S. Lally),
https://commons.wikimedia.org/wiki/File:Electric_and_Magnetic_Fields_for_Microstrip.svg,
CC BY-SA 4.0 (https://creativecommons.org/licenses/by-sa/4.0/).

Chapter 8

Optical Fiber

8.1 Optical Fiber: Method of Operation

[m0178]

In its simplest form, optical fiber consists of concentric regions of dielectric material as shown in Figure 8.1. A cross-section through the fiber reveals a circular region of transparent dielectric material through which light propagates. This is surrounded by a jacket of dielectric material commonly referred to as *cladding*.

A characteristic of the design of any optical fiber is that the permittivity of the fiber is greater than the permittivity of the cladding. As explained in Section 5.11, this creates conditions necessary for total internal reflection. The mechanism of total internal reflection contains the light within the fiber.

In the discipline of optics, the permittivity of a material is commonly quantified in terms of its *index of refraction*. Index of refraction is the square root of relative permittivity, and is usually assigned the symbol n. Thus, if we define the relative permittivities $\epsilon_{r,f} \triangleq \epsilon_f/\epsilon_0$ for the fiber and $\epsilon_{r,c} \triangleq \epsilon_c/\epsilon_0$ for the cladding, then

$$n_f \triangleq \sqrt{\epsilon_{r,f}} \quad (8.1)$$

$$n_c \triangleq \sqrt{\epsilon_{r,c}} \quad (8.2)$$

and

$$n_f > n_c \quad (8.3)$$

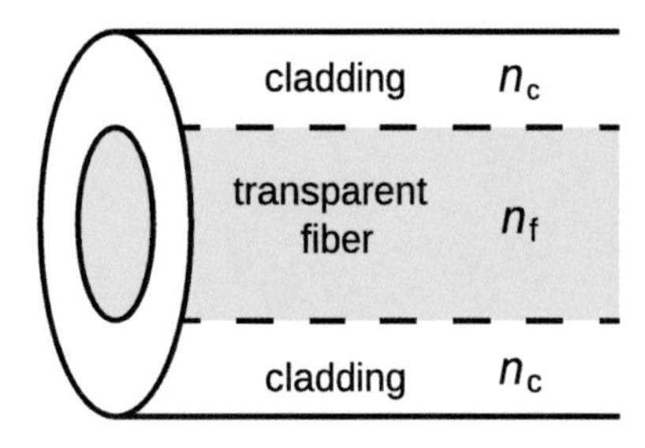

© S. Lally CC BY-SA 4.0

Figure 8.1: Construction of the simplest form of optical fiber.

Figure 8.2 illustrates total internal reflection in an optical fiber. In this case, a ray of light in the fiber is incident on the boundary with the cladding. We may treat the light ray as a uniform plane wave. To see why, consider that optical wavelengths range from 120 nm to 700 nm in free space. Wavelength is slightly shorter than this in fiber; specifically, by a factor equal to the square root of the relative permittivity. The fiber is on the order of millimeters in diameter, which is about 4 orders of magnitude greater than the wavelength. Thus, from the perspective of the light ray, the fiber appears to be an unbounded half-space sharing a planar boundary with the cladding, which also appears to be an unbounded half-space.

Continuing under this presumption, the criterion for total internal reflection is (from Section 5.11):

$$\theta^i \geq \arcsin\sqrt{\frac{\epsilon_{r,c}}{\epsilon_{r,f}}} = \arcsin\frac{n_c}{n_f} \quad (8.4)$$

As long as rays of light approach from angles that satisfy this criterion, the associated power remains in

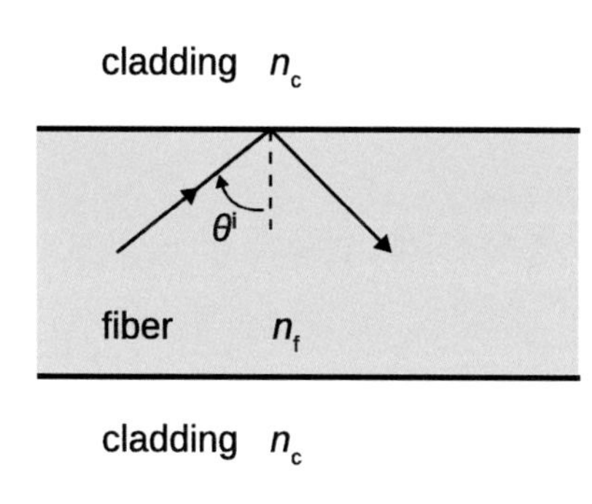

© S. Lally CC BY-SA 4.0

Figure 8.2: Total internal reflection in optical fiber.

the fiber, and is reflected onward. Otherwise, power is lost into the cladding.

Example 8.1. Critical angle for optical fiber.

Typical values of n_f and n_c for an optical fiber are 1.52 and 1.49, respectively. What internal angle of incidence is required to maintain total internal reflection?

Solution. Using Equation 8.4, θ^i must be greater than about 78.8°. In practice this is quite reasonable since we desire light to be traveling approximately parallel the axis of the fiber ($\theta^i \approx 90°$) anyway.

The total internal reflection criterion imposes a limit on the radius of curvature of fiber optic cable. If fiber optic cable is bent such that the radius of curvature is too small, the critical angle will be exceeded at the bend. This will occur even for light rays which are traveling perfectly parallel to the axis of the fiber before they arrive at the bend.

Note that the cladding serves at least two roles. First, it determines the critical angle for total internal reflection, and subsequently determines the minimum radius of curvature for lossless operation of the fiber. Second, it provides a place for the evanescent surface waves associated with total internal reflection (Section 5.12) to exist without interference from objects in contact with the fiber.

Additional Reading:

- "Optical fiber" on Wikipedia.

8.2 Acceptance Angle

[m0192]

In this section, we consider the problem of injecting light into a fiber optic cable. The problem is illustrated in Figure 8.3. In this figure, we see light incident from a medium having index of refraction n_0, with angle of incidence θ^i. The light is transmitted with angle of transmission θ_2 into the fiber, and is subsequently incident on the surface of the cladding with angle of incidence θ_3. For light to propagate without loss within the cable, it is required that

$$\sin\theta_3 \geq \frac{n_c}{n_f} \tag{8.5}$$

since this criterion must be met in order for total internal reflection to occur.

Now consider the constraint that Equation 8.5 imposes on θ^i. First, we note that θ_3 is related to θ_2 as follows:

$$\theta_3 = \frac{\pi}{2} - \theta_2 \tag{8.6}$$

therefore

$$\sin\theta_3 = \sin\left(\frac{\pi}{2} - \theta_2\right) \tag{8.7}$$

$$= \cos\theta_2 \tag{8.8}$$

so

$$\cos\theta_2 \geq \frac{n_c}{n_f} \tag{8.9}$$

Squaring both sides, we find:

$$\cos^2\theta_2 \geq \frac{n_c^2}{n_f^2} \tag{8.10}$$

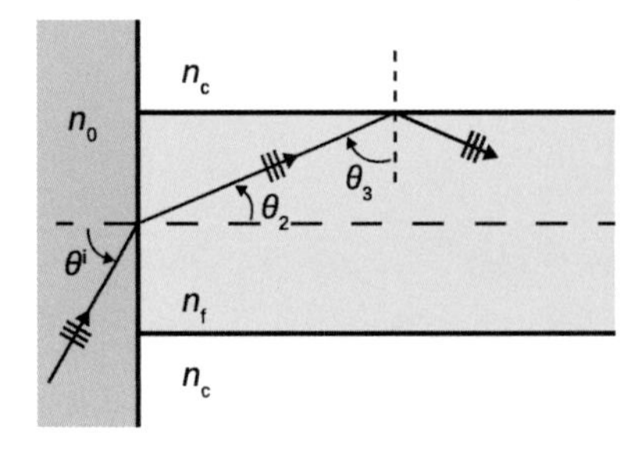

© S. Lally CC BY-SA 4.0

Figure 8.3: Injecting light into a fiber optic cable.

Now invoking a trigonometric identity:

$$1 - \sin^2\theta_2 \geq \frac{n_c^2}{n_f^2} \tag{8.11}$$

so:

$$\sin^2\theta_2 \leq 1 - \frac{n_c^2}{n_f^2} \tag{8.12}$$

Now we relate the θ_2 to θ^i using Snell's law:

$$\sin\theta_2 = \frac{n_0}{n_f}\sin\theta^i \tag{8.13}$$

so Equation 8.12 may be written:

$$\frac{n_0^2}{n_f^2}\sin^2\theta^i \leq 1 - \frac{n_c^2}{n_f^2} \tag{8.14}$$

Now solving for $\sin\theta^i$, we obtain:

$$\sin\theta^i \leq \frac{1}{n_0}\sqrt{n_f^2 - n_c^2} \tag{8.15}$$

This result indicates the range of angles of incidence which result in total internal reflection within the fiber. The maximum value of θ^i which satisfies this condition is known as the *acceptance angle* θ_a, so:

$$\theta_a \triangleq \arcsin\left(\frac{1}{n_0}\sqrt{n_f^2 - n_c^2}\right) \tag{8.16}$$

This leads to the following insight:

> In order to effectively launch light in the fiber, it is necessary for the light to arrive from within a cone having half-angle θ_a with respect to the axis of the fiber.

The associated *cone of acceptance* is illustrated in Figure 8.4.

It is also common to define the quantity *numerical aperture* NA as follows:

$$\text{NA} \triangleq \frac{1}{n_0}\sqrt{n_f^2 - n_c^2} \tag{8.17}$$

Note that n_0 is typically very close to 1 (corresponding to incidence from air), so it is common to see NA defined as simply $\sqrt{n_f^2 - n_c^2}$. This parameter is commonly used in lieu of the acceptance angle in datasheets for fiber optic cable.

Example 8.2. Acceptance angle.

Typical values of n_f and n_c for an optical fiber are 1.52 and 1.49, respectively. What are the numerical aperture and the acceptance angle?

Solution. Using Equation 8.17 and presuming $n_0 = 1$, we find NA $\cong$ $\underline{0.30}$. Since $\sin\theta_a = \text{NA}$, we find $\theta_a = \underline{17.5^\circ}$. Light must arrive from within 17.5° from the axis of the fiber in order to ensure total internal reflection within the fiber.

Additional Reading:

- "Optical fiber" on Wikipedia.
- "Numerical aperture" on Wikipedia.

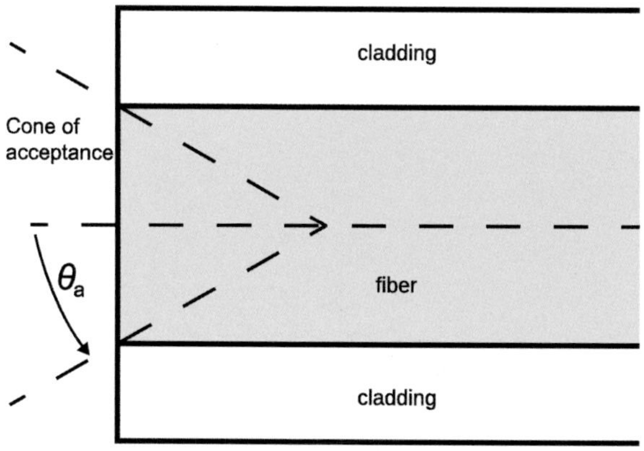

cladding

Cone of acceptance

θ_a

fiber

cladding

© S. Lally CC BY-SA 4.0

Figure 8.4: Cone of acceptance.

8.3 Dispersion in Optical Fiber

[m0193]

Light may follow a variety of paths through a fiber optic cable. Each of the paths has a different length, leading to a phenomenon known as *dispersion*. Dispersion distorts signals and limits the data rate of digital signals sent over fiber optic cable. In this section, we analyze this dispersion and its effect on digital signals.

Figure 8.5 shows the variety of paths that light may take through a straight fiber optic cable. The nominal path is shown in Figure 8.5(a), which is parallel to the axis of the cable. This path has the shortest associated propagation time. The path with the longest associated propagation time is shown in Figure 8.5(c). In this case, light bounces within the fiber, each time approaching the core-clad interface at the critical angle for total internal reflection. Any ray approaching at a greater angle is not completely reflected, and so would likely not survive to the end of

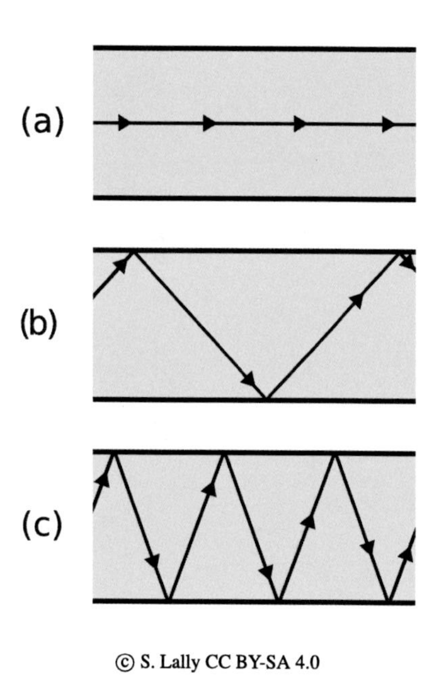

© S. Lally CC BY-SA 4.0

Figure 8.5: Paths that light may take through a straight fiber optic cable: (a) Along axis, corresponding to minimum path length; (b) Intermediate between (a) and (c); (c) Maximum length, corresponding to threshold angle for total internal reflection.

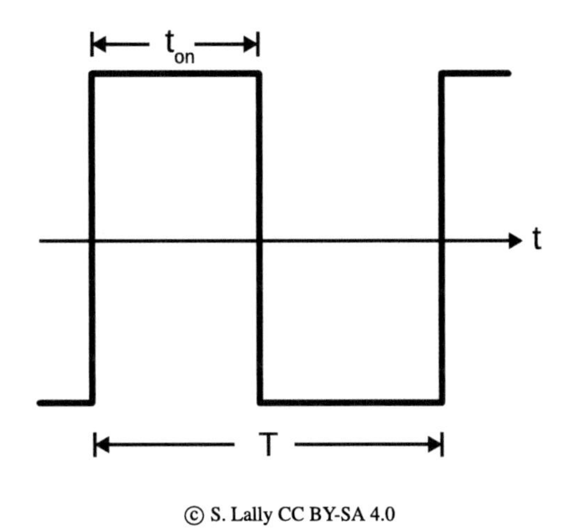

© S. Lally CC BY-SA 4.0

Figure 8.6: A digital signal that might be applied to the input of a fiber optic cable.

the cable. Figure 8.5(b) represents the continuum of possibilities between the extreme cases of (a) and (c), with associated propagation times greater than that of case (a) but less than that of case (c).

Regardless of how light is inserted into the fiber, all possible paths depicted in Figure 8.5 are likely to exist. This is because fiber is rarely installed in a straight line, but rather follows a multiply-curved path. Each curve results in new angles of incidence upon the core-cladding boundary. The existence of these paths leads to dispersion. To see this, consider the input signal shown in Figure 8.6. This signal has period T, during which time a pulse of length $t_{on} < T$ may be present. Let the *minimum* propagation time through the fiber (as in Figure 8.5(a)) be τ_{min}. Let the *maximum* propagation time through the fiber (as in Figure 8.5(c)) be τ_{max}. If $\tau_{max} - \tau_{min} \ll t_{on}$, we see little degradation in the signal output from the fiber. Otherwise, we observe a "smearing" of pulses at the output of the fiber, as shown in Figure 8.7.

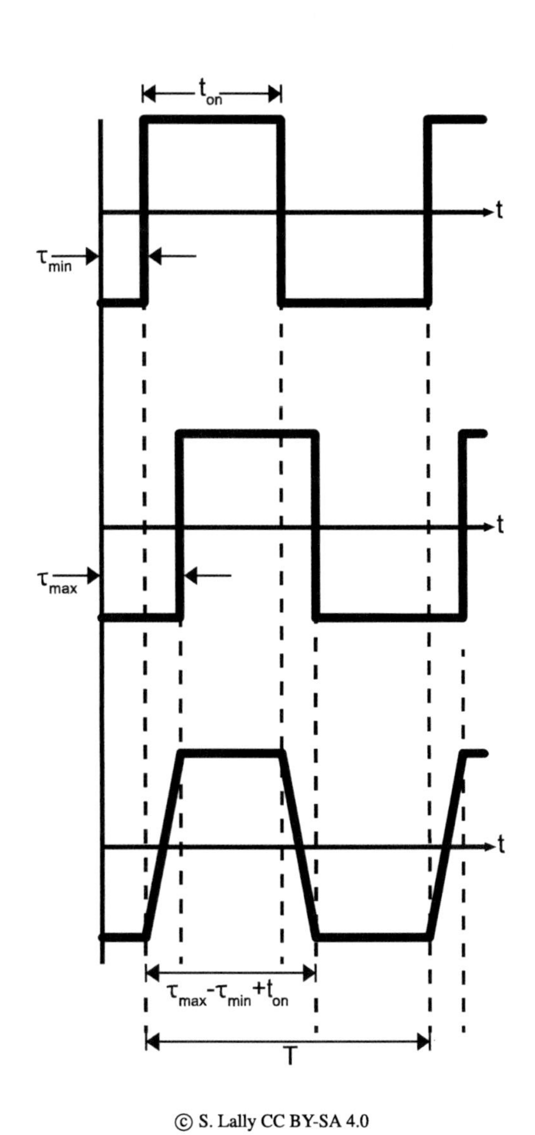

© S. Lally CC BY-SA 4.0

Figure 8.7: The effect of dispersion on the signal output from the fiber optic cable: *Top:* Arriving waveform corresponding to minimum path length, *Middle:* Arriving waveform corresponding to maximum path length, and *Bottom:* Sum of all arriving waveforms.

Any smearing may pose problems for whatever device is detecting pulses at the receiving end. However, as $\tau_{max} - \tau_{min}$ becomes a larger fraction of t_{on}, we see that it becomes possible for adjacent pulses to overlap. This presents a much more serious challenge in detecting individual pulses, so let us examine the overlap problem in greater detail. To avoid overlap:

$$\tau_{max} - \tau_{min} + t_{on} < T \quad (8.18)$$

Let us define the quantity $\tau \triangleq \tau_{max} - \tau_{min}$. This is sometimes referred to as the *delay spread*.[1] Thus, we obtain the following requirement for overlap-free transmission:

$$\tau < T - t_{on} \quad (8.19)$$

Note that the delay spread imposes a minimum value on T, which in turn imposes a maximum value on the rate at which information can be transmitted on the cable. So, we are motivated to calculate delay spread. The minimum propagation time t_{min} is simply the length l of the cable divided by the phase velocity v_p of the light within the core; i.e., $t_{min} = l/v_p$. Recall phase velocity is simply the speed of light in free space c divided by $\sqrt{\epsilon_r}$ where ϵ_r is the relative permittivity of the core material. Thus:

$$t_{min} = \frac{l}{v_p} = \frac{l}{c/\sqrt{\epsilon_r}} = \frac{l}{c/n_f} = \frac{ln_f}{c} \quad (8.20)$$

The maximum propagation time t_{max} is different because the maximum path length is different. Specifically, the maximum path length is not l, but rather $l/\cos\theta_2$ where θ_2 is the angle between the axis and the direction of travel as light crosses the axis. So, for example, $\theta_2 = 0$ for t_{min} since light in that case travels along the axis. The value of θ_2 for t_{max} is determined by the threshold angle for total internal reflection. This was determined in Section 8.2 to be given by:

$$\cos\theta_2 = \frac{n_c}{n_f} \quad \text{(threshold value)} \quad (8.21)$$

so we obtain the following relationship:

$$t_{max} = \frac{l/\cos\theta_2}{v_p} = \frac{ln_f/n_c}{c/n_f} = \frac{ln_f^2}{cn_c} \quad (8.22)$$

and subsequently we find:

$$\boxed{\tau = l\frac{n_f}{c}\left(\frac{n_f}{n_c} - 1\right)} \quad (8.23)$$

[1]Full disclosure: There are many ways to define "delay spread," but this definition is not uncommon and is useful in the present analysis.

Note that τ increases linearly with l. Therefore, the rate at which pulses can be sent without overlap decreases linearly with increasing length. In practical applications, this means that the maximum supportable data rate decreases as the length of the cable increases. This is true independently of media loss within the cable (which we have not yet even considered!). Rather, this is a fundamental limitation resulting from dispersion.

Example 8.3. Maximum supportable data rate in multimode fiber optic cable.

A multimode fiber optic cable of length 1 m is used to transmit data using the scheme shown in Figure 8.6, with $t_{on} = T/2$. Values of n_f and n_c for this fiber are 1.52 and 1.49, respectively. What is the maximum supportable data rate?

Solution. Using Equation 8.23, we find the delay spread $\tau \cong 102$ ps. To avoid overlap, $T > 2\tau$; therefore, T greater than about 204 ps is required. The modulation scheme allows one bit per period, so the maximum data rate is $1/T \cong 4.9 \times 10^9$ bits per second; i.e., $\cong$ 4.9 Gb/s.

The finding of 4.9 Gb/s may seem like a pretty high data rate; however, consider what happens if the length increases to 1 km. It is apparent from Equation 8.23 that the delay spread will increase by a factor of 1000, so the maximum supportable data rate decreases by a factor of 1000 to a scant 4.9 Mb/s. Again, this is independent of any media loss within the fiber. To restore the higher data rate over this longer path, the dispersion must be reduced. One way to do this is to divide the link into smaller links separated by repeaters which can receive the dispersed signal, demodulate it, regenerate the original signal, and transmit the restored signal to the next repeater. Alternatively, one may employ "single mode" fiber, which has intrinsically less dispersion than the multimode fiber presumed in our analysis.

Additional Reading:

- "Optical fiber" on Wikipedia.

[m0209]

Image Credits

Fig. 8.1: © S. Lally, https://commons.wikimedia.org/wiki/File:Figure_8.1-01.svg,
CC BY SA 4.0 (https://creativecommons.org/licenses/by-sa/4.0/). Modified by author.

Fig. 8.2: © Offaperry (S. Lally),
https://commons.wikimedia.org/wiki/File:Internal_Reflection_in_Optical_Fiber.svg,
CC BY SA 4.0 (https://creativecommons.org/licenses/by-sa/4.0/).

Fig. 8.3: © Offaperry (S. Lally),
https://commons.wikimedia.org/wiki/File:Injecting_Light_into_Optical_Fiber.svg,
CC BY SA 4.0 (https://creativecommons.org/licenses/by-sa/4.0/).

Fig. 8.4: © Offaperry (S. Lally), https://commons.wikimedia.org/wiki/File:Cone_of_Acceptance.svg,
CC BY SA 4.0 (https://creativecommons.org/licenses/by-sa/4.0/).

Fig. 8.5: © Offaperry (S. Lally),
https://commons.wikimedia.org/wiki/File:Paths_of_Light_through_Optic_Cable.svg,
CC BY SA 4.0 (https://creativecommons.org/licenses/by-sa/4.0/).

Fig. 8.6: © Offaperry (S. Lally),
https://commons.wikimedia.org/wiki/File:Digital_Signal_on_Fiber_Optic_Cable.svg,
CC BY SA 4.0 (https://creativecommons.org/licenses/by-sa/4.0/).

Fig. 8.7: © Offaperry (S. Lally),
https://commons.wikimedia.org/wiki/File:Dispersion_on_Signal_Output_from_Fiber_Optic_Cable.svg,
CC BY SA 4.0 (https://creativecommons.org/licenses/by-sa/4.0/).

Chapter 9

Radiation

9.1 Radiation from a Current Moment

[m0194]

In this section, we begin to address the following problem: Given a distribution of impressed current density $\mathbf{J}(\mathbf{r})$, what is the resulting electric field intensity $\mathbf{E}(\mathbf{r})$? One route to an answer is via Maxwell's equations. Viewing Maxwell's equations as a system of differential equations, a rigorous mathematical solution is possible given the appropriate boundary conditions. The rigorous solution following that approach is relatively complicated, and is presented beginning in Section 9.2 of this book.

If we instead limit scope to a sufficiently simple current distribution, a simple informal derivation is possible. This section presents such a derivation. The advantage of tackling a simple special case first is that it will allow us to quickly assess the nature of the solution, which will turn out to be useful once we do eventually address the more general problem. Furthermore, the results presented in this section will turn out to be sufficient to tackle many commonly-encountered applications.

The simple current distribution considered in this section is known as a *current moment*. An example of a current moment is shown in Figure 9.1 and in this case is defined as follows:

$$\Delta \mathbf{J}(\mathbf{r}) = \hat{\mathbf{z}}\, I\, \Delta l\, \delta(\mathbf{r}) \tag{9.1}$$

where $I\,\Delta l$ is the scalar component of the current moment, having units of current times length (SI base units of A·m); and $\delta(\mathbf{r})$ is the volumetric sampling function[1] defined as follows:

$$\delta(\mathbf{r}) \triangleq 0 \quad \text{for} \quad \mathbf{r} \neq 0; \quad \text{and} \tag{9.2}$$

$$\int_{\mathcal{V}} \delta(\mathbf{r})\, dv \triangleq 1 \tag{9.3}$$

where $\mathcal{V}$ is any volume which includes the origin ($\mathbf{r} = 0$). It is evident from Equation 9.3 that $\delta(\mathbf{r})$ has SI base units of m^{-3}. Subsequently, $\Delta\mathbf{J}(\mathbf{r})$ has SI base units of A/m^2, confirming that it is a volume current density. However, it is the *simplest possible* form of volume current density, since – as indicated by Equation 9.2 – it exists only at the origin and nowhere else.

Although some current distributions approximate the current moment, current distributions encountered in common engineering practice generally do not exist

[1] Also a form of the *Dirac delta function*; see "Additional Reading" at the end of this section.

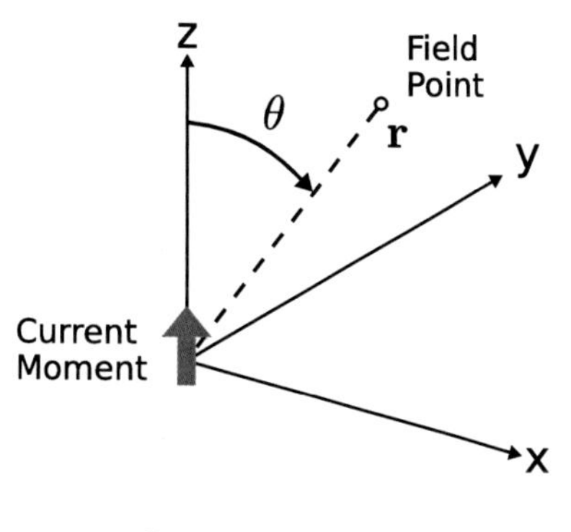

© C. Wang CC BY-SA 4.0

Figure 9.1: A $+\hat{\mathbf{z}}$-directed current moment located at the origin.

in precisely this form. Nevertheless, the current moment turns out to be generally useful as a "building block" from which practical distributions of current can be constructed, via the principle of superposition. Radiation from current distributions constructed in this manner is calculated simply by summing the radiation from each of the constituent current moments.

Now let us consider the electric field intensity $\Delta\mathbf{E}(\mathbf{r})$ that is created by this current distribution. First, if the current is steady (i.e., "DC"), this problem falls within the domain of magnetostatics; i.e., the outcome is completely described by the magnetic field, and there can be no radiation. Therefore, let us limit our attention to the "AC" case, for which radiation is possible. It will be convenient to employ phasor representation. In phasor representation, the current density is

$$\Delta\widetilde{\mathbf{J}}(\mathbf{r}) = \hat{\mathbf{z}}\,\widetilde{I}\,\Delta l\,\delta(\mathbf{r}) \tag{9.4}$$

where $\widetilde{I}\,\Delta l$ is simply the scalar current moment expressed as a phasor.

Now we are ready to address the question "What is $\Delta\widetilde{\mathbf{E}}(\mathbf{r})$ due to $\Delta\widetilde{\mathbf{J}}(\mathbf{r})$?" Without doing any math, we know quite a bit about $\Delta\widetilde{\mathbf{E}}(\mathbf{r})$. For example:

- Since electric fields are proportional to the currents that give rise to them, we expect $\Delta\widetilde{\mathbf{E}}(\mathbf{r})$ to be proportional to $\left|\widetilde{I}\,\Delta l\right|$.
- If we are sufficiently far from the origin, we expect $\Delta\widetilde{\mathbf{E}}(\mathbf{r})$ to be approximately proportional to $1/r$ where $r \triangleq |\mathbf{r}|$ is the distance from the source current. This is because point sources give rise to spherical waves, and the power density in a spherical wave would be proportional to $1/r^2$. Since time-average power density is proportional to $\left|\Delta\widetilde{\mathbf{E}}(\mathbf{r})\right|^2$, $\Delta\widetilde{\mathbf{E}}(\mathbf{r})$ must be proportional to $1/r$.
- If we are sufficiently far from the origin, and the loss due to the medium is negligible, then we expect the phase of $\Delta\widetilde{\mathbf{E}}(\mathbf{r})$ to change approximately at rate β where β is the phase propagation constant $2\pi/\lambda$. Since we expect spherical phasefronts, $\Delta\widetilde{\mathbf{E}}(\mathbf{r})$ should therefore contain the factor $e^{-j\beta r}$.
- Ampere's law indicates that a $\hat{\mathbf{z}}$-directed current at the origin should give rise to a $\hat{\phi}$-directed magnetic field in the $z=0$ plane.[2] At the same time, Poynting's theorem requires the cross product of the electric and magnetic fields to point in the direction of power flow. In the present problem, this direction is away from the source; i.e., $+\hat{\mathbf{r}}$. Therefore, $\Delta\widetilde{\mathbf{E}}(z=0)$ points in the $-\hat{\mathbf{z}}$ direction. The same principle applies outside of the $z=0$ plane, so in general we expect $\Delta\widetilde{\mathbf{E}}(\mathbf{r})$ to point in the $\hat{\theta}$ direction.
- We expect $\Delta\widetilde{\mathbf{E}}(\mathbf{r})=0$ along the z axis. Subsequently $\left|\Delta\widetilde{\mathbf{E}}(\hat{\mathbf{r}})\right|$ must increase from zero at $\theta=0$ and return to zero at $\theta=\pi$. The symmetry of the problem suggests $\left|\Delta\widetilde{\mathbf{E}}(\hat{\mathbf{r}})\right|$ is maximum at $\theta=\pi/2$. This magnitude must vary in the simplest possible way, leading us to conclude that $\Delta\widetilde{\mathbf{E}}(\hat{\mathbf{r}})$ is proportional to $\sin\theta$. Furthermore, the radial symmetry of the problem means that $\Delta\widetilde{\mathbf{E}}(\hat{\mathbf{r}})$ should not depend at all on ϕ.

Putting these ideas together, we conclude that the radiated electric field has the following form:

$$\Delta\widetilde{\mathbf{E}}(\mathbf{r}) \approx \hat{\theta} C \left(\widetilde{I}\,\Delta l\right)(\sin\theta)\,\frac{e^{-j\beta r}}{r} \tag{9.5}$$

where C is a constant which accounts for all of the constants of proportionality identified in the preceding analysis. Since the units of $\Delta\widetilde{\mathbf{E}}(\mathbf{r})$ are V/m, the units of C must be Ω/m. We have not yet accounted for the wave impedance of the medium η, which has units of Ω, so it would be a good bet based on the units that C is proportional to η. However, here the informal analysis reaches a dead end, so we shall simply state the result from the rigorous solution: $C = j\eta\beta/4\pi$. The units are correct, and we finally obtain:

$$\Delta\widetilde{\mathbf{E}}(\mathbf{r}) \approx \hat{\theta}\frac{j\eta\beta}{4\pi}\left(\widetilde{I}\,\Delta l\right)(\sin\theta)\,\frac{e^{-j\beta r}}{r} \tag{9.6}$$

Additional evidence that this solution is correct comes from the fact that it satisfies the wave equation $\nabla^2\Delta\widetilde{\mathbf{E}}(\mathbf{r}) + \beta^2\Delta\widetilde{\mathbf{E}}(\mathbf{r}) = 0$.[3]

[2] This is sometimes described as the "right hand rule" of Ampere's law.

[3] Confirming this is straightforward (simply substitute and evaluate) and is left as an exercise for the student.

Note that the expression we have obtained for the radiated electric field is approximate (hence the "$\approx$"). This is due in part to our presumption of a simple spherical wave, which may only be valid at distances far from the source. But how far? An educated guess would be distances much greater than a wavelength (i.e., $r \gg \lambda$). This will do for now; in another section, we shall show rigorously that this guess is essentially correct.

We conclude this section by noting that the current distribution analyzed in this section is sometimes referred to as a *Hertzian dipole*. A Hertzian dipole is typically defined as a straight infinitesimally-thin filament of current with length which is very small relative to a wavelength, but not precisely zero. This interpretation does not change the solution obtained in this section, thus we may view the current moment and the Hertzian dipole as effectively the same in practical engineering applications.

Additional Reading:

- "Dirac delta function" on Wikipedia.
- "Dipole antenna" (section entitled "Hertzian Dipole") on Wikipedia.

9.2 Magnetic Vector Potential

[m0195]

A common problem in electromagnetics is to determine the fields radiated by a specified current distribution. This problem can be solved using Maxwell's equations along with the appropriate electromagnetic boundary conditions. For time-harmonic (sinusoidally-varying) currents, we use phasor representation.[4] Given the specified current distribution $\widetilde{\mathbf{J}}$ and the desired electromagnetic fields $\widetilde{\mathbf{E}}$ and $\widetilde{\mathbf{H}}$, the appropriate equations are:

$$\nabla \cdot \widetilde{\mathbf{E}} = \widetilde{\rho}_v / \epsilon \tag{9.7}$$

$$\nabla \times \widetilde{\mathbf{E}} = -j\omega\mu\widetilde{\mathbf{H}} \tag{9.8}$$

$$\nabla \cdot \widetilde{\mathbf{H}} = 0 \tag{9.9}$$

$$\nabla \times \widetilde{\mathbf{H}} = \widetilde{\mathbf{J}} + j\omega\epsilon\widetilde{\mathbf{E}} \tag{9.10}$$

where $\widetilde{\rho}_v$ is the volume charge density. In most engineering problems, one is concerned with propagation through media which are well-modeled as homogeneous media with neutral charge, such as free space.[5] Therefore, in this section, we shall limit our scope to problems in which $\widetilde{\rho}_v = 0$. Thus, Equation 9.7 simplifies to:

$$\nabla \cdot \widetilde{\mathbf{E}} = 0 \tag{9.11}$$

To solve the linear system of partial differential Equations 9.8–9.11, it is useful to invoke the concept of *magnetic vector potential*. The magnetic vector potential is a vector field that has the useful property that it is able to represent both the electric and magnetic fields as a single field. This allows the formidable system of equations identified above to be reduced to a single equation which is simpler to solve. Furthermore, this single equation turns out to be the wave equation, with the slight difference that the equation will be mathematically inhomogeneous, with the inhomogeneous part representing the source current.

---

[4]Recall that there is no loss of generality in doing so, since any other time-domain variation in the current distribution can be represented using sums of time-harmonic solutions via the Fourier transform.

[5]A counter-example would be propagation through a plasma, which by definition consists of non-zero net charge.

The magnetic vector potential $\widetilde{\mathbf{A}}$ is defined by the following relationship:

$$\boxed{\widetilde{\mathbf{B}} \triangleq \nabla \times \widetilde{\mathbf{A}}} \tag{9.12}$$

where $\widetilde{\mathbf{B}} = \mu\widetilde{\mathbf{H}}$ is the magnetic flux density. The magnetic field appears in three of Maxwell's equations. For Equation 9.12 to be a reasonable definition, $\nabla \times \widetilde{\mathbf{A}}$ must yield reasonable results when substituted for $\mu\widetilde{\mathbf{H}}$ in each of these equations. Let us first check for consistency with Gauss' law for magnetic fields, Equation 9.9. Making the substitution, we obtain:

$$\nabla \cdot \left(\nabla \times \widetilde{\mathbf{A}}\right) = 0 \tag{9.13}$$

This turns out to be a mathematical identity that applies to *any* vector field (see Equation B.24 in Appendix B.3). Therefore, Equation 9.12 is consistent with Gauss' law for magnetic fields.

Next we check for consistency with Equation 9.8. Making the substitution:

$$\nabla \times \widetilde{\mathbf{E}} = -j\omega\left(\nabla \times \widetilde{\mathbf{A}}\right) \tag{9.14}$$

Gathering terms on the left, we obtain

$$\nabla \times \left(\widetilde{\mathbf{E}} + j\omega\widetilde{\mathbf{A}}\right) = 0 \tag{9.15}$$

Now, for reasons that will become apparent in just a moment, we define a new scalar field $\widetilde{V}$ and require it to satisfy the following relationship:

$$-\nabla\widetilde{V} \triangleq \widetilde{\mathbf{E}} + j\omega\widetilde{\mathbf{A}} \tag{9.16}$$

Using this definition, Equation 9.15 becomes:

$$\nabla \times \left(-\nabla\widetilde{V}\right) = 0 \tag{9.17}$$

which is simply

$$\nabla \times \nabla\widetilde{V} = 0 \tag{9.18}$$

Once again we have obtained a mathematical identity that applies to *any* vector field (see Equation B.25 in Appendix B.3). Therefore, $\widetilde{V}$ can be *any* mathematically-valid scalar field. Subsequently, Equation 9.12 is consistent with Equation 9.8 (Maxwell's curl equation for the electric field) for any choice of $\widetilde{V}$ that we are inclined to make.

Astute readers might already realize what we're up to here. Equation 9.16 is very similar to the relationship $\mathbf{E} = -\nabla V$ from electrostatics,[6] in which V is the scalar electric potential field. Evidently Equation 9.16 is an enhanced version of that relationship that accounts for the coupling with $\mathbf{H}$ (here, represented by $\mathbf{A}$) in the time-varying (decidedly non-static) case. That assessment is correct, but let's not get too far ahead of ourselves: As demonstrated in the previous paragraph, we are not yet compelled to make any particular choice for $\widetilde{V}$, and this freedom will be exploited later in this section.

Next we check for consistency with Equation 9.10. Making the substitution:

$$\nabla \times \left(\frac{1}{\mu}\nabla \times \widetilde{\mathbf{A}}\right) = \widetilde{\mathbf{J}} + j\omega\epsilon\widetilde{\mathbf{E}} \tag{9.19}$$

Multiplying both sides of the equation by μ:

$$\nabla \times \nabla \times \widetilde{\mathbf{A}} = \mu\widetilde{\mathbf{J}} + j\omega\mu\epsilon\widetilde{\mathbf{E}} \tag{9.20}$$

Next we use Equation 9.16 to eliminate $\widetilde{\mathbf{E}}$, yielding:

$$\nabla \times \nabla \times \widetilde{\mathbf{A}} = \mu\widetilde{\mathbf{J}} + j\omega\mu\epsilon\left(-\nabla\widetilde{V} - j\omega\widetilde{\mathbf{A}}\right) \tag{9.21}$$

After a bit of algebra, we obtain

$$\nabla \times \nabla \times \widetilde{\mathbf{A}} = \omega^2\mu\epsilon\widetilde{\mathbf{A}} - j\omega\mu\epsilon\nabla\widetilde{V} + \mu\widetilde{\mathbf{J}} \tag{9.22}$$

Now we replace the left side of this equation using vector identity B.29 in Appendix B.3:

$$\nabla \times \nabla \times \widetilde{\mathbf{A}} \equiv \nabla\left(\nabla \cdot \widetilde{\mathbf{A}}\right) - \nabla^2\widetilde{\mathbf{A}} \tag{9.23}$$

Equation 9.22 becomes:

$$\nabla\left(\nabla \cdot \widetilde{\mathbf{A}}\right) - \nabla^2\widetilde{\mathbf{A}} = \omega^2\mu\epsilon\widetilde{\mathbf{A}} - j\omega\mu\epsilon\nabla\widetilde{V} + \mu\widetilde{\mathbf{J}} \tag{9.24}$$

Now multiplying both sides by -1 and rearranging terms:

$$\nabla^2\widetilde{\mathbf{A}} + \omega^2\mu\epsilon\widetilde{\mathbf{A}} = \nabla\left(\nabla \cdot \widetilde{\mathbf{A}}\right) + j\omega\mu\epsilon\nabla\widetilde{V} - \mu\widetilde{\mathbf{J}} \tag{9.25}$$

Combining terms on the right side:

$$\nabla^2\widetilde{\mathbf{A}} + \omega^2\mu\epsilon\widetilde{\mathbf{A}} = \nabla\left(\nabla \cdot \widetilde{\mathbf{A}} + j\omega\mu\epsilon\widetilde{V}\right) - \mu\widetilde{\mathbf{J}} \tag{9.26}$$

Now consider the expression $\nabla \cdot \widetilde{\mathbf{A}} + j\omega\mu\epsilon\widetilde{V}$ appearing in the parentheses on the right side of the

[6]Note: No tilde in this expression.

equation. We established earlier that $\widetilde{V}$ can be essentially any scalar field – from a mathematical perspective, we are free to choose. Invoking this freedom, we now require $\widetilde{V}$ to satisfy the following expression:

$$\nabla \cdot \widetilde{\mathbf{A}} + j\omega\mu\epsilon\widetilde{V} = 0 \tag{9.27}$$

Clearly this is advantageous in the sense that Equation 9.26 is now dramatically simplified. This equation becomes:

$$\boxed{\nabla^2 \widetilde{\mathbf{A}} + \omega^2 \mu\epsilon \widetilde{\mathbf{A}} = -\mu \widetilde{\mathbf{J}}} \tag{9.28}$$

Note that this expression is a *wave equation*. In fact it is the *same* wave equation that determines $\widetilde{\mathbf{E}}$ and $\widetilde{\mathbf{H}}$ in source-free regions, *except* the right-hand side is not zero. Using mathematical terminology, we have obtained an equation for $\widetilde{\mathbf{A}}$ in the form of an *inhomogeneous* partial differential equation, where the inhomogeneous part includes – no surprise here – the source current $\widetilde{\mathbf{J}}$.

Now we have what we need to find the electromagnetic fields radiated by a current distribution. The procedure is simply as follows:

1. Solve the partial differential Equation 9.28 for $\widetilde{\mathbf{A}}$ along with the appropriate electromagnetic boundary conditions.
2. $\widetilde{\mathbf{H}} = (1/\mu)\nabla \times \widetilde{\mathbf{A}}$
3. $\widetilde{\mathbf{E}}$ may now be determined from $\widetilde{\mathbf{H}}$ using Equation 9.10.

Summarizing:

> The magnetic vector potential $\widetilde{\mathbf{A}}$ is a vector field, defined by Equation 9.12, that is able to represent both the electric and magnetic fields simultaneously.

Also:

> To determine the electromagnetic fields radiated by a current distribution $\widetilde{\mathbf{J}}$, one may solve Equation 9.28 for $\widetilde{\mathbf{A}}$ and then use Equation 9.12 to determine $\widetilde{\mathbf{H}}$ and subsequently $\widetilde{\mathbf{E}}$.

Specific techniques for performing this procedure – in particular, for solving the differential equation – vary depending on the problem, and are discussed in other sections of this book.

We conclude this section with a few comments about Equation 9.27. This equation is known as the *Lorenz gauge condition*. This constraint is not quite as arbitrary as the preceding derivation implies; rather, there is some deep physics at work here. Specifically, the Lorenz gauge leads to the classical interpretation of $\widetilde{V}$ as the familiar scalar electric potential, as noted previously in this section. (For additional information on that idea, recommended starting points are included in "Additional Reading" at the end of this section.)

At this point, it should be clear that the electric and magnetic fields are not merely coupled quantities, but in fact two aspects of the same field; namely, the magnetic vector potential. In fact modern physics (quantum mechanics) yields the magnetic vector potential as a description of the "electromagnetic force," a single entity which constitutes one of the four fundamental forces recognized in modern physics; the others being gravity, the strong nuclear force, and the weak nuclear force. For more information on that concept, an excellent starting point is the video "Quantum Invariance & The Origin of The Standard Model" referenced at the end of this section.

Additional Reading:

- "Lorenz gauge condition" on Wikipedia.
- "Magnetic potential" on Wikipedia.
- PBS Space Time video "Quantum Invariance & The Origin of The Standard Model," available on YouTube.

9.3 Solution of the Wave Equation for Magnetic Vector Potential

[m0196]

The magnetic vector potential $\widetilde{\mathbf{A}}$ due to a current density $\widetilde{\mathbf{J}}$ is given by the following wave equation:

$$\nabla^2\widetilde{\mathbf{A}} - \gamma^2\widetilde{\mathbf{A}} = -\mu\widetilde{\mathbf{J}} \tag{9.29}$$

where γ is the *propagation constant*, defined in the usual manner[7]

$$\gamma^2 \triangleq -\omega^2\mu\epsilon \tag{9.30}$$

Equation 9.29 is a partial differential equation which is inhomogeneous (in the mathematical sense) and can be solved given appropriate boundary conditions. In this section, we present the solution for arbitrary distributions of current in free space.

The strategy is to first identify a solution for a distribution of current that exists at a single point. This distribution is the *current moment*. An example of a current moment is shown in Figure 9.2. A general expression for a current moment located at the origin is:

$$\widetilde{\mathbf{J}}(\mathbf{r}) = \hat{\mathbf{l}}\,\widetilde{I}\,\Delta l\;\delta(\mathbf{r}) \tag{9.31}$$

where $\widetilde{I}$ has units of current (SI base units of A), Δl has units of length (SI base units of m), $\hat{\mathbf{l}}$ is the

[7]Alternatively, $\gamma^2 \triangleq -\omega^2\mu\epsilon_c$ accounting for the possibility of lossy media.

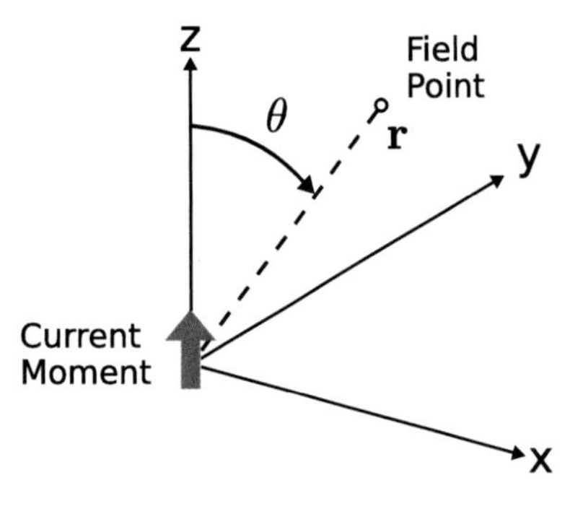

© C. Wang CC BY-SA 4.0

Figure 9.2: An example of a current moment located at the origin. In this case, $\hat{\mathbf{l}} = \hat{\mathbf{z}}$.

direction of current flow, and $\delta(\mathbf{r})$ is the volumetric sampling function[8] defined as follows:

$$\delta(\mathbf{r}) \triangleq 0 \quad \text{for} \quad \mathbf{r} \neq 0; \quad \text{and} \tag{9.32}$$

$$\int_{\mathcal{V}} \delta(\mathbf{r})\, dv \triangleq 1 \tag{9.33}$$

where $\mathcal{V}$ is any volume which includes the origin ($\mathbf{r} = 0$). It is evident from Equation 9.33 that $\delta(\mathbf{r})$ has SI base units of m^{-3}; i.e., inverse volume. Subsequently $\mathbf{J}(\mathbf{r})$ has SI base units of A/m^2, indicating that it is a volume current density.[9] – as indicated by Equation 9.32 – it exists only at the origin and nowhere else.

Substituting Equation 9.31 into Equation 9.29, we obtain:

$$\nabla^2\widetilde{\mathbf{A}} - \gamma^2\widetilde{\mathbf{A}} = -\mu\hat{\mathbf{l}}\,\widetilde{I}\,\Delta l\;\delta(\mathbf{r}) \tag{9.34}$$

The general solution to this equation presuming homogeneous and time-invariant media (i.e., μ and ϵ constant with respect to space and time) is:

$$\widetilde{\mathbf{A}}(\mathbf{r}) = \hat{\mathbf{l}}\,\mu\,\widetilde{I}\,\Delta l\,\frac{e^{\pm\gamma r}}{4\pi r} \tag{9.35}$$

To confirm that this is a solution to Equation 9.34, substitute this expression into Equation 9.29 and observe that the equality holds.

Note that Equation 9.35 indicates two solutions, corresponding to the signs of the exponent in the factor $e^{\pm\gamma r}$. We can actually be a little more specific by applying some common-sense physics. Recall that γ in general may be expressed in terms of real and imaginary components as follows:

$$\gamma = \alpha + j\beta \tag{9.36}$$

where α is a real-valued positive constant known as the *attenuation constant* and β is a real-valued positive constant known as the *phase propagation constant*. Thus, we may rewrite Equation 9.35 as follows:

$$\widetilde{\mathbf{A}}(\mathbf{r}) = \hat{\mathbf{l}}\,\mu\,\widetilde{I}\,\Delta l\,\frac{e^{\pm\alpha r}e^{\pm j\beta r}}{4\pi r} \tag{9.37}$$

[8]Also a form of the *Dirac delta function*; see “Additional Reading” at the end of this section.

[9]Remember, the density of a volume current is with respect to the *area* through which it flows, therefore the units are A/m^2.

Now consider the factor $e^{\pm\alpha r}/r$, which determines the dependence of magnitude on distance r. If we choose the negative sign in the exponent, this factor decays exponentially with increasing distance from the origin, ultimately reaching zero at $r \to \infty$. This is precisely the expected behavior, since we expect the magnitude of a radiated field to diminish with increasing distance from the source. If on the other hand we choose the positive sign in the exponent, this factor increases to infinity as $r \to \infty$. That outcome can be ruled out on physical grounds, since it implies the introduction of energy independently from the source. The requirement that field magnitude diminishes to zero as distance from the source increases to infinity is known as the *radiation condition*, and is essentially a boundary condition that applies at $r \to \infty$. Invoking the radiation condition, Equation 9.35 becomes:

$$\widetilde{\mathbf{A}}(\mathbf{r}) = \hat{\mathbf{l}}\,\mu\,\widetilde{I}\,\Delta l\,\frac{e^{-\gamma r}}{4\pi r} \tag{9.38}$$

In the loss-free ($\alpha = 0$) case, we cannot rely on the radiation condition to constrain the sign of γ. However, in practical engineering work there is always some media loss; i.e., α might be negligible but is not quite zero. Thus, we normally assume that the solution for lossless (including free space) conditions is given by Equation 9.38 with $\alpha = 0$:

$$\widetilde{\mathbf{A}}(\mathbf{r}) = \hat{\mathbf{l}}\,\mu\,\widetilde{I}\,\Delta l\,\frac{e^{-j\beta r}}{4\pi r} \tag{9.39}$$

Now consider the factor $e^{-j\beta r}$ in Equation 9.39. This factor exclusively determines the dependence of the phase of $\widetilde{\mathbf{A}}(\mathbf{r})$ with increasing distance r from the source. In this case, we observe that surfaces of constant phase correspond to spherical shells which are concentric with the source. Thus, $\widetilde{\mathbf{A}}(\mathbf{r})$ is a spherical wave.

Let us now consider a slightly more complicated version of the problem in which the current moment is no longer located at the origin, but rather is located at $\mathbf{r}'$. This is illustrated in Figure 9.3. This current distribution can be expressed as follows:

$$\widetilde{\mathbf{J}}(\mathbf{r}) = \hat{\mathbf{l}}\,\widetilde{I}\,\Delta l\,\delta(\mathbf{r}-\mathbf{r}') \tag{9.40}$$

The solution in this case amounts to a straightforward modification of the existing solution. To see this, note

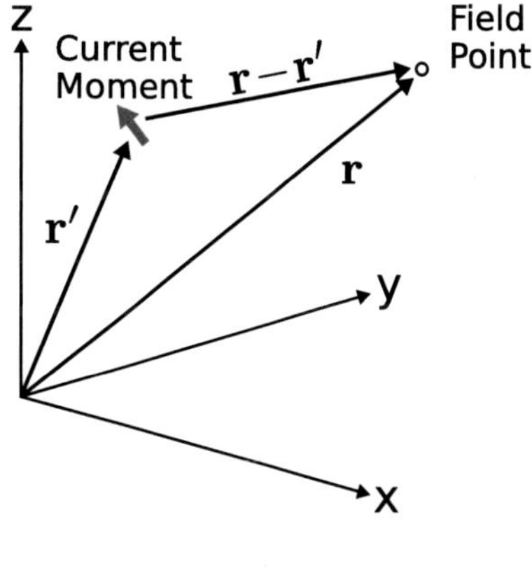

© C. Wang CC BY-SA 4.0

Figure 9.3: Current moment displaced from the origin.

that $\widetilde{\mathbf{A}}$ depends only on r, and not at all on θ or ϕ. In other words, $\widetilde{\mathbf{A}}$ depends only on the distance between the "field point" $\mathbf{r}$ at which we observe $\widetilde{\mathbf{A}}$, and the "source point" $\mathbf{r}'$ at which the current moment lies. Thus we replace r with this distance, which is $|\mathbf{r}-\mathbf{r}'|$. The solution becomes:

$$\widetilde{\mathbf{A}}(\mathbf{r}) = \hat{\mathbf{l}}\,\mu\,\widetilde{I}\,\Delta l\,\frac{e^{-\gamma|\mathbf{r}-\mathbf{r}'|}}{4\pi\,|\mathbf{r}-\mathbf{r}'|} \tag{9.41}$$

Continuing to generalize the solution, let us now consider a scenario consisting of a filament of current following a path $\mathcal{C}$ through space. This is illustrated in Figure 9.4. Such a filament may be viewed as a collection of a large number N of discrete current moments distributed along the path. The contribution of the nth current moment, located at $\mathbf{r}_n$, to the total magnetic vector potential is:

$$\Delta\widetilde{\mathbf{A}}(\mathbf{r};\mathbf{r}_n) = \hat{\mathbf{l}}(\mathbf{r}_n)\,\mu\,\widetilde{I}(\mathbf{r}_n)\,\Delta l\,\frac{e^{-\gamma|\mathbf{r}-\mathbf{r}_n|}}{4\pi\,|\mathbf{r}-\mathbf{r}_n|} \tag{9.42}$$

Note that we are allowing both the current $\widetilde{I}$ and current direction $\hat{\mathbf{l}}$ to vary with position along $\mathcal{C}$. Assuming the medium is linear, superposition applies. So we add these contributions to obtain the total

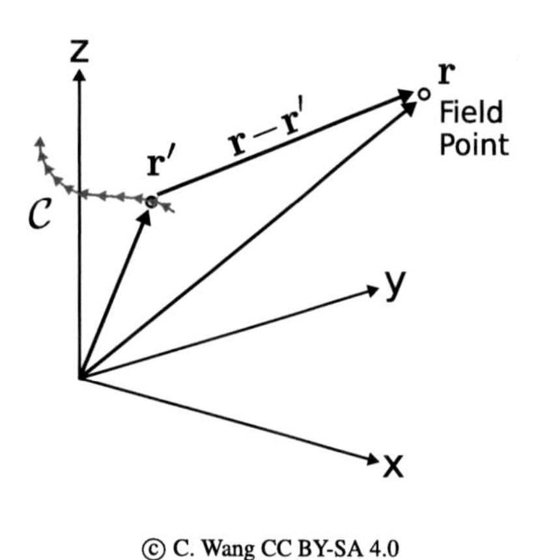

© C. Wang CC BY-SA 4.0

Figure 9.4: A filament of current lying along the path $\mathcal{C}$. This current distribution may be interpreted as a collection of current moments lying along $\mathcal{C}$.

magnetic vector potential:

$$\widetilde{\mathbf{A}}(\mathbf{r}) \approx \sum_{n=1}^{N} \Delta\widetilde{\mathbf{A}}(\mathbf{r};\mathbf{r}_n) \quad (9.43)$$

$$\approx \frac{\mu}{4\pi} \sum_{n=1}^{N} \hat{\mathbf{l}}(\mathbf{r}_n)\, \widetilde{I}(\mathbf{r}_n)\, \frac{e^{-\gamma|\mathbf{r}-\mathbf{r}_n|}}{|\mathbf{r}-\mathbf{r}_n|}\, \Delta l \quad (9.44)$$

Now letting $\Delta l \to 0$ so that we may replace Δl with the differential length dl:

$$\boxed{\widetilde{\mathbf{A}}(\mathbf{r}) = \frac{\mu}{4\pi} \int_{\mathcal{C}} \hat{\mathbf{l}}(\mathbf{r}')\, \widetilde{I}(\mathbf{r}')\, \frac{e^{-\gamma|\mathbf{r}-\mathbf{r}'|}}{|\mathbf{r}-\mathbf{r}'|}\, dl} \quad (9.45)$$

where we have also replaced $\mathbf{r}_n$ with the original notation $\mathbf{r}'$ since we once again have a continuum (as opposed to a discrete set) of source locations.

> The magnetic vector potential corresponding to radiation from a line distribution of current is given by Equation 9.45.

Given $\widetilde{\mathbf{A}}(\mathbf{r})$, the magnetic and electric fields may be determined using the procedure developed in Section 9.2.

Additional Reading:

- "Magnetic potential" on Wikipedia.
- "Dirac delta function" on Wikipedia.

9.4 Radiation from a Hertzian Dipole

[m0197]

Section 9.1 presented an informal derivation of the electromagnetic field radiated by a Hertzian dipole represented by a zero-length current moment. In this section, we provide a rigorous derivation using the concept of magnetic vector potential discussed in Sections 9.2 and 9.3. A review of those sections is recommended before tackling this section.

A Hertzian dipole is commonly defined as an electrically-short and infinitesimally-thin straight filament of current, in which the density of the current is uniform over its length. The Hertzian dipole is commonly used as a "building block" for constructing physically-realizable distributions of current as exhibited by devices such as wire antennas. The method is to model these relatively complex distributions of current as the sum of Hertzian dipoles, which reduces the problem to that of summing the contributions of the individual Hertzian dipoles, with each Hertzian dipole having the appropriate (i.e., different) position, magnitude, and phase.

To facilitate use of the Hertzian dipole as a building block suitable for constructing physically-realizable distributions of current, we choose to represent the Hertzian dipole using an essentially equivalent current distribution which is mathematically more versatile. This description of the Hertzian dipole replaces the notion of constant current over finite length with the notion of a *current moment* located at a single point. This is shown in Figure 9.5, and is given by:

$$\Delta\widetilde{\mathbf{J}}(\mathbf{r}) = \hat{\mathbf{l}}\, \widetilde{I}\, \Delta l\, \delta(\mathbf{r}) \quad (9.46)$$

where the product $\widetilde{I}\Delta l$ (SI base units of A·m) is the current moment, $\hat{\mathbf{l}}$ is the direction of current flow, and $\delta(\mathbf{r})$ is the volumetric sampling function defined as follows:

$$\delta(\mathbf{r}) \triangleq 0 \quad \text{for} \quad \mathbf{r} \neq 0; \quad \text{and} \quad (9.47)$$

$$\int_{\mathcal{V}} \delta(\mathbf{r})\, dv \triangleq 1 \quad (9.48)$$

where $\mathcal{V}$ is any volume which includes the origin ($\mathbf{r} = 0$). In this description, the Hertzian dipole is located at the origin.

The solution for the magnetic vector potential due to a $\hat{\mathbf{z}}$-directed Hertzian dipole located at the origin was presented in Section 9.3. In the present scenario, it is:

$$\widetilde{\mathbf{A}}(\mathbf{r}) = \hat{\mathbf{z}}\,\mu\,\widetilde{I}\,\Delta l\,\frac{e^{-\gamma r}}{4\pi r} \tag{9.49}$$

where the propagation constant $\gamma = \alpha + j\beta$ as usual. Assuming lossless media ($\alpha = 0$), we have

$$\widetilde{\mathbf{A}}(\mathbf{r}) = \hat{\mathbf{z}}\,\mu\,\widetilde{I}\,\Delta l\,\frac{e^{-j\beta r}}{4\pi r} \tag{9.50}$$

We obtain the magnetic field intensity using the definition of magnetic vector potential:

$$\widetilde{\mathbf{H}} \triangleq (1/\mu)\nabla\times\widetilde{\mathbf{A}} \tag{9.51}$$

$$= \frac{\widetilde{I}\,\Delta l}{4\pi}\,\nabla\times\hat{\mathbf{z}}\,\frac{e^{-j\beta r}}{r} \tag{9.52}$$

To proceed, it is useful to convert $\hat{\mathbf{z}}$ into the spherical coordinate system. To do this, we find the component of $\hat{\mathbf{z}}$ that is parallel to $\hat{\mathbf{r}}$, $\hat{\theta}$, and $\hat{\phi}$; and then sum the results:

$$\hat{\mathbf{z}} = \hat{\mathbf{r}}\left(\hat{\mathbf{r}}\cdot\hat{\mathbf{z}}\right) + \hat{\theta}\left(\hat{\theta}\cdot\hat{\mathbf{z}}\right) + \hat{\phi}\left(\hat{\phi}\cdot\hat{\mathbf{z}}\right) \tag{9.53}$$

$$= \hat{\mathbf{r}}\cos\theta - \hat{\theta}\sin\theta + 0 \tag{9.54}$$

Equation 9.52 requires computation of the following quantity:

$$\nabla\times\hat{\mathbf{z}}\frac{e^{-j\beta r}}{r} = \nabla\times\left[\;\hat{\mathbf{r}}\left(\cos\theta\right)\frac{e^{-j\beta r}}{r} - \hat{\theta}\left(\sin\theta\right)\frac{e^{-j\beta r}}{r}\right] \tag{9.55}$$

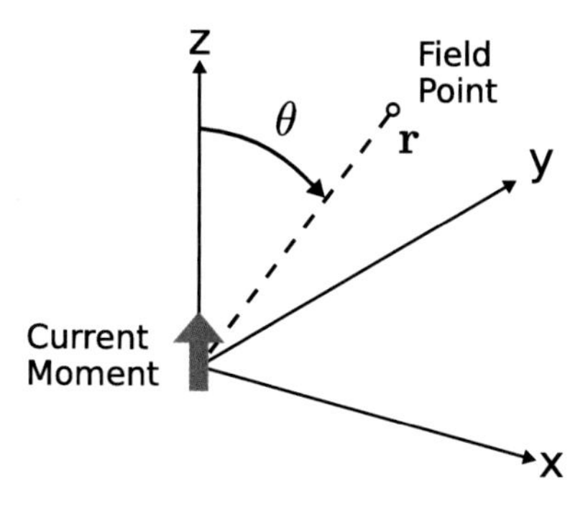

© C. Wang CC BY-SA 4.0

Figure 9.5: A Hertzian dipole located at the origin, represented as a current moment. In this case, $\hat{\mathbf{l}} = \hat{\mathbf{z}}$.

At this point, it is convenient to make the following definitions:

$$C_r \triangleq \left(\cos\theta\right)\frac{e^{-j\beta r}}{r} \tag{9.56}$$

$$C_\theta \triangleq -\left(\sin\theta\right)\frac{e^{-j\beta r}}{r} \tag{9.57}$$

These definitions allow Equation 9.55 to be written compactly as follows:

$$\nabla\times\hat{\mathbf{z}}\frac{e^{-j\beta r}}{r} = \nabla\times\left[\hat{\mathbf{r}}C_r + \hat{\theta}C_\theta\right] \tag{9.58}$$

The right side of Equation 9.58 is evaluated using Equation B.18 (Appendix B.2). Although the complete expression consists of 6 terms, only 2 terms are non-zero.[10] This leaves:

$$\nabla\times\hat{\mathbf{z}}\frac{e^{-j\beta r}}{r} = \hat{\phi}\frac{1}{r}\left[\frac{\partial}{\partial r}\left(rC_\theta\right) - \frac{\partial}{\partial\theta}C_r\right] \tag{9.59}$$

$$= \hat{\phi}\left(\sin\theta\right)\frac{e^{-j\beta r}}{r}\left(j\beta + \frac{1}{r}\right) \tag{9.60}$$

Substituting this result into Equation 9.52, we obtain:

$$\widetilde{\mathbf{H}} = \hat{\phi}\frac{\widetilde{I}\,\Delta l}{4\pi}\left(\sin\theta\right)\frac{e^{-j\beta r}}{r}\left(j\beta + \frac{1}{r}\right) \tag{9.61}$$

Let us further limit our scope to the field far from the antenna. Specifically, let us assume $r \gg \lambda$. Now we use the relationship $\beta = 2\pi/\lambda$ and determine the following:

$$j\beta + \frac{1}{r} = j\frac{2\pi}{\lambda} + \frac{1}{r} \tag{9.62}$$

$$\approx j\frac{2\pi}{\lambda} = j\beta \tag{9.63}$$

Equation 9.61 becomes:

$$\boxed{\widetilde{\mathbf{H}} \approx \hat{\phi}j\frac{\widetilde{I}\cdot\beta\Delta l}{4\pi}\left(\sin\theta\right)\frac{e^{-j\beta r}}{r}} \tag{9.64}$$

where the approximation holds for low-loss media and $r \gg \lambda$. This expression is known as a *far field approximation*, since it is valid only for distances "far" (relative to a wavelength) from the source.

Now let us take a moment to interpret this result:

[10] Specifically, two terms are zero because there is no $\hat{\phi}$ component in the argument of the curl function; and another two terms are zero because the argument of the curl function is independent of ϕ, so partial derivatives with respect to ϕ are zero.

- Notice the factor $\beta\Delta l$ has units of radians; that is, it is *electrical length*. This tells us that the magnitude of the radiated field depends on the electrical length of the current moment.
- The factor $e^{-j\beta r}/r$ indicates that this is a spherical wave; that is, surfaces of constant phase correspond to concentric spheres centered on the source, and magnitude is inversely proportional to distance.
- The direction of the magnetic field vector is always $\hat{\phi}$, which is precisely what we expect; for example, using the Biot-Savart law.
- Finally, note the factor $\sin\theta$. This indicates that the field magnitude is zero along the direction in which the source current flows, and is a maximum in the plane perpendicular to this direction.

Now let us determine the electric field radiated by the Hertzian dipole. The direct method is to employ Ampere's law. That is,

$$\widetilde{\mathbf{E}} = \frac{1}{j\omega\epsilon}\nabla \times \widetilde{\mathbf{H}} \tag{9.65}$$

where $\widetilde{\mathbf{H}}$ is given by Equation 9.64. At field points far from the dipole, the radius of curvature of the spherical phasefronts is very large and so appear to be *locally planar*. That is, from the perspective of an observer far from the dipole, the arriving wave appears to be a plane wave. In this case, we may employ the *plane wave relationships*. The appropriate relationship in this case is:

$$\widetilde{\mathbf{E}} = -\eta\hat{\mathbf{r}} \times \widetilde{\mathbf{H}} \tag{9.66}$$

where η is the wave impedance. So we find:

$$\boxed{\widetilde{\mathbf{E}} \approx \hat{\theta} j\eta \frac{\widetilde{I}\cdot\beta\Delta l}{4\pi}\left(\sin\theta\right)\frac{e^{-j\beta r}}{r}} \tag{9.67}$$

Summarizing:

> The electric and magnetic fields far (i.e., $\gg \lambda$) from a $\hat{\mathbf{z}}$-directed Hertzian dipole having constant current $\widetilde{I}$ over length Δl, located at the origin, are given by Equations 9.67 and 9.64, respectively.

Additional Reading:

- "Dipole antenna" (section entitled "Hertzian Dipole") on Wikipedia.

9.5 Radiation from an Electrically-Short Dipole

[m0198]

The simplest distribution of radiating current that is encountered in common practice is the electrically-short dipole (ESD). This current distribution is shown in Figure 9.6. The two characteristics that define the ESD are (1) the current is aligned along a straight line, and (2) the length L of the line is much less than one-half of a wavelength; i.e., $L \ll \lambda/2$. The latter characteristic is what we mean by "electrically-short."[11]

The current distribution of an ESD is approximately triangular in magnitude, and approximately constant in phase. How do we know this? First, note that distributions of current cannot change in a complex or rapid way over such distances which are much less than a wavelength. If this is not immediately apparent, recall the behavior of transmission lines:

[11]A potential source of confusion is that the *Hertzian dipole* is also a "dipole" which is "electrically-short." The distinction is that the current comprising a Hertzian dipole is *constant* over its length. This condition is rarely and only approximately seen in practice, whereas the triangular magnitude distribution is a relatively good approximation to a broad class of commonly-encountered electrically-short wire antennas. Thus, the term "electrically-short dipole," as used in this book, refers to the triangular distribution unless noted otherwise.

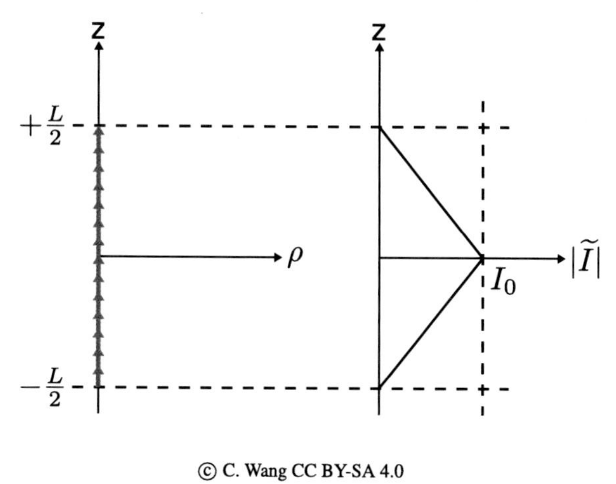

© C. Wang CC BY-SA 4.0

Figure 9.6: Current distribution of the electrically-short dipole (ESD).

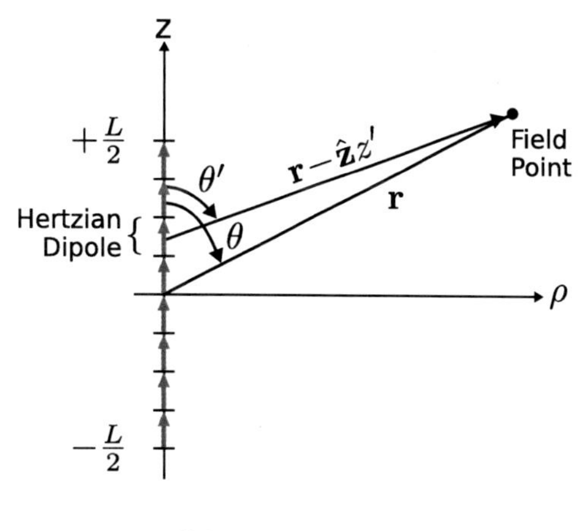

© C. Wang CC BY-SA 4.0

Figure 9.7: Current distribution of the electrically-short dipole (ESD) approximated as a large number of Hertzian dipoles.

The current standing wave on a transmission line exhibits a period of $\lambda/2$, regardless the source or termination. For the ESD, $L \ll \lambda/2$ and so we expect an even simpler variation. Also, we know that the current at the ends of the dipole must be zero, simply because the dipole ends there. These considerations imply that the current distribution of the ESD is well-approximated as triangular in magnitude.[12] Expressed mathematically:

$$\widetilde{I}(z) \approx I_0 \left(1 - \frac{2}{L}|z|\right) \tag{9.68}$$

where I_0 (SI base units of A) is a complex-valued constant indicating the maximum current magnitude and phase.

There are two approaches that we might consider in order to find the electric field radiated by an ESD. The first approach is to calculate the magnetic vector potential $\widetilde{\mathbf{A}}$ by integration over the current distribution, calculate $\widetilde{\mathbf{H}} = (1/\mu)\nabla \times \widetilde{\mathbf{A}}$, and finally calculate $\widetilde{\mathbf{E}}$ from $\widetilde{\mathbf{H}}$ using Ampere's law. We shall employ a simpler approach, shown in Figure 9.7. Imagine the ESD as a collection of many shorter segments of current that radiate independently. The total field is then the sum of these short segments. Because these segments are very short relative to the

[12]A more rigorous analysis leading to the same conclusion is possible, but is beyond the scope of this book.

length of the dipole as well as being short relative to a wavelength, we may approximate the current over each segment as approximately constant. In other words, we may interpret each of these segments as being, to a good approximation, a Hertzian dipole.

The advantage of this approach is that we already have a solution for each of the segments. In Section 9.4, it is shown that a $\hat{\mathbf{z}}$-directed Hertzian dipole at the origin radiates the electric field

$$\widetilde{\mathbf{E}}(\mathbf{r}) \approx \hat{\theta} j\eta \frac{\widetilde{I}\cdot\beta\Delta l}{4\pi}\left(\sin\theta\right)\frac{e^{-j\beta r}}{r} \tag{9.69}$$

where $\widetilde{I}$ and Δl may be interpreted as the current and length of the dipole, respectively. In this expression, η is the wave impedance of medium in which the dipole radiates (e.g., $\approx 377\ \Omega$ for free space), and we have presumed lossless media such that the attenuation constant $\alpha \approx 0$ and the phase propagation constant $\beta = 2\pi/\lambda$. This expression also assumes field points far from the dipole; specifically, distances r that are much greater than λ. Repurposing this expression for the present problem, the segment at the origin radiates the electric field:

$$\widetilde{\mathbf{E}}(\mathbf{r};z'=0) \approx \hat{\theta} j\eta \frac{I_0\cdot\beta\Delta l}{4\pi}\left(\sin\theta\right)\frac{e^{-j\beta r}}{r} \tag{9.70}$$

where the notation $z'=0$ indicates the Hertzian dipole is located at the origin. Letting the length Δl of this segment shrink to differential length dz', we may describe the contribution of this segment to the field radiated by the ESD as follows:

$$d\widetilde{\mathbf{E}}(\mathbf{r};z'=0) \approx \hat{\theta} j\eta \frac{I_0\cdot\beta dz'}{4\pi}\left(\sin\theta\right)\frac{e^{-j\beta r}}{r} \tag{9.71}$$

Using this approach, the electric field radiated by *any* segment can be written:

$$d\widetilde{\mathbf{E}}(\mathbf{r};z') \approx \hat{\theta}' j\eta\beta \frac{\widetilde{I}(z')}{4\pi}\left(\sin\theta'\right)\frac{e^{-j\beta\left|\mathbf{r}-\hat{\mathbf{z}}z'\right|}}{\left|\mathbf{r}-\hat{\mathbf{z}}z'\right|}dz' \tag{9.72}$$

Note that θ is replaced by θ' since the ray $\mathbf{r}-\hat{\mathbf{z}}z'$ forms a different angle (i.e., θ') with respect to $\hat{\mathbf{z}}$. Similarly, $\hat{\theta}$ is replaced by $\hat{\theta}'$, since it also varies with z'. The electric field radiated by the ESD is obtained by integration over these contributions:

$$\widetilde{\mathbf{E}}(\mathbf{r}) \approx \int_{-L/2}^{+L/2} d\widetilde{\mathbf{E}}(\hat{\mathbf{r}};z') \tag{9.73}$$

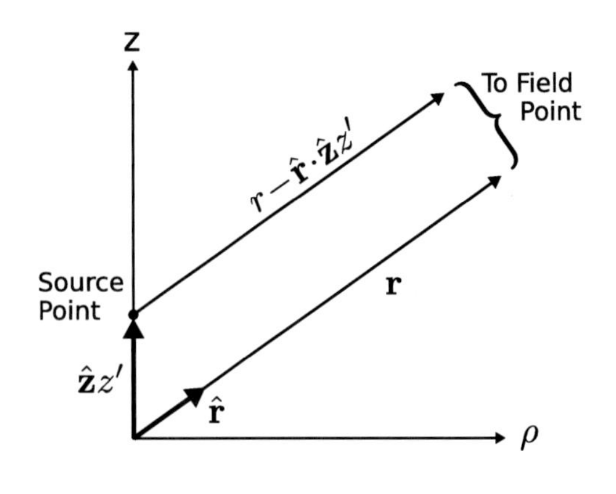

© C. Wang CC BY-SA 4.0

Figure 9.8: Parallel ray approximation for an ESD.

yielding:

$$\widetilde{\mathbf{E}}(\mathbf{r}) \approx j\frac{\eta\beta}{4\pi}\int_{-L/2}^{+L/2}\hat{\theta}'\widetilde{I}(z')\left(\sin\theta'\right)\frac{e^{-j\beta\left|\mathbf{r}-\hat{\mathbf{z}}z'\right|}}{\left|\mathbf{r}-\hat{\mathbf{z}}z'\right|}dz' \tag{9.74}$$

Given some of the assumptions we have already made, this expression can be further simplified. For example, note that $\theta' \approx \theta$ since $L \ll r$. For the same reason, $\hat{\theta}' \approx \hat{\theta}$. Since these variables are approximately constant over the length of the dipole, we may move them outside the integral, yielding:

$$\widetilde{\mathbf{E}}(\mathbf{r}) \approx \hat{\theta} j\frac{\eta\beta}{4\pi}\left(\sin\theta\right)\int_{-L/2}^{+L/2}\widetilde{I}(z')\frac{e^{-j\beta\left|\mathbf{r}-\hat{\mathbf{z}}z'\right|}}{\left|\mathbf{r}-\hat{\mathbf{z}}z'\right|}dz' \tag{9.75}$$

It is also possible to simplify the expression $\left|\mathbf{r}-\hat{\mathbf{z}}z'\right|$. Consider Figure 9.8. Since we have already assumed that $r \gg L$ (i.e., the distance to field points is much greater than the length of the dipole), the vector $\mathbf{r}$ is approximately parallel to the vector $\mathbf{r}-\hat{\mathbf{z}}z'$. Subsequently, it must be true that

$$\left|\mathbf{r}-\hat{\mathbf{z}}z'\right| \approx r - \hat{\mathbf{r}}\cdot\hat{\mathbf{z}}z' \tag{9.76}$$

Note that the magnitude of $r - \hat{\mathbf{r}}\cdot\hat{\mathbf{z}}z'$ must be approximately equal to r, since $r \gg L$. So, insofar as $\left|\mathbf{r}-\hat{\mathbf{z}}z'\right|$ determines the *magnitude* of $\widetilde{\mathbf{E}}(\mathbf{r})$, we may use the approximation:

$$\left|\mathbf{r}-\hat{\mathbf{z}}z'\right| \approx r \quad \text{(magnitude)} \tag{9.77}$$

Insofar as $\left|\mathbf{r}-\hat{\mathbf{z}}z'\right|$ determines *phase*, we have to be a bit more careful. The part of the integrand of

Equation 9.75 that exhibits varying phase is $e^{-j\beta|\mathbf{r}-\hat{\mathbf{z}}z'|}$. Using Equation 9.76, we find

$$e^{-j\beta|\mathbf{r}-\hat{\mathbf{z}}z'|} \approx e^{-j\beta r}e^{+j\beta\hat{\mathbf{r}}\cdot\hat{\mathbf{z}}z'} \tag{9.78}$$

The worst case in terms of phase variation within the integral is for field points along the z axis. For these points, $\hat{\mathbf{r}}\cdot\hat{\mathbf{z}} = \pm 1$ and subsequently $|\mathbf{r}-\hat{\mathbf{z}}z'|$ varies from $z - L/2$ to $z + L/2$ where z is the location of the field point. However, since $L \ll \lambda$ (i.e., because the dipole is electrically short), this difference in lengths is much less than $\lambda/2$. Therefore, the phase $\beta\hat{\mathbf{r}}\cdot\hat{\mathbf{z}}z'$ varies by much less than π radians, and subsequently $e^{-j\beta\hat{\mathbf{r}}\cdot\hat{\mathbf{z}}z'} \approx 1$. We conclude that under these conditions,

$$e^{-j\beta|\mathbf{r}-\hat{\mathbf{z}}z'|} \approx e^{-j\beta r} \quad \text{(phase)} \tag{9.79}$$

Applying these simplifications for magnitude and phase to Equation 9.75, we obtain:

$$\widetilde{\mathbf{E}}(\mathbf{r}) \approx \hat{\theta}j\frac{\eta\beta}{4\pi}(\sin\theta)\,\frac{e^{-j\beta r}}{r}\int_{-L/2}^{+L/2}\widetilde{I}(z')dz' \tag{9.80}$$

The integral in this equation is very easy to evaluate; in fact, from inspection (Figure 9.6), we determine it is equal to $I_0L/2$. Finally, we obtain:

$$\boxed{\widetilde{\mathbf{E}}(\mathbf{r}) \approx \hat{\theta}j\eta\frac{I_0\cdot\beta L}{8\pi}\,(\sin\theta)\,\frac{e^{-j\beta r}}{r}} \tag{9.81}$$

Summarizing:

> The electric field intensity radiated by an ESD located at the origin and aligned along the z axis is given by Equation 9.81. This expression is valid for $r \gg \lambda$.

It is worth noting that the variation in magnitude, phase, and polarization of the ESD with field point location is identical to that of a single Hertzian dipole having current moment $\hat{\mathbf{z}}I_0L/2$ (Section 9.4). However, the magnitude of the field radiated by the ESD is exactly one-half that of the Hertzian dipole. Why one-half? Simply because the integral over the triangular current distribution assumed for the ESD is one-half the integral over the uniform current distribution that defines the Hertzian dipole. This similarly sometimes causes confusion between Hertzian dipoles and ESDs. Remember that ESDs are physically realizable, whereas Hertzian dipoles are not.

It is common to eliminate the factor of β in the magnitude using the relationship $\beta = 2\pi/\lambda$, yielding:

$$\widetilde{\mathbf{E}}(\mathbf{r}) \approx \hat{\theta}j\frac{\eta I_0}{4}\frac{L}{\lambda}\,(\sin\theta)\,\frac{e^{-j\beta r}}{r} \tag{9.82}$$

At field points $r \gg \lambda$, the wave appears to be locally planar. Therefore, we are justified using the plane wave relationship $\widetilde{\mathbf{H}} = \frac{1}{\eta}\hat{\mathbf{r}}\times\widetilde{\mathbf{E}}$ to calculate $\widetilde{\mathbf{H}}$. The result is:

$$\widetilde{\mathbf{H}}(\mathbf{r}) \approx \hat{\phi}j\frac{I_0}{4}\frac{L}{\lambda}\,(\sin\theta)\,\frac{e^{-j\beta r}}{r} \tag{9.83}$$

Finally, let us consider the spatial characteristics of the radiated field. Figures 9.9 and 9.10 show the result in a plane of constant ϕ. Figures 9.11 and 9.12 show the result in the $z = 0$ plane. Note that the orientations of the electric and magnetic field vectors indicate a Poynting vector $\widetilde{\mathbf{E}}\times\widetilde{\mathbf{H}}$ that is always directed radially outward from the location of the dipole. This confirms that power flow is always directed radially outward from the dipole. Due to the symmetry of the problem, Figures 9.9–9.12 provide a complete characterization of the relative magnitudes and orientations of the radiated fields.

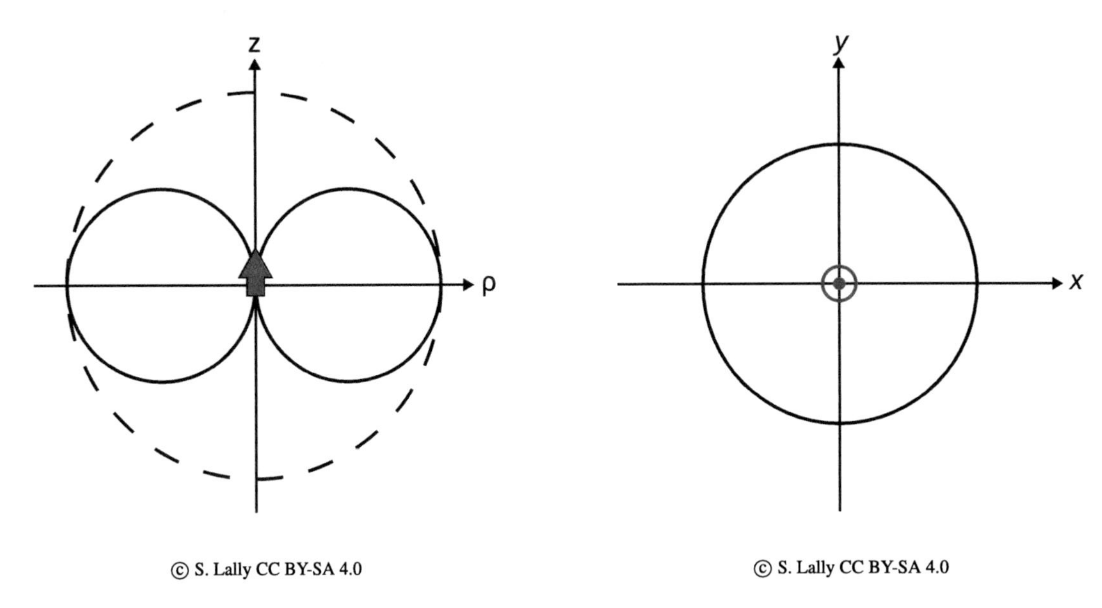

Figure 9.9: Magnitude of the radiated field in any plane of constant ϕ.

Figure 9.11: Magnitude of the radiated field in any plane of constant z.

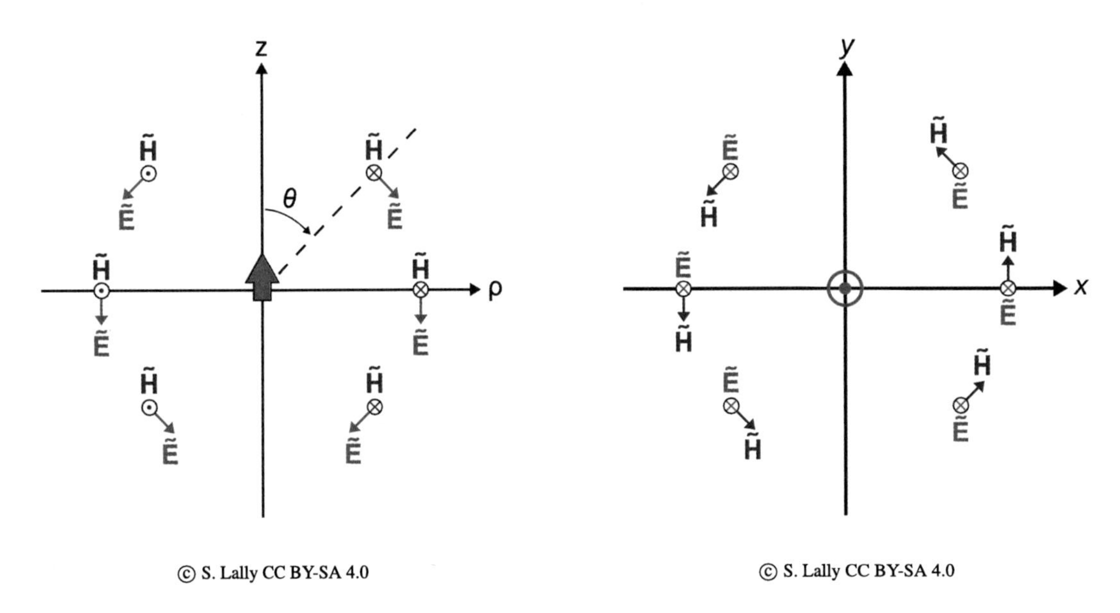

Figure 9.10: Orientation of the electric and magnetic fields in any plane of constant ϕ.

Figure 9.12: Orientation of the electric and magnetic fields in the $z = 0$ plane.

9.6 Far-Field Radiation from a Thin Straight Filament of Current

[m0199]

A simple distribution of radiating current that is encountered in common practice is the thin straight current filament, shown in Figure 9.13. The defining characteristic of this distribution is that the current filament is aligned along a straight line, and that the maximum dimension of the cross-section of the filament is much less than a wavelength. The latter characteristic is what we mean by "thin" – i.e., the filament is "electrically thin." Physical distributions of current that meet this description include the electrically-short dipole (Section 9.5) and the half-wave dipole (Section 9.7) among others. A gentler introduction to this distribution is via Section 9.5 ("Radiation from an Electrically-Short Dipole"), so students may want to review that section first. This section presents the more general case.

Let the magnitude and phase of current along the filament be given by the phasor quantity $\widetilde{I}(z)$ (SI base units of A). In principle, the only constraint on $\widetilde{I}(z)$ that applies generally is that it must be zero at the ends of the distribution; i.e., $\widetilde{I}(z) = 0$ for $|z| \geq L/2$. Details beyond this constraint depend on L and perhaps other factors. Nevertheless, the characteristics of radiation from members of this class of current distributions have much in common, regardless of L. These become especially apparent if we limit our scope to field points far from the current, as we shall do here.

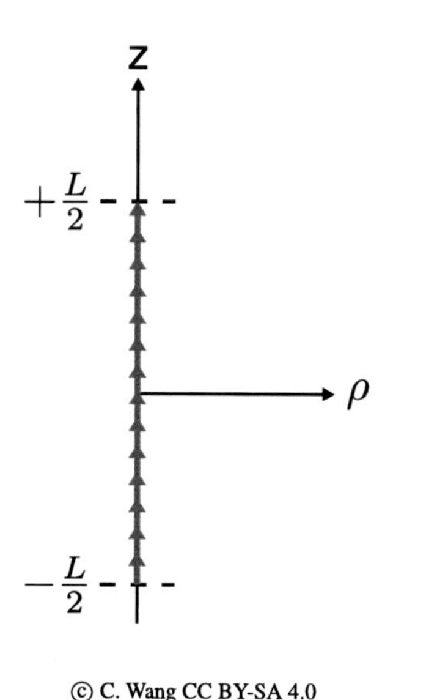

© C. Wang CC BY-SA 4.0

Figure 9.13: A thin straight distribution of radiating current.

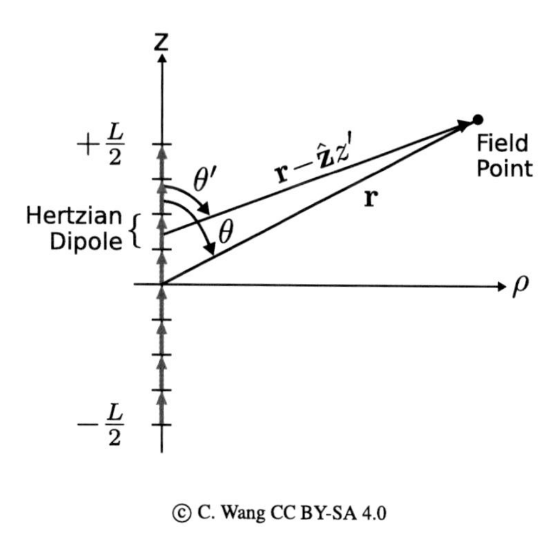

© C. Wang CC BY-SA 4.0

Figure 9.14: Current distribution approximated as a set of Hertzian dipoles.

There are two approaches that we might consider in order to find the electric field radiated by this distribution. The first approach is to calculate the magnetic vector potential $\widetilde{\mathbf{A}}$ by integration over the current distribution (Section 9.3), calculate $\widetilde{\mathbf{H}} = (1/\mu)\nabla \times \widetilde{\mathbf{A}}$, and finally calculate $\widetilde{\mathbf{E}}$ from $\widetilde{\mathbf{H}}$ using the differential form of Ampere's law. In this section, we shall employ a simpler approach, shown in Figure 9.14. Imagine the filament as a collection of many shorter segments of current that radiate independently. The total field is then the sum of these short segments. Because these segments are very short relative to the length of the filament as well as being short relative to a wavelength, we may approximate the current over each segment as constant. In other words, we may interpret each segment as being, to a good approximation, a Hertzian dipole.

The advantage of this approach is that we already have a solution for every segment. In Section 9.4, it is shown that a $\hat{\mathbf{z}}$-directed Hertzian dipole at the origin radiates the electric field

$$\widetilde{\mathbf{E}}(\mathbf{r}) \approx \hat{\theta} j\eta \frac{\widetilde{I}\,(\beta\Delta l)}{4\pi}\,(\sin\theta)\,\frac{e^{-j\beta r}}{r} \tag{9.84}$$

where $\widetilde{I}$ and Δl may be interpreted as the current and length of the filament, respectively. In this expression, η is the wave impedance of medium in which the filament radiates (e.g., $\approx 377\ \Omega$ for free space), and we have presumed lossless media such that the attenuation constant $\alpha \approx 0$ and the phase propagation constant $\beta = 2\pi/\lambda$. This expression also assumes field points far from the filament; specifically, distances r that are much greater than λ. Repurposing this expression for the present problem, we note that the segment at the origin radiates the electric field:

$$\widetilde{\mathbf{E}}(\mathbf{r}; z'=0) \approx \hat{\theta} j\eta \frac{\widetilde{I}(0)\,(\beta\Delta l)}{4\pi}\,(\sin\theta)\,\frac{e^{-j\beta r}}{r} \tag{9.85}$$

where the notation $z'=0$ indicates the Hertzian dipole is located at the origin. Letting the length Δl of this segment shrink to differential length dz', we may describe the contribution of this segment to the field radiated by the ESD as follows:

$$d\widetilde{\mathbf{E}}(\mathbf{r}; z'=0) \approx \hat{\theta} j\eta \frac{\widetilde{I}(0)\,(\beta dz')}{4\pi}\,(\sin\theta)\,\frac{e^{-j\beta r}}{r} \tag{9.86}$$

Using this approach, the electric field radiated by *any* segment can be written:

$$d\widetilde{\mathbf{E}}(\mathbf{r}; z') \approx \hat{\theta}' j\eta\beta \frac{\widetilde{I}(z')}{4\pi}\,(\sin\theta')\,\frac{e^{-j\beta|\mathbf{r}-\hat{\mathbf{z}}z'|}}{|\mathbf{r}-\hat{\mathbf{z}}z'|}\,dz' \tag{9.87}$$

Note that θ is replaced by θ' since the ray $\mathbf{r}-\hat{\mathbf{z}}z'$ forms a different angle (i.e., θ') with respect to $\hat{\mathbf{z}}$. Subsequently, $\hat{\theta}$ is replaced by $\hat{\theta}'$, which varies similarly with z'. The electric field radiated by the filament is obtained by integration over these contributions, yielding:

$$\widetilde{\mathbf{E}}(\mathbf{r}) \approx \int_{-L/2}^{+L/2} d\widetilde{\mathbf{E}}(\hat{\mathbf{r}}; z') \tag{9.88}$$

Expanding this expression:

$$\widetilde{\mathbf{E}}(\mathbf{r}) \approx j\frac{\eta\beta}{4\pi}\int_{-L/2}^{+L/2} \hat{\theta}'\widetilde{I}(z')\,(\sin\theta')\,\frac{e^{-j\beta|\mathbf{r}-\hat{\mathbf{z}}z'|}}{|\mathbf{r}-\hat{\mathbf{z}}z'|}\,dz' \tag{9.89}$$

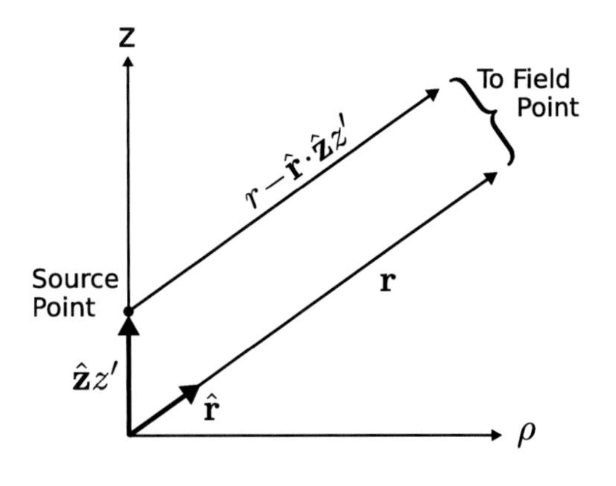

© C. Wang CC BY-SA 4.0

Figure 9.15: Parallel ray approximation.

Given some of the assumptions we have already made, this expression can be further simplified. For example, note that $\theta' \approx \theta$ since $L \ll r$. For the same reason, $\hat{\theta}' \approx \hat{\theta}$. Since these variables are approximately constant over the length of the filament, we may move them outside the integral, yielding:

$$\widetilde{\mathbf{E}}(\mathbf{r}) \approx \hat{\theta} j\frac{\eta\beta}{4\pi}\,(\sin\theta)\int_{-L/2}^{+L/2} \widetilde{I}(z')\frac{e^{-j\beta|\mathbf{r}-\hat{\mathbf{z}}z'|}}{|\mathbf{r}-\hat{\mathbf{z}}z'|}\,dz' \tag{9.90}$$

It is also possible to simplify the expression $|\mathbf{r}-\hat{\mathbf{z}}z'|$. Consider Figure 9.15. Since we have already assumed that $r \gg L$ (i.e., the distance to field points is much greater than the length of the filament), the vector $\mathbf{r}$ is approximately parallel to the vector $\mathbf{r}-\hat{\mathbf{z}}z'$. Subsequently, it must be true that

$$|\mathbf{r}-\hat{\mathbf{z}}z'| \approx r - \hat{\mathbf{r}}\cdot\hat{\mathbf{z}}z' \tag{9.91}$$

$$\approx r - z'\cos\theta \tag{9.92}$$

Note that the magnitude of $r - \hat{\mathbf{r}}\cdot\hat{\mathbf{z}}z'$ must be approximately equal to r, since $r \gg L$. So, insofar as $|\mathbf{r}-\hat{\mathbf{z}}z'|$ determines the *magnitude* of $\widetilde{\mathbf{E}}(\mathbf{r})$, we may use the approximation:

$$|\mathbf{r}-\hat{\mathbf{z}}z'| \approx r \quad \text{(magnitude)} \tag{9.93}$$

Insofar as $|\mathbf{r}-\hat{\mathbf{z}}z'|$ determines *phase*, we have to be more careful. The part of the integrand of Equation 9.90 that exhibits varying phase is $e^{-j\beta|\mathbf{r}-\hat{\mathbf{z}}z'|}$. Using Equation 9.91, we find

$$e^{-j\beta|\mathbf{r}-\hat{\mathbf{z}}z'|} \approx e^{-j\beta r}e^{+j\beta z'\cos\theta} \tag{9.94}$$

These simplifications are known collectively as a *far field approximation*, since they are valid only for distances "far" from the source.

Applying these simplifications for magnitude and phase to Equation 9.90, we obtain:

$$\widetilde{\mathbf{E}}(\mathbf{r}) \approx \hat{\theta} j \frac{\eta\beta}{4\pi} \frac{e^{-j\beta r}}{r} \left(\sin\theta\right) \cdot \int_{-L/2}^{+L/2} \widetilde{I}(z') e^{+j\beta z' \cos\theta} dz' \tag{9.95}$$

Finally, it is common to eliminate the factor of β in the magnitude using the relationship $\beta = 2\pi/\lambda$, yielding:

$$\widetilde{\mathbf{E}}(\mathbf{r}) \approx \hat{\theta} j \frac{\eta}{2} \frac{e^{-j\beta r}}{r} \left(\sin\theta\right) \cdot \left[\frac{1}{\lambda} \int_{-L/2}^{+L/2} \widetilde{I}(z') e^{+j\beta z' \cos\theta} dz' \right] \tag{9.96}$$

> The electric field radiated by a thin, straight, $\hat{\mathbf{z}}$-directed current filament of length L located at the origin and aligned along the z axis is given by Equation 9.96. This expression is valid for $r \gg L$ and $r \gg \lambda$.

At field points satisfying the conditions $r \gg L$ and $r \gg \lambda$, the wave appears to be locally planar. Therefore, we are justified using the plane wave relationship $\widetilde{\mathbf{H}} = (1/\eta)\hat{\mathbf{r}} \times \widetilde{\mathbf{E}}$ to calculate $\widetilde{\mathbf{H}}$.

As a check, one may readily verify that Equation 9.96 yields the expected result for the electrically-short dipole (Section 9.5).

9.7 Far-Field Radiation from a Half-Wave Dipole

[m0200]

A simple and important current distribution is that of the thin half-wave dipole (HWD), shown in Figure 9.16. This is the distribution expected on a thin straight wire having length $L = \lambda/2$, where λ is wavelength. This distribution is described mathematically as follows:

$$\widetilde{I}(z) \approx I_0 \cos\left(\pi \frac{z}{L}\right) \quad \text{for } |z| \leq \frac{L}{2} \tag{9.97}$$

where I_0 (SI base units of A) is a complex-valued constant indicating the maximum magnitude of the current and its phase. Note that the current is zero at the ends of the dipole; i.e., $\widetilde{I}(z) = 0$ for $|z| = L/2$. Note also that this "cosine pulse" distribution is very similar to the triangular distribution of the ESD, and is reminiscent of the sinusoidal variation of current in a standing wave.

Since $L = \lambda/2$ for the HWD, Equation 9.97 may equivalently be written:

$$\widetilde{I}(z) \approx I_0 \cos\left(2\pi \frac{z}{\lambda}\right) \tag{9.98}$$

The electromagnetic field radiated by this distribution

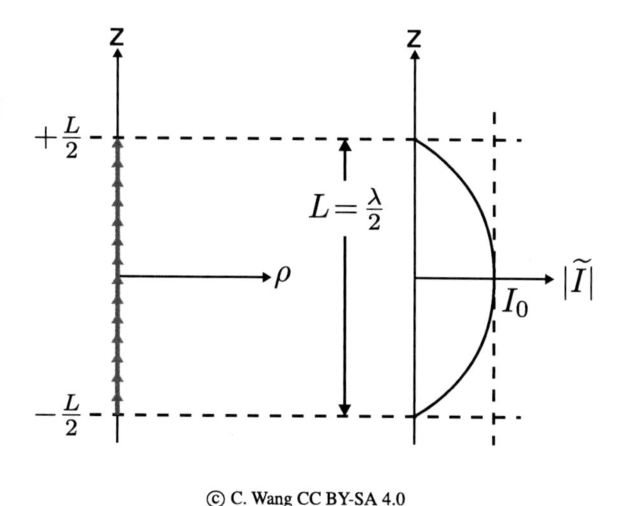

© C. Wang CC BY-SA 4.0

Figure 9.16: Current distribution of the half-wave dipole (HWD).

of current may be calculated using the method described in Section 9.6, in particular:

$$\widetilde{\mathbf{E}}(\mathbf{r}) \approx \hat{\theta} j \frac{\eta}{2} \frac{e^{-j\beta r}}{r} (\sin\theta) \cdot \left[\frac{1}{\lambda} \int_{-L/2}^{+L/2} \widetilde{I}(z') e^{+j\beta z' \cos\theta} dz' \right] \quad (9.99)$$

which is valid for field points $\mathbf{r}$ far from the dipole; i.e., for $r \gg L$ and $r \gg \lambda$. For the HWD, the quantity in square brackets is

$$\frac{I_0}{\lambda} \int_{-\lambda/4}^{+\lambda/4} \cos\left(2\pi \frac{z'}{\lambda}\right) e^{+j\beta z' \cos\theta} dz' \quad (9.100)$$

The evaluation of this integral is straightforward, but tedious. The integral reduces to

$$\frac{I_0}{\pi} \frac{\cos\left[(\pi/2)\cos\theta\right]}{\sin^2\theta} \quad (9.101)$$

Substitution into Equation 9.99 yields

$$\widetilde{\mathbf{E}}(\mathbf{r}) \approx \hat{\theta} j \frac{\eta I_0}{2\pi} \frac{\cos\left[(\pi/2)\cos\theta\right]}{\sin\theta} \frac{e^{-j\beta r}}{r} \quad (9.102)$$

The magnetic field may be determined from this result using Ampere's law. However, a simpler method is to use the fact that the electric field, magnetic field, and direction of propagation $\hat{\mathbf{r}}$ are mutually perpendicular and related by:

$$\widetilde{\mathbf{H}} = \frac{1}{\eta} \hat{\mathbf{r}} \times \widetilde{\mathbf{E}} \quad (9.103)$$

This relationship indicates that the magnetic field will be $+\hat{\phi}$-directed.

The magnitude and polarization of the radiated field is similar to that of the electrically-short dipole (ESD; Section 9.5). A comparison of the magnitudes in any radial plane containing the z-axis is shown in Figure 9.17. For either current distribution, the maximum magnitude of the fields occurs in the $z = 0$ plane. For a given terminal current I_0, the maximum magnitude is greater for the HWD than for the ESD. Both current distributions yield zero magnitude along the axis of the dipole. The polarization characteristics of the fields of both current distributions are identical.

Additional Reading:

- "Dipole antenna" (section entitled "Half-wave dipole") on Wikipedia.

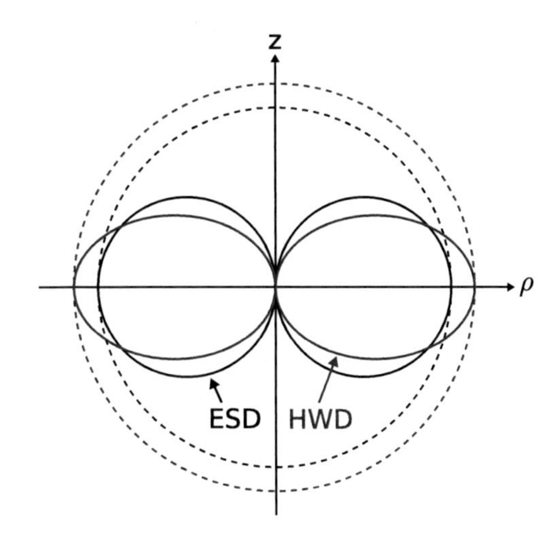

© C. Wang CC BY-SA 4.0

Figure 9.17: Comparison of the magnitude of the radiated field of the HWD to that of an electrically-short dipole also oriented along the z-axis. This result is for any radial plane that includes the z-axis.

9.8 Radiation from Surface and Volume Distributions of Current

[m0221]

In Section 9.3, a solution was developed for radiation from current located at a single point $\mathbf{r}'$. This current distribution was expressed mathematically as a *current moment*, as follows:

$$\widetilde{\mathbf{J}}(\mathbf{r}) = \hat{\mathbf{l}}\, \widetilde{I}\, \Delta l\, \delta(\mathbf{r} - \mathbf{r}') \quad (9.104)$$

where $\hat{\mathbf{l}}$ is the direction of current flow, $\widetilde{I}$ has units of current (SI base units of A), Δl has units of length (SI base units of m), and $\delta(\mathbf{r})$ is the volumetric sampling function (Dirac "delta" function; SI base units of m^{-3}). In this formulation, $\widetilde{\mathbf{J}}$ has SI base units of A/m^2. The magnetic vector potential radiated by this current, observed at the field point $\mathbf{r}$, was found to be

$$\widetilde{\mathbf{A}}(\mathbf{r}) = \hat{\mathbf{l}}\, \mu\, \widetilde{I}\, \Delta l\, \frac{e^{-\gamma|\mathbf{r}-\mathbf{r}'|}}{4\pi\, |\mathbf{r}-\mathbf{r}'|} \quad (9.105)$$

This solution was subsequently generalized to obtain the radiation from any distribution of *line* current; i.e., any distribution of current that is constrained to flow along a single path through space, as along an infinitesimally-thin wire.

In this section, we derive an expression for the radiation from current that is constrained to flow along a surface and from current which flows through a volume. The solution in both cases can be obtained by "recycling" the solution for line current as follows. Letting Δl shrink to the differential length dl, Equation 9.104 becomes:

$$d\widetilde{\mathbf{J}}(\mathbf{r}) = \hat{\mathbf{l}}\,\widetilde{I}\,dl\,\delta(\mathbf{r}-\mathbf{r}') \tag{9.106}$$

Subsequently, Equation 9.105 becomes:

$$d\widetilde{\mathbf{A}}(\mathbf{r};\mathbf{r}') = \hat{\mathbf{l}}\,\mu\,\widetilde{I}\,dl\,\frac{e^{-\gamma|\mathbf{r}-\mathbf{r}'|}}{4\pi\,|\mathbf{r}-\mathbf{r}'|} \tag{9.107}$$

where the notation $d\widetilde{\mathbf{A}}(\mathbf{r};\mathbf{r}')$ is used to denote the magnetic vector potential at the field point $\mathbf{r}$ due to the differential-length current moment at the source point $\mathbf{r}'$. Next, consider that any distribution of current can be described as a distribution of current moments. By the principle of superposition, the radiation from this distribution of current moments can be calculated as the sum of the radiation from the individual current moments. This is expressed mathematically as follows:

$$\widetilde{\mathbf{A}}(\mathbf{r}) = \int d\widetilde{\mathbf{A}}(\mathbf{r};\mathbf{r}') \tag{9.108}$$

where the integral is over $\mathbf{r}'$; i.e., summing over the source current.

If we substitute Equation 9.107 into Equation 9.108, we obtain the solution derived in Section 9.3, which is specific to line distributions of current. To obtain the solution for surface and volume distributions of current, we reinterpret the definition of the differential current moment in Equation 9.106. Note that this current is completely specified by its direction ($\hat{\mathbf{l}}$) and the quantity $\widetilde{I}\,dl$, which has SI base units of A·m. We may describe the same current distribution alternatively as follows:

$$d\widetilde{\mathbf{J}}(\mathbf{r}) = \hat{\mathbf{l}}\,\widetilde{J}_s\,ds\,\delta(\mathbf{r}-\mathbf{r}') \tag{9.109}$$

where $\widetilde{J}_s$ has units of surface current density (SI base units of A/m) and ds has units of area (SI base units of m^2). To emphasize that this is precisely the same current moment, note that $\widetilde{J}_s\,ds$, like $\widetilde{I}\,dl$, has units of A·m. Similarly,

$$d\widetilde{\mathbf{J}}(\mathbf{r}) = \hat{\mathbf{l}}\,\widetilde{J}\,dv\,\delta(\mathbf{r}-\mathbf{r}') \tag{9.110}$$

where $\widetilde{J}$ has units of volume current density (SI base units of A/m^2) and dv has units of volume (SI base units of m^3). Again, $\widetilde{J}\,dv$ has units of A·m. Summarizing, we have found that

$$\widetilde{I}\,dl = \widetilde{J}_s\,ds = \widetilde{J}\,dv \tag{9.111}$$

all describe the same differential current moment.

Thus, we may obtain solutions for surface and volume distributions of current simply by replacing $\widetilde{I}\,dl$ in Equation 9.107, and subsequently in Equation 9.108, with the appropriate quantity from Equation 9.111. For a surface current distribution, we obtain:

$$\boxed{\widetilde{\mathbf{A}}(\mathbf{r}) = \frac{\mu}{4\pi}\int_{\mathcal{S}} \widetilde{\mathbf{J}}_s(\mathbf{r}')\,\frac{e^{-\gamma|\mathbf{r}-\mathbf{r}'|}}{|\mathbf{r}-\mathbf{r}'|}\,ds} \tag{9.112}$$

where $\widetilde{\mathbf{J}}_s(\mathbf{r}') \triangleq \hat{\mathbf{l}}(\mathbf{r}')\widetilde{J}_s(\mathbf{r}')$ and where $\mathcal{S}$ is the surface over which the current flows. Similarly for a volume current distribution, we obtain:

$$\boxed{\widetilde{\mathbf{A}}(\mathbf{r}) = \frac{\mu}{4\pi}\int_{\mathcal{V}} \widetilde{\mathbf{J}}(\mathbf{r}')\,\frac{e^{-\gamma|\mathbf{r}-\mathbf{r}'|}}{|\mathbf{r}-\mathbf{r}'|}\,dv} \tag{9.113}$$

where $\widetilde{\mathbf{J}}(\mathbf{r}') \triangleq \hat{\mathbf{l}}(\mathbf{r}')\widetilde{J}(\mathbf{r}')$ and where $\mathcal{V}$ is the volume in which the current flows.

> The magnetic vector potential corresponding to radiation from a surface and volume distribution of current is given by Equations 9.112 and 9.113, respectively.

Given $\widetilde{\mathbf{A}}(\mathbf{r})$, the magnetic and electric fields may be determined using the procedure developed in Section 9.2.

[m0217]

Image Credits

Fig. 9.1: © Sevenchw (C. Wang),
https://commons.wikimedia.org/wiki/File:A_z-directed_current_moment_located_at_the_origin.svg,
CC BY-SA 4.0 (https://creativecommons.org/licenses/by-sa/4.0/).

Fig. 9.2: © Sevenchw (C. Wang),
https://commons.wikimedia.org/wiki/File:A_z-directed_current_moment_located_at_the_origin.svg,
CC BY-SA 4.0 (https://creativecommons.org/licenses/by-sa/4.0/).

Fig. 9.3: © Sevenchw (C. Wang),
https://commons.wikimedia.org/wiki/File:Current_moment_displaced_from_the_origin.svg,
CC BY-SA 4.0 (https://creativecommons.org/licenses/by-sa/4.0/).

Fig. 9.4: © Sevenchw (C. Wang),
https://commons.wikimedia.org/wiki/File:A_filament_of_current_lying_along_the_path_c.svg,
CC BY-SA 4.0 (https://creativecommons.org/licenses/by-sa/4.0/).

Fig. 9.5: © Sevenchw (C. Wang),
https://commons.wikimedia.org/wiki/File:A_z-directed_current_moment_located_at_the_origin.svg,
CC BY-SA 4.0 (https://creativecommons.org/licenses/by-sa/4.0/).

Fig. 9.6: © Sevenchw (C. Wang),
https://commons.wikimedia.org/wiki/File:Current_distribution_of_the_esd.svg,
CC BY-SA 4.0 (https://creativecommons.org/licenses/by-sa/4.0/).

Fig. 9.7: © Sevenchw (C. Wang),
https://commons.wikimedia.org/wiki/File:Esd_approximated_as_a_large_number_of_hertzian_dipoles.svg,
CC BY-SA 4.0 (https://creativecommons.org/licenses/by-sa/4.0/).

Fig. 9.8: © Sevenchw (C. Wang),
https://commons.wikimedia.org/wiki/File:Parallel_ray_approximation_for_an_esd.svg,
CC BY-SA 4.0 (https://creativecommons.org/licenses/by-sa/4.0/).

Fig. 9.9: © Offaperry (S. Lally),
https://commons.wikimedia.org/wiki/File:Magnitude_of_the_Radiated_Field.svg,
CC BY-SA 4.0 (https://creativecommons.org/licenses/by-sa/4.0/).

Fig. 9.10: © Offaperry (S. Lally),
https://commons.wikimedia.org/wiki/File:Electric_and_Magnetic_Fields_in_Plane_of_Constant_Theta.svg,
CC BY-SA 4.0 (https://creativecommons.org/licenses/by-sa/4.0/).

Fig. 9.11: © Offaperry (S. Lally), https://commons.wikimedia.org/wiki/File:FHplaneMag.svg,
CC BY-SA 4.0 (https://creativecommons.org/licenses/by-sa/4.0/).

Fig. 9.12: © Offaperry (S. Lally), https://commons.wikimedia.org/wiki/File:FHplanePol.svg,
CC BY-SA 4.0 (https://creativecommons.org/licenses/by-sa/4.0/).

Fig. 9.13: © Sevenchw (C. Wang),
https://commons.wikimedia.org/wiki/File:A_thin_straight_distribution_of_radiating_current.svg,
CC BY-SA 4.0 (https://creativecommons.org/licenses/by-sa/4.0/).

Fig. 9.14: © Sevenchw (C. Wang),
https://commons.wikimedia.org/wiki/File:Esd_approximated_as_a_large_number_of_hertzian_dipoles.svg,
CC BY-SA 4.0 (https://creativecommons.org/licenses/by-sa/4.0/).

Fig. 9.15: © Sevenchw (C. Wang),
https://commons.wikimedia.org/wiki/File:Parallel_ray_approximation_for_an_esd.svg,
CC BY-SA 4.0 (https://creativecommons.org/licenses/by-sa/4.0/).

Fig. 9.16: © Sevenchw (C. Wang),
https://commons.wikimedia.org/wiki/File:Current_distribution_of_the_hwd.svg,
CC BY-SA 4.0 (https://creativccommons.org/licenses/by-sa/4.0/).

Fig. 9.17: © Sevenchw (C. Wang),
https://commons.wikimedia.org/wiki/File:Comparison_radiated_field_magnitude_of_hwd_to_esd.svg,
CC BY-SA 4.0 (https://creativecommons.org/licenses/by-sa/4.0/).

Chapter 10

Antennas

10.1 How Antennas Radiate

[m0201]

An antenna is a *transducer*; that is, a device which converts signals in one form into another form. In the case of an antenna, these two forms are (1) conductor-bound voltage and current signals and (2) electromagnetic waves. Traditional passive antennas are capable of this conversion in either direction. In this section, we consider the transmit case, in which a conductor-bound signal is converted into a radiating electromagnetic wave. Radiation from an antenna is due to the time-varying current that is excited by the bound electrical signal applied to the antenna terminals.

Why ideal transmission lines *don't* radiate. To describe the process that allows an antenna to transmit, it is useful to first consider the scenario depicted in Figure 10.1. Here a sinusoidal source is applied to the input of an ideal twin lead transmission line. The spacing between conductors is much less than a wavelength, and the output of the transmission line is terminated into an open circuit.

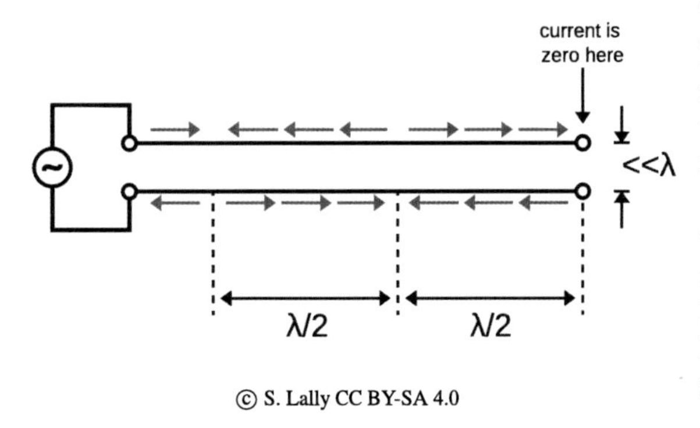

Figure 10.1: Twin lead transmission line terminated into an open circuit, giving rise to a standing wave.

Without any additional information, we already know two things about the current on this transmission line. First, we know the current must be identically zero at the end of the transmission line. Second, we know the current on the two conductors comprising the transmission line must be related as indicated in Figure 10.1. That is, at any given position on the transmission line, the current on each conductor is equal in magnitude and flows in opposite directions.

Further note that Figure 10.1 depicts only the situation over an interval of one-half of the period of the sinusoidal source. For the other half-period, the direction of current will be in the direction *opposite* that depicted in Figure 10.1. In other words: The source is varying periodically, so the sign of the current is changing every half-period. Generally, time-varying currents give rise to radiation. Therefore, we should expect the currents depicted in Figure 10.1 might radiate. We can estimate the radiation from the transmission line by interpreting the current as a collection of Hertzian dipoles. For a review of Hertzian dipoles, see Section 9.4; however, all we need to know to address the present problem is that superposition applies. That is, the total radiation is the sum of the radiation from the individual Hertzian dipoles. Once again looking back at Figure 10.1, note that each Hertzian dipole representing current on one conductor has an associated Hertzian dipole representing the current on the other conductor, and is only a tiny fraction of a wavelength distant. Furthermore, these pairs of

Hertzian dipoles are identical in magnitude but opposite in sign. Therefore, the radiated field from any such pair of Hertzian dipoles is approximately zero at distances sufficiently far from the transmission line. Continuing to sum all such pairs of Hertzian dipoles, the radiated field remains approximately zero at distances sufficiently far from the transmission line. We come to the following remarkable conclusion:

> The radiation from an ideal twin lead transmission line with open circuit termination is negligible at distances much greater than the separation between the conductors.

Before proceeding, let us be clear about one thing: The situation at distances which are *not* large relative to separation between the conductors is quite different. This is because the Hertzian dipole pairs do not appear to be quite so precisely collocated at field points close to the transmission line. Subsequently the cancellation of fields from Hertzian dipole pairs is less precise. The resulting sum fields are not negligible and depend on the separation between the conductors. For the present discussion, it suffices to restrict our attention to the simpler "far field" case.

A simple antenna formed by modifying twin lead transmission line. Let us now consider a modification to the previous scenario, shown in Figure 10.2. In the new scenario, the ends of the twin lead are bent into right angles. This new section has an overall length which is much less than one-half wavelength. To determine the current distribution on the modified section, we first note that the current must still be precisely zero at the ends of the conductors, but not necessarily at the point at which

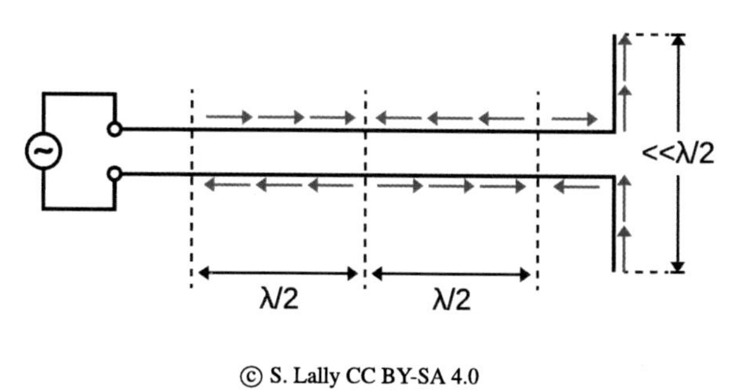

© S. Lally CC BY-SA 4.0

Figure 10.2: End of the twin lead transmission line fashioned into an electrically-short dipole (ESD).

they are bent. Since the modified section is much shorter than one-half wavelength, the current distribution on this section must be very simple. In fact, the current distribution must be that of the electrically-short dipole (ESD), exhibiting magnitude which is maximum at the center and decreasing approximately linearly to zero at the ends. (See Section 9.5 for a review of the ESD.) Finally, we note that the current should be continuous at the junction between the unmodified and modified sections.

Having established that the modified section exhibits the current distribution of an ESD, and having previously determined that the unmodified section of transmission line does not radiate, we conclude that this system radiates precisely as an ESD does. Note also that we need not interpret the ESD portion of the transmission line as a modification of the transmission line: Instead, we may view this system as an unmodified transmission line attached to an antenna, which in this case in an ESD.

The general case. Although we developed this insight for the ESD specifically, the principle applies generally. That is, any antenna – not just dipoles – can be viewed as a structure that can support a current distribution that radiates. Elaborating:

> A transmitting antenna is a device that, when driven by an appropriate source, supports a time-varying distribution of current resulting in an electromagnetic wave that radiates away from the device.

Although this may seem to be simply a restatement of the definition at the beginning of this section – and it is – we now see *how* this can happen, and also why transmission lines typically aren't also antennas.

10.2 Power Radiated by an Electrically-Short Dipole

[m0207]

In this section, we determine the total power radiated by an electrically-short dipole (ESD) antenna in response to a sinusoidally-varying current applied to the antenna terminals. This result is both useful on its own and necessary as an intermediate result in determining the impedance of the ESD. The ESD is introduced in Section 9.5, and a review of that section is suggested before attempting this section.

In Section 9.5, it is shown that the electric field intensity in the far field of a $\hat{\mathbf{z}}$-oriented ESD located at the origin is

$$\widetilde{\mathbf{E}}(\mathbf{r}) \approx \hat{\theta} j\eta \frac{I_0 \cdot \beta L}{8\pi} (\sin\theta) \frac{e^{-j\beta r}}{r} \tag{10.1}$$

where $\mathbf{r}$ is the field point, I_0 is a complex number representing the peak magnitude and phase of the sinusoidally-varying terminal current, L is the length of the ESD, and β is the phase propagation constant $2\pi/\lambda$ where λ is wavelength. Note that $L \ll \lambda$ since this is an ESD. Also note that Equation 10.1 is valid only for the far-field conditions $r \gg L$ and $r \gg \lambda$, and presumes propagation in simple (linear, homogeneous, time-invariant, isotropic) media with negligible loss.

Given that we have already limited scope to the far field, it is reasonable to approximate the electromagnetic field at each field point $\mathbf{r}$ as a plane wave propagating radially away from the antenna; i.e., in the $\hat{\mathbf{r}}$ direction. Under this assumption, the time-average power density is

$$\mathbf{S}(\mathbf{r}) = \hat{\mathbf{r}} \frac{\left|\widetilde{\mathbf{E}}(\mathbf{r})\right|^2}{2\eta} \tag{10.2}$$

where η is the wave impedance of the medium. The total power P_{rad} radiated by the antenna is simply $\mathbf{S}(\mathbf{r})$ integrated over any closed surface $\mathcal{S}$ that encloses the antenna. Thus:

$$P_{rad} = \oint_{\mathcal{S}} \mathbf{S}(\mathbf{r}) \cdot d\mathbf{s} \tag{10.3}$$

where $d\mathbf{s}$ is the outward-facing differential element of surface area. In other words, power density (W/m^2) integrated over an area (m^2) gives power (W). Anticipating that this problem will be addressed in spherical coordinates, we note that

$$d\mathbf{s} = \hat{\mathbf{r}} r^2 \sin\theta \, d\theta \, d\phi \tag{10.4}$$

and subsequently:

$$\begin{aligned} P_{rad} &= \int_{\theta=0}^{\pi} \int_{\phi=0}^{2\pi} \left(\hat{\mathbf{r}} \frac{\left|\widetilde{\mathbf{E}}(\mathbf{r})\right|^2}{2\eta} \right) \cdot \left(\hat{\mathbf{r}} r^2 \sin\theta \, d\theta \, d\phi \right) \\ &= \frac{1}{2\eta} \int_{\theta=0}^{\pi} \int_{\phi=0}^{2\pi} \left|\widetilde{\mathbf{E}}(\mathbf{r})\right|^2 r^2 \sin\theta \, d\theta \, d\phi \end{aligned} \tag{10.5}$$

Returning to Equation 10.1, we note:

$$\left|\widetilde{\mathbf{E}}(\mathbf{r})\right|^2 \approx \eta^2 \frac{|I_0|^2 (\beta L)^2}{64\pi^2} (\sin\theta)^2 \frac{1}{r^2} \tag{10.6}$$

Substitution into Equation 10.5 yields:

$$P_{rad} \approx \eta \frac{|I_0|^2 (\beta L)^2}{128\pi^2} \int_{\theta=0}^{\pi} \int_{\phi=0}^{2\pi} \sin^3\theta \, d\theta \, d\phi \tag{10.7}$$

Note that this may be factored into separate integrals over θ and ϕ. The integral over ϕ is simply 2π, leaving:

$$P_{rad} \approx \eta \frac{|I_0|^2 (\beta L)^2}{64\pi} \int_{\theta=0}^{\pi} \sin^3\theta \, d\theta \tag{10.8}$$

The remaining integral is equal to $4/3$, leaving:

$$\boxed{P_{rad} \approx \eta \frac{|I_0|^2 (\beta L)^2}{48\pi}} \tag{10.9}$$

This completes the derivation, but it is useful to check units. Recall that β has SI base units of rad/m, so βL has units of radians. This leaves $\eta \left|I_0\right|^2$, which has SI base units of $\Omega \cdot \text{A}^2 = \text{W}$, as expected.

> The power radiated by an ESD in response to the current I_0 applied at the terminals is given by Equation 10.9.

Finally, it is useful to consider how various parameters affect the radiated power. First, note that the radiated power is proportional to the square of the terminal current. Second, note that the product $\beta L = 2\pi L/\lambda$ is the electrical length of the antenna;

that is, the length of the antenna expressed in radians, where 2π radians is one wavelength. Thus, we see that the power radiated by the antenna increases as the square of electrical length.

Example 10.1. Power radiated by an ESD.

A dipole is 10 cm in length and is surrounded by free space. A sinusoidal current having frequency 30 MHz and peak magnitude 100 mA is applied to the antenna terminals. What is the power radiated by the antenna?

Solution. If no power is dissipated within the antenna, then all power is radiated. The wavelength $\lambda = c/f \cong 10$ m, so $L \cong 0.01\lambda$. This certainly qualifies as electrically-short, so we may use Equation 10.9. In the present problem, $\eta \cong 376.7\ \Omega$ (the free space wave impedance), $I_0 = 100$ mA, and $\beta = 2\pi/\lambda \cong 0.628$ rad/m. Thus, we find that the radiated power is $\approx$ 98.6 μW.

10.3 Power Dissipated by an Electrically-Short Dipole

[m0208]

The power delivered to an antenna by a source connected to the terminals is nominally radiated. However, it is possible that some fraction of the power delivered by the source will be dissipated within the antenna. In this section, we consider the dissipation due to the finite conductivity of materials comprising the antenna. Specifically, we determine the total power dissipated by an electrically-short dipole (ESD) antenna in response to a sinusoidally-varying current applied to the antenna terminals. (The ESD is introduced in Section 9.5, and a review of that section is suggested before attempting this section.) The result allows us to determine *radiation efficiency* and is a step toward determining the impedance of the ESD.

Consider an ESD centered at the origin and aligned along the z axis. In Section 9.5, it is shown that the current distribution is:

$$\widetilde{I}(z) \approx I_0 \left(1 - \frac{2}{L}|z|\right) \tag{10.10}$$

where I_0 (SI base units of A) is a complex-valued constant indicating the maximum current magnitude and phase, and L is the length of the ESD. This current distribution may be interpreted as a set of discrete very-short segments of constant-magnitude current (sometimes referred to as "Hertzian dipoles"). In this interpretation, the nth current segment is located at $z = z_n$ and has magnitude $\widetilde{I}(z_n)$.

Now let us assume that the material comprising the ESD is a homogeneous good conductor. Then each segment exhibits the same resistance R_{seg}. Subsequently, the power dissipated in the nth segment is

$$P_{seg}(z_n) = \frac{1}{2}\left|\widetilde{I}(z_n)\right|^2 R_{seg} \tag{10.11}$$

The segment resistance can be determined as follows. Let us assume that the wire comprising the ESD has circular cross-section of radius a. Since the wire is a good conductor, the segment resistance may be calculated using Equation 4.17 (Section 4.2, "Impedance of a Wire"):

$$R_{seg} \approx \frac{1}{2}\sqrt{\frac{\mu f}{\pi\sigma}} \cdot \frac{\Delta l}{a} \tag{10.12}$$

where μ is permeability, f is frequency, σ is conductivity, and Δl is the length of the segment. Substitution into Equation 10.11 yields:

$$P_{seg}(z_n) \approx \frac{1}{4a}\sqrt{\frac{\mu f}{\pi\sigma}} \left|\widetilde{I}(z_n)\right|^2 \Delta l \tag{10.13}$$

Now the total power dissipated in the antenna, P_{loss}, can be expressed as the sum of the power dissipated in each segment:

$$P_{loss} \approx \sum_{n=1}^{N} \left[\frac{1}{4a}\sqrt{\frac{\mu f}{\pi\sigma}} \left|\widetilde{I}(z_n)\right|^2 \Delta l \right] \tag{10.14}$$

where N is the number of segments. This may be rewritten as follows:

$$P_{loss} \approx \frac{1}{4a}\sqrt{\frac{\mu f}{\pi\sigma}} \sum_{n=1}^{N} \left|\widetilde{I}(z_n)\right|^2 \Delta l \tag{10.15}$$

Reducing Δl to the differential length dz', we may write this in the following integral form:

$$P_{loss} \approx \frac{1}{4a}\sqrt{\frac{\mu f}{\pi\sigma}} \int_{z'=-L/2}^{+L/2} \left|\widetilde{I}(z')\right|^2 dz' \tag{10.16}$$

It is worth noting that the above expression applies to *any* straight wire antenna of length L. For the ESD specifically, the current distribution is given by Equation 10.10. Making the substitution:

$$\begin{aligned} P_{loss} &\approx \frac{1}{4a}\sqrt{\frac{\mu f}{\pi\sigma}} \int_{z'=-L/2}^{+L/2} \left|I_0\left(1 - \frac{2}{L}\left|z'\right|\right)\right|^2 dz' \\ &\approx \frac{1}{4a}\sqrt{\frac{\mu f}{\pi\sigma}} \left|I_0\right|^2 \int_{z'=-L/2}^{+L/2} \left|1 - \frac{2}{L}\left|z'\right|\right|^2 dz' \end{aligned} \tag{10.17}$$

The integral is straightforward to solve, albeit a bit tedious. The integral is found to be equal to $L/3$, so we obtain:

$$\begin{aligned} P_{loss} &\approx \frac{1}{4a}\sqrt{\frac{\mu f}{\pi\sigma}} \left|I_0\right|^2 \cdot \frac{L}{3} \\ &\approx \frac{L}{12a}\sqrt{\frac{\mu f}{\pi\sigma}} \left|I_0\right|^2 \end{aligned} \tag{10.18}$$

Now let us return to interpretation of the ESD as a circuit component. We have found that applying the current I_0 to the terminals results in the dissipated power indicated in Equation 10.18. A current source driving the ESD does not perceive the current distribution of the ESD nor does it perceive the varying power over the length of the ESD. Instead, the current source perceives only a net resistance R_{loss} such that

$$P_{loss} = \frac{1}{2}\left|I_0\right|^2 R_{loss} \tag{10.19}$$

Comparing Equations 10.18 and 10.19, we find

$$\boxed{R_{loss} \approx \frac{L}{6a}\sqrt{\frac{\mu f}{\pi\sigma}}} \tag{10.20}$$

The power dissipated within an ESD in response to a sinusoidal current I_0 applied at the terminals is $\frac{1}{2}\left|I_0\right|^2 R_{loss}$ where R_{loss} (Equation 10.20) is the resistance perceived by a source applied to the ESD's terminals.

Note that R_{loss} is *not* the impedance of the ESD. R_{loss} is merely the contribution of internal loss to the impedance of the ESD. The impedance of the ESD must also account for contributions from radiation resistance (an additional real-valued contribution) and energy storage (perceived as a reactance). These quantities are addressed in other sections of this book.

Example 10.2. Power dissipated within an ESD.

A dipole is 10 cm in length, 1 mm in radius, and is surrounded by free space. The antenna is comprised of aluminum having conductivity $\approx 3.7 \times 10^7$ S/m and $\mu \approx \mu_0$. A sinusoidal current having frequency 30 MHz and peak magnitude 100 mA is applied to the antenna terminals. What is the power dissipated within this antenna?

Solution. The wavelength $\lambda = c/f \cong 10$ m, so $L = 10$ cm $\cong 0.01\lambda$. This certainly qualifies as electrically-short, so we may use Equation 10.20. In the present problem, $a = 1$ mm and $\sigma \approx 3.7 \times 10^7$ S/m. Thus, we find that the loss resistance $R_{loss} \approx 9.49$ mΩ. Subsequently, the power dissipated within this antenna is

$$P_{loss} = \frac{1}{2} |I_0|^2 R_{loss} \approx \underline{47.5\ \mu\text{W}} \quad (10.21)$$

We conclude this section with one additional caveat: Whereas this section focuses on the limited conductivity of wire, other physical mechanisms may contribute to the loss resistance of the ESD. In particular, materials used to coat the antenna or to provide mechanical support near the terminals may potentially absorb and dissipate power that might otherwise be radiated.

10.4 Reactance of the Electrically-Short Dipole

[m0210]

For any given time-varying voltage appearing across the terminals of an electrically-short antenna, there will be a time-varying current that flows in response. The ratio of voltage to current is impedance. Just as a resistor, capacitor, or inductor may be characterized in terms of an impedance, any antenna may be characterized in terms of this impedance. The real-valued component of this impedance accounts for power which is radiated away from the antenna (Section 10.2) and dissipated within the antenna (Section 10.3). The imaginary component of this impedance – i.e., the reactance – typically represents energy storage within the antenna, in the same way that the reactance of a capacitor or inductor represents storage of electrical or magnetic energy, respectively. In this section, we determine the reactance of the electrically-short dipole (ESD).

Reactance of a zero-length dipole. We begin with what might seem initially to be an absurd notion: A dipole antenna having zero length. However, such a dipole is certainly electrically-short, and in fact serves as an extreme condition from which we can deduce some useful information.

Consider Figure 10.3, which shows a zero-length dipole being driven by a source via a transmission line. It is immediately apparent that such a dipole is equivalent to an open circuit. So, the impedance of a zero-length dipole is equal to that of an open circuit.

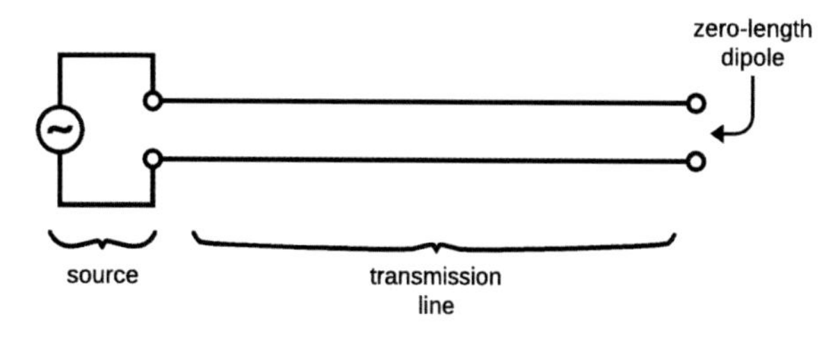

© S. Lally CC BY-SA 4.0

Figure 10.3: Transmission line terminated into a zero-length dipole, which is equivalent to an open circuit.

What is the impedance of an open circuit? One might be tempted to say "infinite," since the current is zero independently of the voltage. However, we must now be careful to properly recognize the real and imaginary components of this infinite number, and signs of these components. In fact, the impedance of an open circuit is $0 - j\infty$. One way to confirm this is via basic transmission line theory; i.e., the input impedance of transmission line stubs. A more direct justification is as follows: The real part of the impedance is zero because there is no transfer of power into the termination. The magnitude of the imaginary part of the impedance must be infinite because the current is zero. The sign of the imaginary component is negative because the reflected current experiences a sign change (required to make the total current zero), whereas the reflected voltage does not experience a sign change (and so is not canceled at the terminals). Thus, the impedance of an open circuit, and the zero-length dipole, is $0 - j\infty$.

Reactance of a nearly-zero-length dipole. Let us now consider what happens as the length of the dipole increases from zero. Since such a dipole is short compared to a wavelength, the variation with length must be very simple. The reactance remains large and negative, but can only increase (become less negative) monotonically with increasing electrical length. This trend continues until the dipole is no longer electrically short. Thus, we conclude that the reactance of an ESD is always large and negative.

> The reactance of an ESD is very large and negative, approaching the reactance of an open circuit termination as length decreases to zero.

Note that this behavior is similar to that of a capacitor, whose impedance is also negative and increases toward zero with increasing frequency. Thus, the reactance of an ESD is sometimes represented in circuit diagrams as a capacitor. However, the specific dependence of reactance on frequency is different from that of a capacitor (as we shall see in a moment), so this model is generally valid only for analysis at one frequency at time.

An approximate expression for the reactance of an ESD. Sometimes it is useful to be able to estimate the reactance X_A of an ESD. Although a derivation is beyond the scope of this text, a suitable expression is (see, e.g., Johnson (1993) in "Additional References" at the end of this section):

$$X_A \approx -\frac{120\ \Omega}{\pi L/\lambda}\left[\ln\left(\frac{L}{2a}\right) - 1\right] \tag{10.22}$$

where L is length and $a \ll L$ is the radius of the wire comprising the ESD. Note that this expression yields the expected behavior; i.e., $X_A \to -\infty$ as $L \to 0$, and increases monotonically as L increases from zero.

Example 10.3. Reactance of an ESD.

A dipole is 10 cm in length, 1 mm in radius, and is surrounded by free space. What is the reactance of this antenna at 30 MHz?

Solution. The wavelength $\lambda = c/f \cong 10$ m, so $L = 10$ cm $\cong 0.01\lambda$. This certainly qualifies as electrically-short, so we may use Equation 10.22. Given $a = 1$ mm, we find the reactance $X_A \approx \underline{-11.1\ \text{k}\Omega}$. For what it's worth, this antenna exhibits approximately the same reactance as a 0.47 pF capacitor at the same frequency.

The reactance of the ESD is typically orders of magnitude larger than the real part of the impedance of the ESD. The reactance of the ESD is also typically very large compared to the characteristic impedance of typical transmission lines (usually 10s to 100s of ohms). This makes ESDs quite difficult to use in practical transmit applications.

Additional Reading:

- R.C. Johnson (Ed.), *Antenna Systems Handbook* (Ch. 4), McGraw-Hill, 1993.

10.5 Equivalent Circuit Model for Transmission; Radiation Efficiency

[m0202]

A radio transmitter consists of a source which generates the electrical signal intended for transmission, and an antenna which converts this signal into a propagating electromagnetic wave. Since the transmitter is an electrical system, it is useful to be able to model the antenna as an equivalent circuit. From a circuit analysis point of view, it should be possible to describe the antenna as a passive one-port circuit that presents an impedance to the source. Thus, we have the following question: What is the equivalent circuit for an antenna which is transmitting?

We begin by emphasizing that the antenna is passive. That is, the antenna does not add power. Invoking the principle of conservation of power, there are only three possible things that *can* happen to power that is delivered to the antenna by the transmitter:[1]

- Power can be converted to a propagating electromagnetic wave. (The desired outcome.)
- Power can be dissipated within the antenna.
- Energy can be stored by the antenna, analogous to the storage of energy in a capacitor or inductor.

We also note that these outcomes can occur in any combination. Taking this into account, we model the antenna using the equivalent circuit shown in Figure 10.4. Since the antenna is passive, it is reasonable to describe it as an impedance Z_A which is (by definition) the ratio of voltage $\widetilde{V}_A$ to current $\widetilde{I}_A$ at the terminals; i.e.,

$$Z_A \triangleq \frac{\widetilde{V}_A}{\widetilde{I}_A} \tag{10.23}$$

[1]Note that "delivered" power means power accepted by the antenna. We are not yet considering power reflected from the antenna due to impedance mismatch.

In the phasor domain, Z_A is a complex-valued quantity and therefore has, in general, a real-valued component and an imaginary component. We may identify those components using the power conservation argument made previously: Since the real-valued component must represent power transfer and the imaginary component must represent energy storage, we infer:

$$Z_A \triangleq R_A + jX_A \tag{10.24}$$

where R_A represents power transferred to the antenna, and X_A represents energy stored by the antenna. Note that the energy stored by the antenna is being addressed in precisely the same manner that we address energy storage in a capacitor or an inductor; in all cases, as reactance. Further, we note that R_A consists of components R_{rad} and R_{loss} as follows:

$$Z_A = R_{rad} + R_{loss} + jX_A \tag{10.25}$$

where R_{rad} represents power transferred to the antenna and subsequently radiated, and R_{loss} represents power transferred to the antenna and subsequently dissipated.

To confirm that this model works as expected, consider what happens when a voltage is applied across the antenna terminals. The current $\widetilde{I}_A$ flows and the time-average power P_A transferred to the

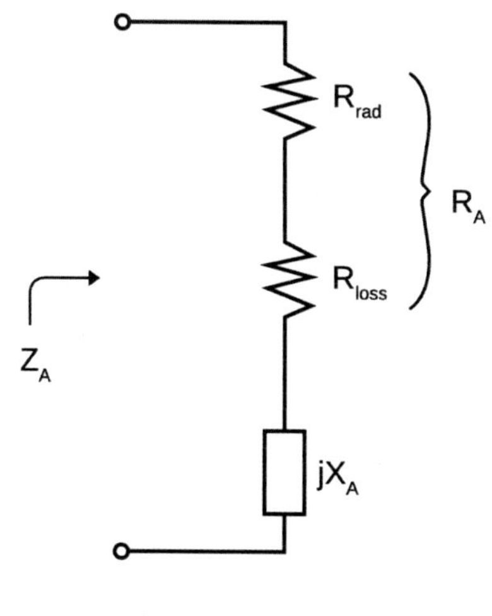

© S. Lally CC BY-SA 4.0

Figure 10.4: Equivalent circuit for an antenna which is transmitting.

antenna is

$$P_A = \frac{1}{2}\text{Re}\left\{\widetilde{V}_A \widetilde{I}_A^*\right\} \quad (10.26)$$

where we have assumed peak (as opposed to root mean squared) units for voltage and current. Since $\widetilde{V}_A = Z_A \widetilde{I}_A$, we have:

$$P_A = \frac{1}{2}\text{Re}\left\{(R_{rad} + R_{loss} + jX_A)\,\widetilde{I}_A \widetilde{I}_A^*\right\} \quad (10.27)$$

which reduces to:

$$P_A = \frac{1}{2}\left|\widetilde{I}_A\right|^2 R_{rad} + \frac{1}{2}\left|\widetilde{I}_A\right|^2 R_{loss} \quad (10.28)$$

As expected, the power transferred to the antenna is the sum of

$$P_{rad} \triangleq \frac{1}{2}\left|\widetilde{I}_A\right|^2 R_{rad} \quad (10.29)$$

representing power transferred to the radiating electromagnetic field, and

$$P_{loss} \triangleq \frac{1}{2}\left|\widetilde{I}_A\right|^2 R_{loss} \quad (10.30)$$

representing power dissipated within the antenna.

The reactance X_A will play a role in determining $\widetilde{I}_A$ given $\widetilde{V}_A$ (and vice versa), but does not by itself account for disposition of power. Again, this is exactly analogous to the role played by inductors and capacitors in a circuit.

The utility of this equivalent circuit formalism is that it allows us to treat the antenna in the same manner as any other component, and thereby facilitates analysis using conventional electric circuit theory and transmission line theory. For example: Given Z_A, we know how to specify the output impedance Z_S of the transmitter so as to minimize reflection from the antenna: We would choose $Z_S = Z_A$, since in this case the voltage reflection coefficient would be

$$\Gamma = \frac{Z_A - Z_S}{Z_A + Z_S} = 0 \quad (10.31)$$

Alternatively, we might specify Z_S so as to maximize power transfer to the antenna: We would choose $Z_S = Z_A^*$; i.e., conjugate matching.

In order to take full advantage of this formalism, we require values for R_{rad}, R_{loss}, and X_A. These quantities are considered below.

Radiation resistance. R_{rad} is referred to as *radiation resistance*. Equation 10.29 tells us that

$$R_{rad} = 2P_{rad}\left|\widetilde{I}_A\right|^{-2} \quad (10.32)$$

This equation suggests the following procedure: We apply current $\widetilde{I}_A$ to the antenna terminals, and then determine the total power P_{rad} radiated from the antenna in response. For an example of this procedure, see Section 10.2 ("Total Power Radiated by an Electrically-Short Dipole"). Given $\widetilde{I}_A$ and P_{rad}, one may then use Equation 10.32 to determine R_{rad}.

Loss resistance. *Loss resistance* represents the dissipation of power within the antenna, which is usually attributable to loss intrinsic to materials comprising or surrounding the antenna. In many cases, antennas are made from good conductors – metals, in particular – so that R_{loss} is very low compared to R_{rad}. For such antennas, loss is often so low compared to R_{rad} that R_{loss} may be neglected. In the case of the electrically-short dipole, R_{loss} is typically very small but R_{rad} is also very small, so both must be considered. In many other cases, antennas contain materials with substantially greater loss than metal. For example, a microstrip patch antenna implemented on a printed circuit board typically has non-negligible R_{loss} because the dielectric material comprising the antenna exhibits significant loss.

Antenna reactance. The reactance term jX_A accounts for energy stored by the antenna. This may be due to reflections internal to the antenna, or due to energy associated with non-propagating electric and magnetic fields surrounding the antenna. The presence of significant reactance (i.e., $|X_A|$ comparable to or greater than $|R_A|$) complicates efforts to establish the desired impedance match to the source. For an example, see Section 10.4 ("Reactance of the Electrically-Short Dipole").

Radiation efficiency. When R_{loss} is non-negligible, it is useful to characterize antennas in terms of their *radiation efficiency* e_{rad}, defined as the fraction of power which is radiated compared to the total power delivered to the antenna; i.e.,

$$e_{rad} \triangleq \frac{P_{rad}}{P_A} \quad (10.33)$$

Using Equations 10.28–10.30, we see that this efficiency can be expressed as follows:

$$e_{rad} = \frac{R_{rad}}{R_{rad} + R_{loss}} \quad (10.34)$$

Once again, the equivalent circuit formalism proves useful.

Example 10.4. Impedance of an antenna.

The total power radiated by an antenna is 60 mW when 20 mA (rms) is applied to the antenna terminals. The radiation efficiency of the antenna is known to be 70%. It is observed that voltage and current are in-phase at the antenna terminals. Determine (a) the radiation resistance, (b) the loss resistance, and (c) the impedance of the antenna.

Solution. From the problem statement, $P_{rad} = 60$ mW, $\left|\widetilde{I}_A\right| = 20$ mA (rms), and $e_{rad} = 0.7$. Also, the fact that voltage and current are in-phase at the antenna terminals indicates that $X_A = 0$. From Equation 10.32, the radiation resistance is

$$R_{rad} \approx \frac{2 \cdot (60\text{ mW})}{\left|\sqrt{2} \cdot 20\text{ mA}\right|^2} = \underline{150\ \Omega} \quad (10.35)$$

Solving Equation 10.34 for the loss resistance, we find:

$$R_{loss} = \frac{1 - e_{rad}}{e_{rad}} R_{rad} \cong \underline{64.3\ \Omega} \quad (10.36)$$

Since $Z_A = R_{rad} + R_{loss} + jX_A$, we find $Z_A \cong \underline{214.3 + j0\ \Omega}$. This will be the ratio of voltage to current at the antenna terminals regardless of the source current.

10.6 Impedance of the Electrically-Short Dipole

[m0204]

In this section, we determine the impedance of the electrically-short dipole (ESD) antenna. The physical theory of operation for the ESD is introduced in Section 9.5, and additional relevant aspects of the ESD antenna are addressed in Sections 10.1–10.4. The concept of antenna impedance is addressed in Section 10.5. Review of those sections is suggested before attempting this section.

The impedance of any antenna may be expressed as

$$Z_A = R_{rad} + R_{loss} + jX_A \quad (10.37)$$

where the real-valued quantities R_{rad}, R_{loss}, and X_A represent the radiation resistance, loss resistance, and reactance of the antenna, respectively.

Radiation resistance. The radiation resistance of any antenna can be expressed as:

$$R_{rad} = 2P_{rad} \left|I_0\right|^{-2} \quad (10.38)$$

where $|I_0|$ is the magnitude of the current at the antenna terminals, and P_{rad} is the resulting total power radiated. For an ESD (Section 10.2):

$$P_{rad} \approx \eta \frac{|I_0|^2 (\beta L)^2}{48\pi} \quad (10.39)$$

so

$$R_{rad} \approx \eta \frac{(\beta L)^2}{24\pi} \quad (10.40)$$

It is useful to have an alternative form of this expression in terms of wavelength λ. This is derived as follows. First, note:

$$\beta L = \frac{2\pi}{\lambda} L = 2\pi \frac{L}{\lambda} \quad (10.41)$$

where L/λ is the antenna length in units of wavelength. Substituting this expression into Equation 10.40:

$$\begin{aligned} R_{rad} &\approx \eta \left(2\pi \frac{L}{\lambda}\right)^2 \frac{1}{24\pi} \\ &\approx \eta \frac{\pi}{6} \left(\frac{L}{\lambda}\right)^2 \end{aligned} \quad (10.42)$$

Assuming free-space conditions, $\eta \cong 376.7\ \Omega$, which is $\approx 120\pi\ \Omega$. Subsequently,

$$\boxed{R_{rad} \approx 20\pi^2 \left(\frac{L}{\lambda}\right)^2} \quad (10.43)$$

This remarkably simple expression indicates that the radiation resistance of an ESD is very small (since $L \ll \lambda$ for an ESD), but increases as the square of the length.

At this point, a warning is in order. The radiation resistance of an "electrically-short dipole" is sometimes said to be $80\pi^2 (L/\lambda)^2$; i.e., 4 times the right side of Equation 10.43. This higher value is not for a *physically-realizable* ESD, but rather for the *Hertzian dipole* (sometimes also referred to as an "ideal dipole"). The Hertzian dipole is an electrically-short dipole with a current distribution that has uniform magnitude over the length of the dipole.[2] The Hertzian dipole is quite difficult to realize in practice, and nearly all practical electrically-short dipoles exhibit a current distribution that is closer to that of the ESD. The ESD has a current distribution which is maximum in the center and goes approximately linearly to zero at the ends. The factor-of-4 difference in the radiation resistance of the Hertzian dipole relative to the (practical) ESD is a straightforward consequence of the difference in the current distributions.

Loss resistance. The loss resistance of the ESD is derived in Section 10.3 and is found to be

$$R_{loss} \approx \frac{L}{6a}\sqrt{\frac{\mu f}{\pi\sigma}} \quad (10.44)$$

where a, μ, and σ are the radius, permeability, and conductivity of the wire comprising the antenna, and f is frequency.

Reactance. The reactance of the ESD is addressed in Section 10.4. A suitable expression for this reactance is (see, e.g., Johnson (1993) in "Additional References" at the end of this section):

$$X_A \approx -\frac{120\ \Omega}{\pi L/\lambda}\left[\ln\left(\frac{L}{2a}\right) - 1\right] \quad (10.45)$$

where $a \ll L$ is assumed.

Example 10.5. Impedance of an ESD.

A thin, straight dipole antenna operates at 30 MHz in free space. The length and radius of the dipole are 1 m and 1 mm respectively. The dipole is comprised of aluminum having conductivity $\approx 3.7 \times 10^7$ S/m and $\mu \approx \mu_0$. What is the impedance and radiation efficiency of this antenna?

Solution. The free-space wavelength at $f = 30$ MHz is $\lambda = c/f \cong 10$ m. Therefore, $L \cong 0.1\lambda$, and this is an ESD. Since this is an ESD, we may compute the radiation resistance using Equation 10.43, yielding $R_{rad} \approx 1.97\ \Omega$. The radius $a = 1$ mm and $\sigma \approx 3.7 \times 10^7$ S/m; thus, we find that the loss resistance $R_{loss} \approx 94.9$ mΩ using Equation 10.44. Using Equation 10.45, the reactance is found to be $X_A \approx -1991.8\ \Omega$. The impedance of this antenna is therefore

$$\begin{aligned} Z_A &= R_{rad} + R_{loss} + jX_A \\ &\approx \underline{2.1 - j1991.8\ \Omega} \end{aligned} \quad (10.46)$$

and the radiation efficiency of this antenna is

$$e_{rad} = \frac{R_{rad}}{R_{rad} + R_{loss}} \approx \underline{95.4\%} \quad (10.47)$$

In the preceding example, the radiation efficiency is a respectable 95.4%. However, the real part of the impedance of the ESD is much less than the characteristic impedance of typical transmission lines (typically 10s to 100s of ohms). Another problem is that the reactance of the ESD is very large. Some form of impedance matching is required to efficiently transfer power from a transmitter or transmission line to this form of antenna. Failure to do so will result in reflection of a large fraction of the power incident on antenna terminals. A common solution is to insert series inductance to reduce – nominally, cancel – the negative reactance of the ESD. In the preceding example, about 10 μH would be needed. The remaining mismatch in the real-valued components of impedance is then relatively easy to mitigate using common "real-to-real" impedance matching

[2]See Section 9.4 for additional information about the Hertzian dipole.

techniques.

Additional Reading:

- R.C. Johnson (Ed.), *Antenna Systems Handbook* (Ch. 4), McGraw-Hill, 1993.

10.7 Directivity and Gain

[m0203]

A transmitting antenna does not radiate power uniformly in all directions. Inevitably more power is radiated in some directions than others. *Directivity* quantifies this behavior. In this section, we introduce the concept of directivity and the related concepts of *maximum directivity* and *antenna gain.*

Consider an antenna located at the origin. The power radiated in a single direction (θ, ϕ) is formally zero. This is because a single direction corresponds to a solid angle of zero, which intercepts an area of zero at any given distance from the antenna. Since the power flowing through any surface having zero area is zero, the power flowing in a single direction is formally zero. Clearly we need a different metric of power in order to develop a sensible description of the spatial distribution of power flow.

The appropriate metric is *spatial power density*; that is, power per unit area, having SI base units of W/m^2. Therefore, directivity is defined in terms of spatial power density in a particular direction, as opposed to power in a particular direction. Specifically, directivity in the direction (θ, ϕ) is:

$$D(\theta, \phi) \triangleq \frac{S(\mathbf{r})}{S_{ave}(r)} \tag{10.48}$$

In this expression, $S(\mathbf{r})$ is the power density at (r, θ, ϕ); i.e., at a distance r in the direction (θ, ϕ). $S_{ave}(r)$ is the *average* power density at that distance; that is, $S(\mathbf{r})$ averaged over all possible directions at distance r. Since directivity is a ratio of power densities, it is unitless. Summarizing:

> Directivity is ratio of power density in a specified direction to the power density averaged over all directions at the same distance from the antenna.

Despite Equation 10.48, directivity does not depend on the distance from the antenna. To be specific, directivity is the same at every distance r. Even though the numerator and denominator of Equation 10.48 both vary with r, one finds that the distance dependence always cancels because power density and average power density are both proportional to r^{-2}. This is a key point: Directivity is a convenient way to characterize an antenna because it does not change with distance from the antenna.

In general, directivity is a function of direction. However, one is often not concerned about all directions, but rather only the directivity in the direction in which it is maximum. In fact it is quite common to use the term "directivity" informally to refer to the maximum directivity of an antenna. This is usually what is meant when the directivity is indicated to be a single number; in any event, the intended meaning of the term is usually clear from context.

Example 10.6. Directivity of the electrically-short dipole.

An electrically-short dipole (ESD) consists of a straight wire having length $L \ll \lambda/2$. What is the directivity of the ESD?

Solution. The field radiated by an ESD is derived in Section 9.5. In that section, we find that the electric field intensity in the far field of a $\hat{\mathbf{z}}$-oriented ESD located at the origin is:

$$\widetilde{\mathbf{E}}(\mathbf{r}) \approx \hat{\theta} j\eta \frac{I_0 \cdot \beta L}{8\pi} (\sin\theta) \frac{e^{-j\beta r}}{r} \tag{10.49}$$

where I_0 represents the magnitude and phase of the current applied to the terminals, η is the wave impedance of the medium, and $\beta = 2\pi/\lambda$. In Section 10.2, we find that the power density of this field is:

$$S(\mathbf{r}) \approx \eta \frac{|I_0|^2 (\beta L)^2}{128\pi^2} (\sin\theta)^2 \frac{1}{r^2} \tag{10.50}$$

and we subsequently find that the total power radiated is:

$$P_{rad} \approx \eta \frac{|I_0|^2 (\beta L)^2}{48\pi} \tag{10.51}$$

The average power density S_{ave} is simply the total power divided by the area of a sphere centered on the ESD. Let us place this sphere at distance r, with $r \gg L$ and $r \gg \lambda$ as required for the validity of Equations 10.49 and 10.50. Then:

$$S_{ave} = \frac{P_{rad}}{4\pi r^2} \approx \eta \frac{|I_0|^2 (\beta L)^2}{192\pi^2 r^2} \tag{10.52}$$

Finally the directivity is determined by applying the definition:

$$D(\theta,\phi) \triangleq \frac{S(\mathbf{r})}{S_{ave}(r)} \tag{10.53}$$

$$\approx \underline{1.5\,(\sin\theta)^2} \tag{10.54}$$

The maximum directivity occurs in the $\theta = \pi/2$ plane. Therefore, the maximum directivity is <u>1.5</u>, meaning the maximum power density is 1.5 times greater than the power density averaged over all directions.

Since directivity is a unitless ratio, it is common to express it in decibels. For example, the maximum directivity of the ESD in the preceding example is $10\log_{10} 1.5 \cong 1.76$ dB. (Note "$10\log_{10}$" here since directivity is the ratio of power-like quantities.)

Gain. The gain $G(\theta,\phi)$ of an antenna is its directivity modified to account for loss within the antenna. Specifically:

$$G(\theta,\phi) \triangleq \frac{S(\mathbf{r}) \text{ for actual antenna}}{S_{ave}(r) \text{ for identical but lossless antenna}} \tag{10.55}$$

In this equation, the numerator is the actual power density radiated by the antenna, which is less than the nominal power density due to losses within the antenna. The denominator is the average power density for an antenna which is identical, but lossless. Since the actual antenna radiates less power than an identical but lossless version of the same antenna, gain in any particular direction is always less than directivity in that direction. Therefore, an equivalent definition of antenna gain is

$$G(\theta,\phi) \triangleq e_{rad} D(\theta,\phi) \tag{10.56}$$

where e_{rad} is the radiation efficiency of the antenna (Section 10.5).

> Gain is directivity times radiation efficiency; that is, directivity modified to account for loss within the antenna.

The receive case. To conclude this section, we make one additional point about directivity, which applies equally to gain. The preceding discussion has presumed an antenna which is radiating; i.e., transmitting. Directivity can also be defined for the receive case, in which it quantifies the effectiveness of the antenna in converting power in an incident wave to power in a load attached to the antenna. Receive directivity is formally introduced in Section 10.13 ("Effective Aperture"). When receive directivity is defined as specified in Section 10.13, it is equal to transmit directivity as defined in this section. Thus, it is commonly said that the directivity of an antenna is the same for receive and transmit.

Additional Reading:

- "Directivity" on Wikipedia.

10.8 Radiation Pattern

[m0205]

The *radiation pattern* of a transmitting antenna describes the magnitude and polarization of the field radiated by the antenna as a function of angle relative to the antenna. A pattern may also be defined for a receiving antenna, however, we defer discussion of the receive case to a later section.

The concept of radiation pattern is closely related to the concepts of directivity and gain (Section 10.7). The principal distinction is the explicit consideration of polarization. In many applications, the polarization of the field radiated by a transmit antenna is as important as the power density radiated by the antenna. For example, a radio communication link consists of an antenna which is transmitting separated by some distance from an antenna which is receiving. Directivity determines the power density delivered to the receive antenna, but the receive antenna must be co-polarized with the arriving wave in order to capture all of this power.

The radiation pattern concept is perhaps best explained by example. The simplest antenna encountered in common practice is the electrically-short dipole (ESD), which consists of a straight wire of length L that is much less than one-half of a wavelength. In Section 9.5, it is shown that the field radiated by an ESD which is located at the origin and aligned along the z-axis is:

$$\widetilde{\mathbf{E}}(\mathbf{r}) \approx \hat{\theta} j\eta \frac{I_0 \cdot \beta L}{8\pi} \left(\sin\theta\right) \frac{e^{-j\beta r}}{r} \tag{10.57}$$

where I_0 represents the magnitude and phase of the current applied to the terminals, η is the wave impedance of the medium, and $\beta = 2\pi/\lambda$ is the phase propagation constant of the medium. Note that the reference direction of the electric field is in the $\hat{\theta}$ direction; therefore, a receiver must be $\hat{\theta}$-polarized relative to the transmitter's coordinate system in order to capture all available power. A receiver which is not fully $\hat{\theta}$-polarized will capture less power. In the extreme, a receiver which is $\hat{\phi}$-polarized with respect to the transmitter's coordinate system will capture zero power. Thus, for the $\hat{\mathbf{z}}$-oriented ESD, we refer to the $\hat{\theta}$-polarization of the transmitted field as "co-polarized" or simply "co-pol," and the $\hat{\phi}$-polarization of the transmitted field as "cross-pol."

At this point, the reader may wonder what purpose is served by defining cross polarization, since the definition given above seems to suggest that cross-pol should always be zero. In common engineering practice, cross-pol is non-zero when co-pol is different from the *intended* or *nominal* polarization of the field radiated by the antenna. In the case of the ESD, we observe that the electric field is always $\hat{\theta}$-polarized, and therefore we consider that to be the nominal polarization. Since the actual polarization of the ESD in the example is precisely the same as the nominal polarization of the ESD, the cross-pol of the ideal ESD is zero. If, on the other hand, we arbitrarily define $\hat{\theta}$ to be the nominal polarization and apply this definition to a different antenna that does not produce a uniformly $\hat{\theta}$-polarized electric field, then we observe non-zero cross-pol. Cross-pol is similarly used to quantify effects due to errors in position or orientation, or due to undesired modification of the field due to materials (e.g., feed or mounting structures) near the transmit antenna. Summarizing:

> *Co-pol* is commonly defined to be the intended or nominal polarization for a particular application, which is not necessarily the actual polarization radiated by the antenna under consideration. *Cross-pol* measures polarization in the orthogonal plane; i.e., deviation from the presumed co-pol.

Returning to the ESD: Since $\widetilde{\mathbf{E}}(\mathbf{r})$ depends only on θ and not ϕ, the co-pol pattern is the same in any plane that contains the z axis. We refer to any such plane as the *E-plane*. In general:

> The *E-plane* is any plane in which the nominal or intended vector $\widetilde{\mathbf{E}}$ lies.

Since the ESD is $\hat{\theta}$-polarized, the E-plane pattern of the ESD is simply:

$$\left|\widetilde{\mathbf{E}}(\mathbf{r})\right| \approx \eta \frac{I_0 \cdot \beta L}{8\pi} (\sin\theta) \frac{1}{r} \tag{10.58}$$

This pattern is shown in Figure 10.5.

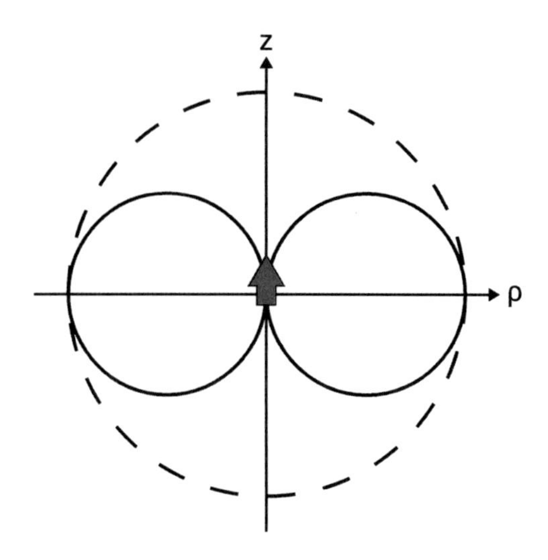

© S. Lally CC BY-SA 4.0

Figure 10.5: E-plane co-pol pattern for the $\hat{\mathbf{z}}$-oriented ESD. In the unnormalized pattern scaling, the dashed circle indicates the maximum value of Equation 10.58.

Equation 10.58 is referred to as an *unnormalized* pattern. The associated normalized pattern is addressed later in this section.

Similarly, we define the *H-plane* as follows:

> The *H-plane* is any plane in which the nominal or intended vector $\widetilde{\mathbf{H}}$ lies, and so is perpendicular to both the E-plane and the direction of propagation.

In the case of the ESD, the one and only H-plane is the $z = 0$ plane. The H-plane pattern is shown in Figure 10.6.

It is often useful to normalize the pattern, meaning that we scale the pattern so that its maximum magnitude corresponds to a convenient value. There are two common scalings. One common scaling sets the maximum value of the pattern equal to 1, and is therefore independent of source magnitude and distance. This is referred to as the *normalized pattern*. The normalized co-pol pattern can be defined as follows:

$$F(\theta,\phi) \triangleq \frac{\left|\hat{\mathbf{e}} \cdot \widetilde{\mathbf{E}}(\mathbf{r})\right|}{\left|\hat{\mathbf{e}} \cdot \widetilde{\mathbf{E}}(\mathbf{r})\right|_{max}} \tag{10.59}$$

where $\hat{\mathbf{e}}$ is the co-pol reference direction, and the

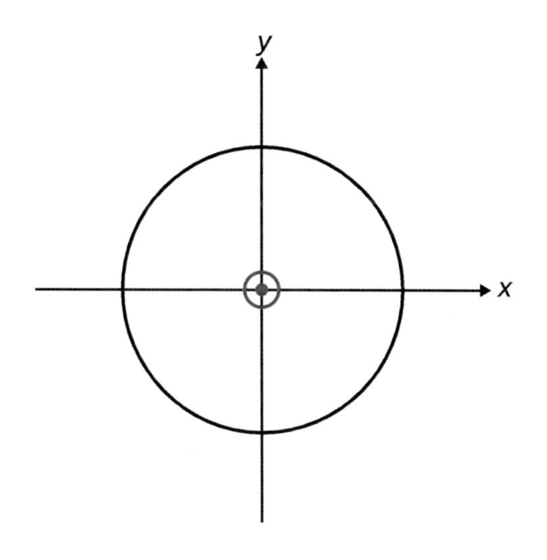

© S. Lally CC BY-SA 4.0

Figure 10.6: H-plane co-pol pattern for the $\hat{\mathbf{z}}$-oriented ESD. In the unnormalized pattern scaling, the radius of the circle is the maximum value of Equation 10.58.

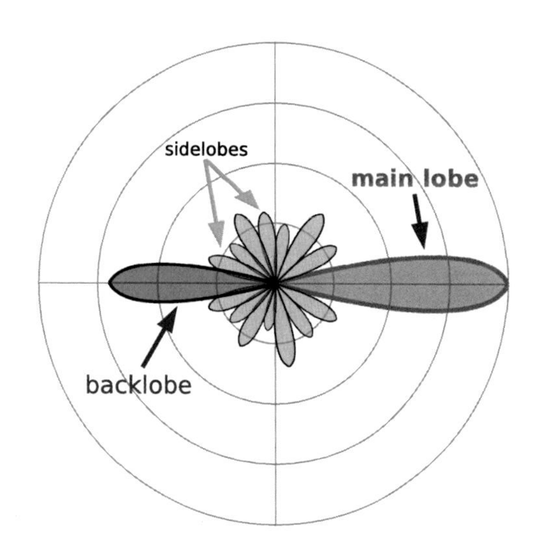

© T. Truckle CC BY-SA 4.0 (modified)

Figure 10.7: Co-pol pattern typical of a highly directional antenna, such as a yagi.

denominator is the maximum value of the electric field at distance r.

> A *normalized pattern* is scaled to a maximum magnitude of 1, using the definition expressed in Equation 10.59.

Note that the value of r is irrelevant, since numerator and denominator both scale with r in the same way. Thus, the normalized pattern, like directivity, does not change with distance from the antenna.

For the ESD, $\hat{e} = \hat{\theta}$, so the normalized co-pol pattern is:

$$F(\theta,\phi) = \frac{\left|\hat{\theta}\cdot\widetilde{\mathbf{E}}(\mathbf{r})\right|}{\left|\hat{\theta}\cdot\widetilde{\mathbf{E}}(\mathbf{r})\right|_{max}} \quad \text{(ESD)} \tag{10.60}$$

which yields simply

$$F(\theta,\phi) \approx \sin\theta \quad \text{(ESD)} \tag{10.61}$$

Thus, the E-plane normalized co-pol pattern of the ESD is Figure 10.5 where the radius of the maximum value circle is equal to 1, which is 0 dB. Similarly, the H-plane normalized co-pol pattern of the ESD is Figure 10.6 where the radius of the circle is equal to 1 (0 dB).

The other common scaling for patterns sets the maximum value equal to maximum directivity. Directivity is proportional to power density, which is proportional to $\left|\widetilde{\mathbf{E}}(\mathbf{r})\right|^2$. Therefore, this "directivity normalized" pattern can be expressed as:

$$D_{max}\left|F(\theta,\phi)\right|^2 \tag{10.62}$$

where D_{max} is the directivity in whichever direction it is maximum. For the ESD considered previously, $D_{max} = 1.5$ (Section 10.7). Therefore, the co-pol pattern of the ESD using this particular scaling is

$$1.5\sin^2\theta \quad \text{(ESD)} \tag{10.63}$$

Thus, the E-plane co-pol pattern of the ESD using this scaling is similar to Figure 10.5, except that it is squared in magnitude and the radius of the maximum value circle is equal to 1.5, which is 1.76 dB. The H-plane co-pol pattern of the ESD, using this scaling, is Figure 10.6 where the radius of the circle is equal to 1.5 (1.76 dB).

Pattern lobes. Nearly all antennas in common use exhibit directivity that is greater than that of the ESD. The patterns of these antennas subsequently exhibit more complex structure. Figure 10.7 shows an example. The region around the direction of maximum directivity is referred to as the *main lobe*.

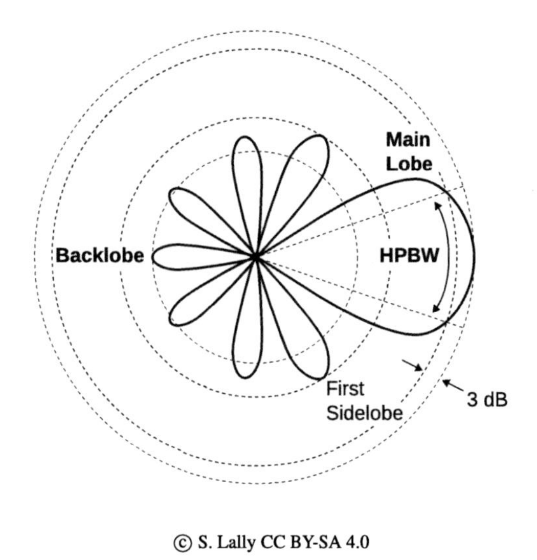

© S. Lally CC BY-SA 4.0

Figure 10.8: Half-power beamwidth (HPBW).

The main lobe is bounded on each side by a *null*, where the magnitude reaches a local minimum, perhaps zero. Many antennas also exhibit a lobe in the opposite direction, known as a *backlobe*. (Many other antennas exhibit a null in this direction.) Lobes between the main lobe and the backlobe are referred to as *sidelobes*. Other commonly-used pattern metrics include *first sidelobe level*, which is the ratio of the maximum magnitude of the sidelobe closest to the main lobe to that of the main lobe; and *front-to-back ratio*, which is the ratio of the maximum magnitude of the backlobe to that of the main lobe.

When the main lobe is narrow, it is common to characterize the pattern in terms of *half-power beamwidth* (HPBW). This is shown in Figure 10.8. HPBW is the width of the main lobe measured between two points at which the directivity is one-half its maximum value. As a pattern metric, HPBW depends on the plane in which it is measured. In particular, HPBW may be different in the E- and H-planes. For example, the E-plane HPBW of the ESD is found to be 90°, whereas the H-plane HPBW is undefined since the pattern is constant in the H-plane.

Omnidirectional and isotropic antennas. The ESD is an example of an *omnidirectional* antenna. An omnidirectional antenna is an antenna whose pattern magnitude is nominally constant in a plane containing the maximum directivity. For the ESD, this plane is the H-plane, so the ESD is said to be omnidirectional in the H-plane. The term "omnidirectional" does *not* indicate constant pattern in all directions. (In fact, note that the ESD exhibits pattern nulls in two directions.)

> An *omnidirectional* antenna, such as the ESD, exhibits constant and nominally maximum directivity in one plane.

An antenna whose pattern is uniform in all directions is said to be *isotropic*. No physically-realizable antenna is isotropic; in fact, the ESD is about as close as one can get. Nevertheless, the "isotropic antenna" concept is useful as a standard against which other antennas can be quantified. Since the pattern of an isotropic antenna is constant with direction, the power density radiated by such an antenna in any direction is equal to the power density averaged over all directions. Thus, the directivity of an isotropic antenna is exactly 1. The directivity of any other antenna may be expressed in units of "dBi," which is simply dB relative to that of an isotropic antenna. For example, the maximum directivity of the ESD is 1.5, which is $10\log_{10}(1.5/1) = 1.76$ dBi. Summarizing:

> An *isotropic* antenna exhibits constant directivity in every direction. Such an antenna is not physically-realizable, but is nevertheless useful as a baseline for describing other antennas.

Additional Reading:

- "Radiation pattern" on Wikipedia.

10.9 Equivalent Circuit Model for Reception

[m0206]

In this section, we begin to address antennas as devices that convert incident electromagnetic waves into potentials and currents in a circuit. It is convenient to represent this process in the form of a Thévenin equivalent circuit. The particular circuit addressed in this section is shown in Figure 10.9. The circuit consists of a voltage source $\widetilde{V}_{OC}$ and a series impedance Z_A. The source potential $\widetilde{V}_{OC}$ is the potential at the terminals of the antenna when there is no termination; i.e., when the antenna is open-circuited. The series impedance Z_A is the output impedance of the circuit, and so determines the magnitude and phase of the current at the terminals once a load is connected. Given $\widetilde{V}_{OC}$ and the current through the equivalent circuit, it is possible to determine the power delivered to the load. Thus, this model is quite useful, but only if we are able to determine $\widetilde{V}_{OC}$ and Z_A. This section provides an informal derivation of these quantities that is sufficient to productively address the subsequent important topics of effective aperture and impedance matching of receive antennas.[3]

Vector effective length. With no derivation required, we can deduce the following about $\widetilde{V}_{OC}$:

- $\widetilde{V}_{OC}$ must depend on the incident electric field intensity $\widetilde{\mathbf{E}}^i$. Presumably the relationship is linear, so $\widetilde{V}_{OC}$ is proportional to the magnitude of $\widetilde{\mathbf{E}}^i$.
- Since $\widetilde{\mathbf{E}}^i$ is a vector whereas $\widetilde{V}_{OC}$ is a scalar, there must be some vector $\mathbf{l}_e$ for which

$$\widetilde{V}_{OC} = \widetilde{\mathbf{E}}^i \cdot \mathbf{l}_e \tag{10.64}$$

- Since $\widetilde{\mathbf{E}}^i$ has SI base units of V/m and $\widetilde{V}_{OC}$ has SI base units of V, $\mathbf{l}_e$ must have SI base units of m; i.e., length.
- We expect that $\widetilde{V}_{OC}$ increases as the size of the antenna increases, so the magnitude of $\mathbf{l}_e$ likely increases with the size of the antenna.
- The direction of $\mathbf{l}_e$ must be related to the orientation of the incident electric field relative to that of the antenna, since this is clearly important yet we have not already accounted for this.

[3] Formal derivations of these quantities are provided in subsequent sections. The starting point is the section on reciprocity.

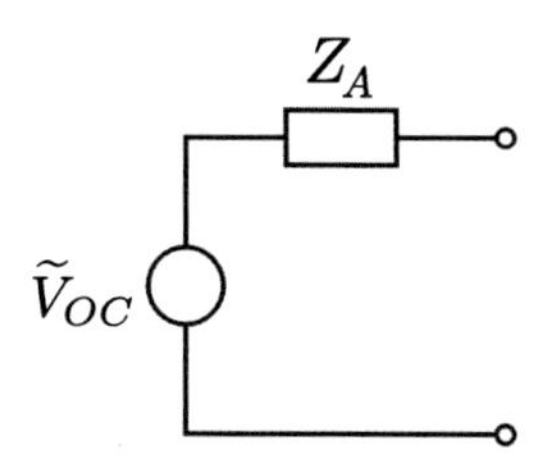

© S. Lally, CC BY-SA 4.0 (modified)

Figure 10.9: Thévenin equivalent circuit for an antenna in the presence of an incident electromagnetic wave.

It may seem at this point that $\mathbf{l}_e$ is unambiguously determined, and we need merely to derive its value. However, this is not the case. There are in fact multiple unique definitions of $\mathbf{l}_e$ that will reduce the vector $\widetilde{\mathbf{E}}^i$ to the observed scalar $\widetilde{V}_{OC}$ via Equation 10.64. In this section, we shall employ the most commonly-used definition, in which $\mathbf{l}_e$ is referred to as *vector effective length*. Following this definition, the scalar part l_e of $\mathbf{l}_e = \hat{\mathbf{l}} l_e$ is commonly referred to as any of the following: *effective length* (the term used in this book), *effective height*, or *antenna factor*.

In this section, we shall merely define vector effective length, and defer a formal derivation to Section 10.11. In this definition, we arbitrarily set $\hat{\mathbf{l}}$, the real-valued unit vector indicating the direction of $\mathbf{l}_e$, equal to the direction in which the electric field transmitted from this antenna would be polarized in the far field. For example, consider a $\hat{\mathbf{z}}$-oriented electrically-short dipole (ESD) located at the origin. The electric field transmitted from this antenna would have only a $\hat{\theta}$ component, and no $\hat{\phi}$ component (and certainly no $\hat{\mathbf{r}}$ component). Thus, $\hat{\mathbf{l}} = \hat{\theta}$ in this case.

Applying this definition, $\widetilde{\mathbf{E}}^i \cdot \hat{\mathbf{l}}$ yields the scalar component of $\widetilde{\mathbf{E}}^i$ that is co-polarized with electric field radiated by the antenna when transmitting. Now

l_e is uniquely defined to be the factor that converts this component into $\widetilde{V}_{OC}$. Summarizing:

> The *vector effective length* $\mathbf{l}_e = \hat{\mathbf{l}} l_e$ is defined as follows: $\hat{\mathbf{l}}$ is the real-valued unit vector corresponding to the polarization of the electric field that would be transmitted from the antenna in the far field. Subsequently, the *effective length* l_e is
>
> $$l_e \triangleq \frac{\widetilde{V}_{OC}}{\widetilde{\mathbf{E}}^i \cdot \hat{\mathbf{l}}} \tag{10.65}$$
>
> where $\widetilde{V}_{OC}$ is the open-circuit potential induced at the antenna terminals in response to the incident electric field intensity $\widetilde{\mathbf{E}}^i$.

While this definition yields an unambiguous value for l_e, it is not yet clear what that value is. For most antennas, effective length is quite difficult to determine directly, and one must instead determine effective length indirectly from the transmit characteristics via reciprocity. This approach is relatively easy (although still quite a bit of effort) for thin dipoles, and is presented in Section 10.11.

To provide an example of how effective length works right away, consider the $\hat{\mathbf{z}}$-oriented ESD described earlier in this section. Let the length of this ESD be L. Let $\widetilde{\mathbf{E}}^i$ be a $\hat{\theta}$-polarized plane wave arriving at the ESD. The ESD is open-circuited, so the potential induced in its terminals is $\widetilde{V}_{OC}$. One observes the following:

- When $\widetilde{\mathbf{E}}^i$ arrives from anywhere in the $\theta = \pi/2$ plane (i.e., broadside to the ESD), $\widetilde{\mathbf{E}}^i$ points in the $-\hat{\mathbf{z}}$ direction, and we find that $l_e \approx L/2$. It should not be surprising that l_e is proportional to L; this expectation was noted earlier in this section.

- When $\widetilde{\mathbf{E}}^i$ arrives from the directions $\theta = 0$ or $\theta = \pi$ – i.e., along the axis of the ESD – $\widetilde{\mathbf{E}}^i$ is perpendicular to the axis of the ESD. In this case, we find that l_e equals zero.

Taken together, these findings suggest that l_e should contain a factor of $\sin\theta$. We conclude that the vector effective length for a $\hat{\mathbf{z}}$-directed ESD of length L is

$$\mathbf{l}_e \approx \hat{\theta}\frac{L}{2}\sin\theta \quad \text{(ESD)} \tag{10.66}$$

Example 10.7. Potential induced in an ESD.

A thin straight dipole of length 10 cm is located at the origin and aligned with the z-axis. A plane wave is incident on the dipole from the direction $(\theta = \pi/4, \phi = \pi/2)$. The frequency of the wave is 30 MHz. The magnitude of the incident electric field is 10 μV/m (rms). What is the magnitude of the induced open-circuit potential when the electric field is (a) $\hat{\theta}$-polarized and (b) $\hat{\phi}$-polarized?

Solution. The wavelength in this example is $c/f \cong 10$ m, so this dipole is electrically-short. Using Equation 10.66:

$$\begin{aligned}\mathbf{l}_e &\approx \hat{\theta}\frac{10\text{ cm}}{2}\sin\frac{\pi}{4} \\ &\approx \hat{\theta}\,(3.54\text{ cm})\end{aligned}$$

Thus, the effective length $l_e = 3.54$ cm. When the electric field is $\hat{\theta}$-polarized, the magnitude of the induced open-circuit voltage is

$$\begin{aligned}\left|\widetilde{V}_{OC}\right| &= \left|\widetilde{\mathbf{E}}^i \cdot \mathbf{l}_e\right| \\ &\approx (10\ \mu\text{V/m})\,\hat{\theta}\cdot\hat{\theta}\,(3.54\text{ cm}) \\ &\approx \underline{354\text{ nV rms}} \quad \text{(a)}\end{aligned}$$

When the electric field is $\hat{\phi}$-polarized:

$$\begin{aligned}\left|\widetilde{V}_{OC}\right| &\approx (10\ \mu\text{V/m})\,\hat{\phi}\cdot\hat{\theta}\,(3.54\text{ cm}) \\ &\approx \underline{0} \quad \text{(b)}\end{aligned}$$

This is because the polarization of the incident electric field is orthogonal to that of the ESD. In fact, the answer to part (b) is zero for *any* angle of incidence (θ, ϕ).

Output impedance. The output impedance Z_A is somewhat more difficult to determine without a formal derivation, which is presented in Section 10.12. For the purposes of this section, it suffices to jump directly to the result:

The output impedance Z_A of the equivalent circuit for an antenna in the receive case is equal to the input impedance of the same antenna in the *transmit* case.

This remarkable fact is a consequence of the reciprocity property of antenna systems, and greatly simplifies the analysis of receive antennas.

Now a demonstration of how the antenna equivalent circuit can be used to determine the power delivered by an antenna to an attached electrical circuit:

Example 10.8. Power captured by an ESD.

Continuing with part (a) of Example 10.7: If this antenna is terminated into a conjugate-matched load, then what is the power delivered to that load? Assume the antenna is lossless.

Solution. First, we determine the impedance Z_A of the equivalent circuit of the antenna. This is equal to the input impedance of the antenna in transmission. Let R_A and X_A be the real and imaginary parts of this impedance; i.e., $Z_A = R_A + jX_A$. Further, R_A is the sum of the radiation resistance R_{rad} and the loss resistance. The loss resistance is zero because the antenna is lossless. Since this is an ESD:

$$R_{rad} \approx 20\pi^2 \left(\frac{L}{\lambda}\right)^2 \quad (10.67)$$

Therefore, $R_A = R_{rad} \approx 4.93\ \mathrm{m}\Omega$. We do not need to calculate X_A, as will become apparent in the next step.

A conjugate-matched load has impedance Z_A^*, so the potential $\widetilde{V}_L$ across the load is

$$\widetilde{V}_L = \widetilde{V}_{OC} \frac{Z_A^*}{Z_A + Z_A^*} = \widetilde{V}_{OC} \frac{Z_A^*}{2R_A} \quad (10.68)$$

The current $\widetilde{I}_L$ through the load is

$$\widetilde{I}_L = \frac{\widetilde{V}_{OC}}{Z_A + Z_A^*} = \frac{\widetilde{V}_{OC}}{2R_A} \quad (10.69)$$

Taking $\widetilde{V}_{OC}$ as an RMS quantity, the power P_L delivered to the load is

$$P_L = \mathrm{Re}\left\{V_L I_L^*\right\} = \frac{\left|\widetilde{V}_{OC}\right|^2}{4R_A} \quad (10.70)$$

In part (a) of Example 10.7, $\left|\widetilde{V}_{OC}\right|$ is found to be ≈ 354 nV rms, so $P_L \approx 6.33$ pW.

Additional Reading:

- "Thévenin's Theorem" on Wikipedia.
- W.L. Stutzman & G.A. Thiele, *Antenna Theory and Design*, 3rd Ed., Wiley, 2012. Sec. 4.2 ("Receiving Properties of Antennas").

10.10 Reciprocity

[m0214]

The term "reciprocity" refers to a class of theorems that relate the inputs and outputs of a linear system to those of an identical system in which the inputs and outputs are swapped. The importance of reciprocity in electromagnetics is that it simplifies problems that would otherwise be relatively difficult to solve. An example of this is the derivation of the receiving properties of antennas, which is addressed in other sections using results derived in this section.

As an initial and relatively gentle introduction, consider a well-known special case that emerges in basic circuit theory: The two-port device shown in Figure 10.10. The two-port is said to be reciprocal if the voltage v_2 appearing at port 2 due to a current applied at port 1 is the same as v_1 when the same current is applied instead at port 2. This is normally the case when the two-port consists exclusively of linear passive devices such as ideal resistors, capacitors, and inductors. The fundamental underlying requirement is linearity: That is, outputs must be proportional to inputs, and superposition must apply.

This result from basic circuit theory is actually a special case of a more general theorem of electromagnetics, which we shall now derive. Figure 10.11 shows a scenario in which a current distribution $\widetilde{\mathbf{J}}_1$ is completely contained within a volume $\mathcal{V}$. This current is expressed as a volume current density, having SI base units of A/m^2. Also, the current is expressed in phasor form, signaling that we are considering a single frequency. This current distribution gives rise to an electric field intensity $\widetilde{\mathbf{E}}_1$,

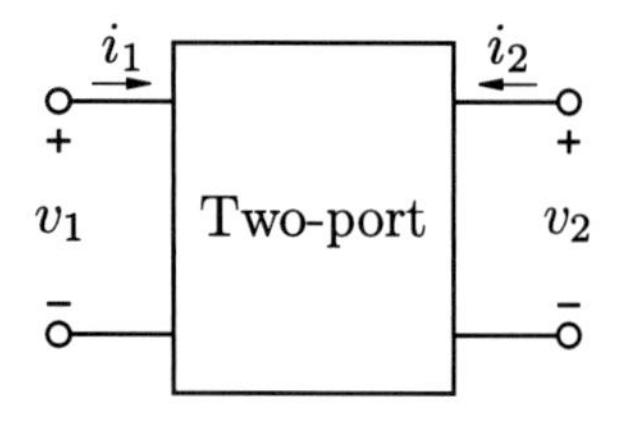

Inductiveload, public domain (modified)

Figure 10.10: Two-port device.

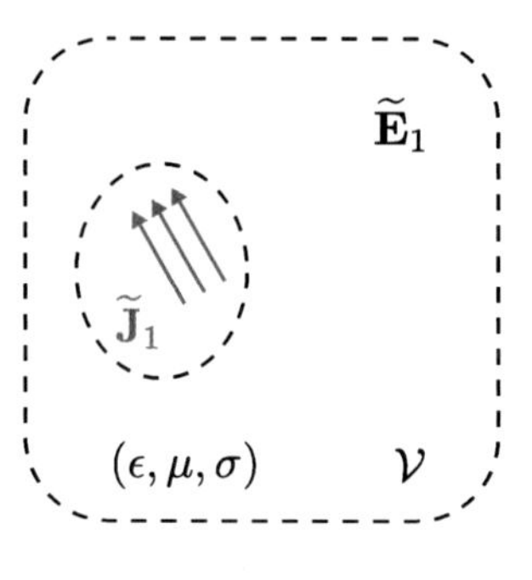

© C. Wang CC BY-SA 4.0

Figure 10.11: An electromagnetic system consisting of a current distribution $\widetilde{\mathbf{J}}_1$ radiating an electric field $\widetilde{\mathbf{E}}_1$ in the presence of linear matter.

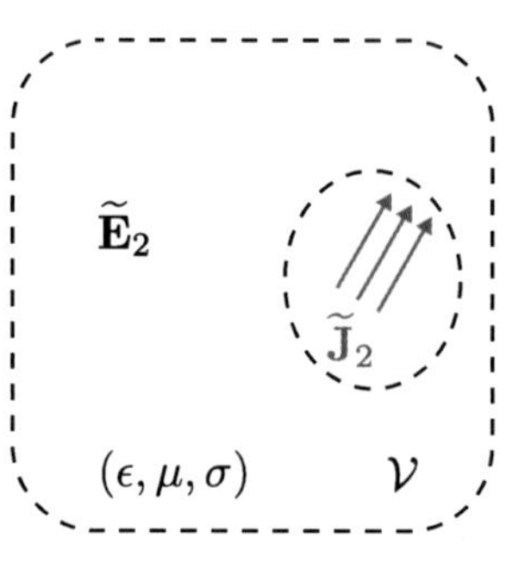

© C. Wang CC BY-SA 4.0

Figure 10.12: The same electromagnetic system as shown in Figure 10.11 (including the same distribution of matter), but now with a different input, $\widetilde{\mathbf{J}}_2$, resulting in a different output, $\widetilde{\mathbf{E}}_2$.

having SI base units of V/m. The volume may consist of any combination of linear time-invariant matter; i.e., permittivity ϵ, permeability μ, and conductivity σ are constants that may vary arbitrarily with position but not with time.

Here's a key idea: We may interpret this scenario as a "two-port" system in which $\widetilde{\mathbf{J}}_1$ is the input, $\widetilde{\mathbf{E}}_1$ is the output, and the system's behavior is completely defined by Maxwell's equations in differential phasor form:

$$\nabla \times \widetilde{\mathbf{E}}_1 = -j\omega\mu\widetilde{\mathbf{H}}_1 \tag{10.71}$$

$$\nabla \times \widetilde{\mathbf{H}}_1 = \widetilde{\mathbf{J}}_1 + j\omega\epsilon\widetilde{\mathbf{E}}_1 \tag{10.72}$$

along with the appropriate electromagnetic boundary conditions. (For the purposes of our present analysis, $\widetilde{\mathbf{H}}_1$ is neither an input nor an output; it is merely a coupled quantity that appears in this particular formulation of the relationship between $\widetilde{\mathbf{E}}_1$ and $\widetilde{\mathbf{J}}_1$.)

Figure 10.12 shows a scenario in which a different current distribution $\widetilde{\mathbf{J}}_2$ is completely contained within the same volume $\mathcal{V}$ containing the same distribution of linear matter. This new current distribution gives rise to an electric field intensity $\widetilde{\mathbf{E}}_2$. The relationship between $\widetilde{\mathbf{E}}_2$ and $\widetilde{\mathbf{J}}_2$ is governed by the same equations:

$$\nabla \times \widetilde{\mathbf{E}}_2 = -j\omega\mu\widetilde{\mathbf{H}}_2 \tag{10.73}$$

$$\nabla \times \widetilde{\mathbf{H}}_2 = \widetilde{\mathbf{J}}_2 + j\omega\epsilon\widetilde{\mathbf{E}}_2 \tag{10.74}$$

along with the same electromagnetic boundary conditions. Thus, we may interpret this scenario as the *same* electromagnetic system depicted in Figure 10.11, except now with $\widetilde{\mathbf{J}}_2$ as the input and $\widetilde{\mathbf{E}}_2$ is the output.

The input current and output field in the second scenario are, in general, completely different from the input current and output field in the first scenario. However, both scenarios involve precisely the same electromagnetic system; i.e., the same governing equations and the same distribution of matter. This leads to the following question: Let's say you know nothing about the system, aside from the fact that it is linear and time-invariant. However, you are able to observe the first scenario; i.e., you know $\widetilde{\mathbf{E}}_1$ in response to $\widetilde{\mathbf{J}}_1$. Given this very limited look into the behavior of the system, what can you infer about $\widetilde{\mathbf{E}}_2$ given $\widetilde{\mathbf{J}}_2$, or vice-versa? At first glance, the answer might seem to be nothing, since you lack a description of the system. However, the answer turns out to be that a surprising bit more information is available. This information is provided by reciprocity. To show this, we must engage in some pure mathematics.

Derivation of the Lorentz reciprocity theorem. First, let us take the dot product of $\widetilde{\mathbf{H}}_2$ with each side of Equation 10.71:

$$\widetilde{\mathbf{H}}_2 \cdot \left(\nabla \times \widetilde{\mathbf{E}}_1\right) = -j\omega\mu\widetilde{\mathbf{H}}_1 \cdot \widetilde{\mathbf{H}}_2 \tag{10.75}$$

Similarly, let us take the dot product of $\widetilde{\mathbf{E}}_1$ with each side of Equation 10.74:

$$\widetilde{\mathbf{E}}_1 \cdot \left(\nabla \times \widetilde{\mathbf{H}}_2\right) = \widetilde{\mathbf{E}}_1 \cdot \widetilde{\mathbf{J}}_2 + j\omega\epsilon\widetilde{\mathbf{E}}_1 \cdot \widetilde{\mathbf{E}}_2 \tag{10.76}$$

Next, let us subtract Equation 10.75 from Equation 10.76. The left side of the resulting equation is

$$\widetilde{\mathbf{E}}_1 \cdot \left(\nabla \times \widetilde{\mathbf{H}}_2\right) - \widetilde{\mathbf{H}}_2 \cdot \left(\nabla \times \widetilde{\mathbf{E}}_1\right) \tag{10.77}$$

This can be simplified using the vector identity (Appendix B.3):

$$\nabla \cdot (\mathbf{A} \times \mathbf{B}) = \mathbf{B} \cdot (\nabla \times \mathbf{A}) - \mathbf{A} \cdot (\nabla \times \mathbf{B}) \tag{10.78}$$

Yielding

$$\widetilde{\mathbf{E}}_1 \cdot \left(\nabla \times \widetilde{\mathbf{H}}_2\right) - \widetilde{\mathbf{H}}_2 \cdot \left(\nabla \times \widetilde{\mathbf{E}}_1\right) = \nabla \cdot \left(\widetilde{\mathbf{H}}_2 \times \widetilde{\mathbf{E}}_1\right) \tag{10.79}$$

So, by subtracting Equation 10.75 from Equation 10.76, we have found:

$$\nabla \cdot \left(\widetilde{\mathbf{H}}_2 \times \widetilde{\mathbf{E}}_1\right) = \widetilde{\mathbf{E}}_1 \cdot \widetilde{\mathbf{J}}_2 + j\omega\epsilon\widetilde{\mathbf{E}}_1 \cdot \widetilde{\mathbf{E}}_2 + j\omega\mu\widetilde{\mathbf{H}}_1 \cdot \widetilde{\mathbf{H}}_2 \tag{10.80}$$

Next, we repeat the process represented by Equations 10.75–10.80 above to generate a complementary equation to Equation 10.80. This time we take the dot product of $\widetilde{\mathbf{E}}_2$ with each side of Equation 10.72:

$$\widetilde{\mathbf{E}}_2 \cdot \left(\nabla \times \widetilde{\mathbf{H}}_1\right) = \widetilde{\mathbf{E}}_2 \cdot \widetilde{\mathbf{J}}_1 + j\omega\epsilon\widetilde{\mathbf{E}}_1 \cdot \widetilde{\mathbf{E}}_2 \tag{10.81}$$

Similarly, let us take the dot product of $\widetilde{\mathbf{H}}_1$ with each side of Equation 10.73:

$$\widetilde{\mathbf{H}}_1 \cdot \left(\nabla \times \widetilde{\mathbf{E}}_2\right) = -j\omega\mu\widetilde{\mathbf{H}}_1 \cdot \widetilde{\mathbf{H}}_2 \tag{10.82}$$

Next, let us subtract Equation 10.82 from Equation 10.81. Again using the vector identity, the left side of the resulting equation is

$$\widetilde{\mathbf{E}}_2 \cdot \left(\nabla \times \widetilde{\mathbf{H}}_1\right) - \widetilde{\mathbf{H}}_1 \cdot \left(\nabla \times \widetilde{\mathbf{E}}_2\right) = \nabla \cdot \left(\widetilde{\mathbf{H}}_1 \times \widetilde{\mathbf{E}}_2\right) \tag{10.83}$$

So we find:

$$\nabla \cdot \left(\widetilde{\mathbf{H}}_1 \times \widetilde{\mathbf{E}}_2\right) = \widetilde{\mathbf{E}}_2 \cdot \widetilde{\mathbf{J}}_1 + j\omega\epsilon \widetilde{\mathbf{E}}_1 \cdot \widetilde{\mathbf{E}}_2 + j\omega\mu \widetilde{\mathbf{H}}_1 \cdot \widetilde{\mathbf{H}}_2 \tag{10.84}$$

Finally, subtracting Equation 10.84 from Equation 10.80, we obtain:

$$\nabla \cdot \left(\widetilde{\mathbf{H}}_2 \times \widetilde{\mathbf{E}}_1 - \widetilde{\mathbf{H}}_1 \times \widetilde{\mathbf{E}}_2\right) = \widetilde{\mathbf{E}}_1 \cdot \widetilde{\mathbf{J}}_2 - \widetilde{\mathbf{E}}_2 \cdot \widetilde{\mathbf{J}}_1 \tag{10.85}$$

This equation is commonly known by the name of the theorem it represents: The *Lorentz reciprocity theorem*. The theorem is a very general statement about the relationship between fields and currents at each point in space. An associated form of the theorem applies to contiguous regions of space. To obtain this form, we simply integrate both sides of Equation 10.85 over the volume $\mathcal{V}$:

$$\int_{\mathcal{V}} \nabla \cdot \left(\widetilde{\mathbf{H}}_2 \times \widetilde{\mathbf{E}}_1 - \widetilde{\mathbf{H}}_1 \times \widetilde{\mathbf{E}}_2\right) dv = \int_{\mathcal{V}} \left(\widetilde{\mathbf{E}}_1 \cdot \widetilde{\mathbf{J}}_2 - \widetilde{\mathbf{E}}_2 \cdot \widetilde{\mathbf{J}}_1\right) dv \tag{10.86}$$

We now take the additional step of using the divergence theorem (Appendix B.3) to transform the left side of the equation into a surface integral:

$$\oint_{\mathcal{S}} \left(\widetilde{\mathbf{H}}_2 \times \widetilde{\mathbf{E}}_1 - \widetilde{\mathbf{H}}_1 \times \widetilde{\mathbf{E}}_2\right) \cdot d\mathbf{s} = \int_{\mathcal{V}} \left(\widetilde{\mathbf{E}}_1 \cdot \widetilde{\mathbf{J}}_2 - \widetilde{\mathbf{E}}_2 \cdot \widetilde{\mathbf{J}}_1\right) dv \tag{10.87}$$

where $\mathcal{S}$ is the closed mathematical surface which bounds $\mathcal{V}$. This is also the Lorentz reciprocity theorem, but now in integral form. This version of the theorem relates fields on the bounding surface to sources within the volume.

The integral form of the theorem has a particularly useful feature. Let us confine the sources to a finite region of space, while allowing $\mathcal{V}$ to grow infinitely large, expanding to include all space. In this situation, the closest distance between any point containing non-zero source current and $\mathcal{S}$ is infinite. Because field magnitude diminishes with distance from the source, the fields $(\widetilde{\mathbf{E}}_1, \widetilde{\mathbf{H}}_1)$ and $(\widetilde{\mathbf{E}}_2, \widetilde{\mathbf{H}}_2)$ are all effectively zero on $\mathcal{S}$. In this case, the left side of Equation 10.87 is zero, and we find:

$$\boxed{\int_{\mathcal{V}} \left(\widetilde{\mathbf{E}}_1 \cdot \widetilde{\mathbf{J}}_2 - \widetilde{\mathbf{E}}_2 \cdot \widetilde{\mathbf{J}}_1\right) dv = 0} \tag{10.88}$$

for any volume $\mathcal{V}$ which contains *all* the current.

> The *Lorentz reciprocity theorem* (Equation 10.88) describes a relationship between one distribution of current and the resulting fields, and a second distribution of current and resulting fields, when both scenarios take place in identical regions of space filled with identical distributions of linear matter.

Why do we refer to this relationship as reciprocity? Simply because the expression is identical when the subscripts "1" and "2" are swapped. In other words, the relationship does not recognize a distinction between "inputs" and "outputs;" there are only "ports."

A useful special case pertains to scenarios in which the current distributions $\widetilde{\mathbf{J}}_1$ and $\widetilde{\mathbf{J}}_2$ are *spatially disjoint*. By "spatially disjoint," we mean that there is no point in space at which both $\widetilde{\mathbf{J}}_1$ and $\widetilde{\mathbf{J}}_2$ are non-zero; in other words, these distributions do not overlap. (Note that the currents shown in Figures 10.11 and 10.12 are depicted as spatially disjoint.) To see what happens in this case, let us first rewrite Equation 10.88 as follows:

$$\int_{\mathcal{V}} \widetilde{\mathbf{E}}_1 \cdot \widetilde{\mathbf{J}}_2 \, dv = \int_{\mathcal{V}} \widetilde{\mathbf{E}}_2 \cdot \widetilde{\mathbf{J}}_1 \, dv \tag{10.89}$$

Let $\mathcal{V}_1$ be the contiguous volume over which $\widetilde{\mathbf{J}}_1$ is non-zero, and let $\mathcal{V}_2$ be the contiguous volume over which $\widetilde{\mathbf{J}}_2$ is non-zero. Then Equation 10.89 may be written as follows:

$$\int_{\mathcal{V}_2} \widetilde{\mathbf{E}}_1 \cdot \widetilde{\mathbf{J}}_2 \, dv = \int_{\mathcal{V}_1} \widetilde{\mathbf{E}}_2 \cdot \widetilde{\mathbf{J}}_1 \, dv \tag{10.90}$$

The utility of this form is that we have reduced the region of integration to just those regions where the current exists.

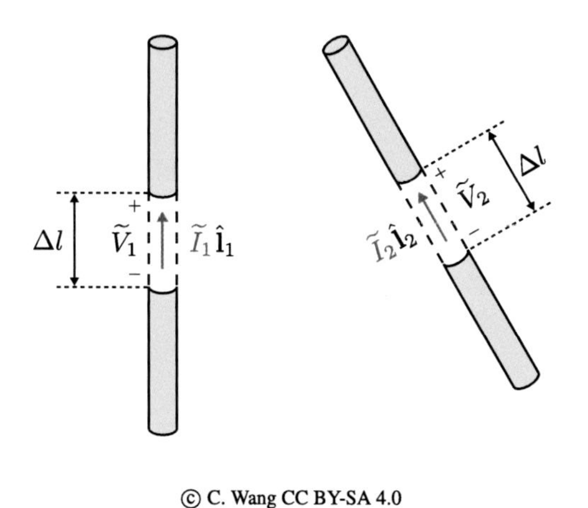

© C. Wang CC BY-SA 4.0

Figure 10.13: A two-port consisting of two dipole antennas.

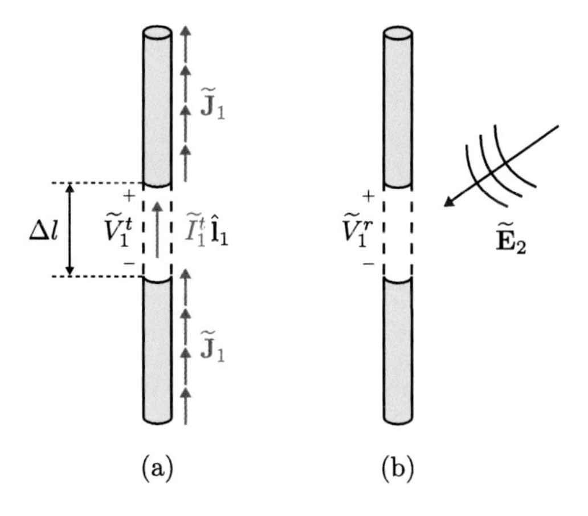

© C. Wang CC BY-SA 4.0

Figure 10.14: The port 1 antenna (a) transmitting and (b) receiving.

Reciprocity of two-ports consisting of antennas. Equation 10.90 allows us to establish the reciprocity of two-ports consisting of pairs of antennas. This is most easily demonstrated for pairs of thin dipole antennas, as shown in Figure 10.13. Here, port 1 is defined by the terminal quantities $(\widetilde{V}_1, \widetilde{I}_1)$ of the antenna on the left, and port 2 is defined by the terminal quantities $(\widetilde{V}_2, \widetilde{I}_2)$ of the antenna on the right. These quantities are defined with respect to a small gap of length Δl between the perfectly-conducting arms of the dipole. Either antenna may transmit or receive, so $(\widetilde{V}_1, \widetilde{I}_1)$ depends on $(\widetilde{V}_2, \widetilde{I}_2)$, and vice-versa.

The transmit and receive cases for port 1 are illustrated in Figure 10.14(a) and (b), respectively. Note that $\widetilde{\mathbf{J}}_1$ is the current distribution on this antenna when transmitting (i.e., when driven by the impressed current $\widetilde{I}_1^t$) and $\widetilde{\mathbf{E}}_2$ is the electric field incident on the antenna when the other antenna is transmitting. Let us select $\mathcal{V}_1$ to be the cylindrical volume defined by the exterior surface of the dipole, including the gap between the arms of the dipole. We are now ready to consider the right side of Equation 10.90:

$$\int_{\mathcal{V}_1} \widetilde{\mathbf{E}}_2 \cdot \widetilde{\mathbf{J}}_1 \, dv \qquad (10.91)$$

The electromagnetic boundary conditions applicable to the perfectly-conducting dipole arms allow this integral to be dramatically simplified. First, recall that all current associated with a perfect conductor must flow on the surface of the material, and therefore $\widetilde{\mathbf{J}}_1 = 0$ everywhere except on the surface. Therefore, the direction of $\widetilde{\mathbf{J}}_1$ is always tangent to the surface. The tangent component of $\widetilde{\mathbf{E}}_2$ is zero on the surface of a perfectly-conducting material, as required by the applicable boundary condition. Therefore, $\widetilde{\mathbf{E}}_2 \cdot \widetilde{\mathbf{J}}_1 = 0$ everywhere $\widetilde{\mathbf{J}}_1$ is non-zero.

There is only one location where the current is non-zero and yet there is no conductor: This location is the gap located precisely at the terminals. Thus, we find:

$$\int_{\mathcal{V}_1} \widetilde{\mathbf{E}}_2 \cdot \widetilde{\mathbf{J}}_1 \, dv = \int_{gap} \widetilde{\mathbf{E}}_2 \cdot \widetilde{I}_1^t \hat{\mathbf{l}}_1 \, dl \qquad (10.92)$$

where the right side is a line integral crossing the gap that defines the terminals of the antenna. We assume the current $\widetilde{I}_1^t$ is constant over the gap, and so may be factored out of the integral:

$$\int_{\mathcal{V}_1} \widetilde{\mathbf{E}}_2 \cdot \widetilde{\mathbf{J}}_1 \, dv = \widetilde{I}_1^t \int_{gap} \widetilde{\mathbf{E}}_2 \cdot \hat{\mathbf{l}}_1 \, dl \qquad (10.93)$$

Recall that potential between two points in space is given by the integral of the electric field over any path between those two points. In particular, we may calculate the open-circuit potential $\widetilde{V}_1^r$ as follows:

$$\widetilde{V}_1^r = -\int_{gap} \widetilde{\mathbf{E}}_2 \cdot \hat{\mathbf{l}}_1 \, dl \qquad (10.94)$$

Remarkably, we have found:

$$\int_{\mathcal{V}_1} \widetilde{\mathbf{E}}_2 \cdot \widetilde{\mathbf{J}}_1 \, dv = -\widetilde{I}_1^t \widetilde{V}_1^r \qquad (10.95)$$

Applying the exact same procedure for port 2 (or by simply exchanging subscripts), we find:

$$\int_{\mathcal{V}_2} \widetilde{\mathbf{E}}_1 \cdot \widetilde{\mathbf{J}}_2 \, dv = -\widetilde{I}_2^t \widetilde{V}_2^r \tag{10.96}$$

Now substituting these results into Equation 10.90, we find:

$$\boxed{\widetilde{I}_1^t \widetilde{V}_1^r = \widetilde{I}_2^t \widetilde{V}_2^r} \tag{10.97}$$

At the beginning of this section, we stated that a two-port is reciprocal if $\widetilde{V}_2$ appearing at port 2 due to a current applied at port 1 is the same as $\widetilde{V}_1$ when the same current is applied instead at port 2. If the present two-dipole problem is reciprocal, then $\widetilde{V}_2^r$ due to $\widetilde{I}_1^t$ should be the same as $\widetilde{V}_1^r$ when $\widetilde{I}_2^t = \widetilde{I}_1^t$. Is it? Let us set $\widetilde{I}_1^t$ equal to some particular value I_0, then the resulting value of $\widetilde{V}_2^r$ will be some particular value V_0. If we subsequently set $\widetilde{I}_2^t$ equal to I_0, then the resulting value of $\widetilde{V}_1^r$ will be, according to Equation 10.97:

$$\widetilde{V}_1^r = \frac{\widetilde{I}_2^t \widetilde{V}_2^r}{\widetilde{I}_1^t} = \frac{I_0 V_0}{I_0} = V_0 \tag{10.98}$$

Therefore, Equation 10.97 is simply a mathematical form of the familiar definition of reciprocity from basic circuit theory, and we have found that our system of antennas is reciprocal in precisely this same sense.

The above analysis presumed pairs of straight, perfectly conducting dipoles of arbitrary length. However, the result is readily generalized – in fact, is the same – for *any* pair of passive antennas in linear time-invariant media. Summarizing:

> The potential induced at the terminals of one antenna due to a current applied to a second antenna is equal to the potential induced in the second antenna by the same current applied to the first antenna (Equation 10.97).

Additional Reading:

- "Reciprocity (electromagnetism)" on Wikipedia.
- "Two-port network" on Wikipedia.

10.11 Potential Induced in a Dipole

[m0215]

An electromagnetic wave incident on an antenna will induce a potential at the terminals of the antenna. In this section, we shall derive this potential. To simplify the derivation, we shall consider the special case of a straight thin dipole of arbitrary length that is illuminated by a plane wave. However, certain aspects of the derivation will apply to antennas generally. In particular, the concepts of *effective length* (also known as *effective height*) and *vector effective length* emerge naturally from this derivation, so this section also serves as a stepping stone in the development of an equivalent circuit model for a receiving antenna. The derivation relies on the transmit properties of dipoles as well as the principle of reciprocity, so familiarity with those topics is recommended before reading this section.

The scenario of interest is shown in Figure 10.15. Here a thin $\hat{\mathbf{z}}$-aligned straight dipole is located at the origin. The total length of the dipole is L. The arms of the dipole are perfectly-conducting. The terminals consist of a small gap of length Δl between the arms. The incident plane wave is described in terms of its electric field intensity $\widetilde{\mathbf{E}}^i$. The question is: What is $\widetilde{V}_{OC}$, the potential at the terminals when the terminals are open-circuited?

There are multiple approaches to solve this problem. A direct attack is to invoke the principle that potential is equal to the integral of the electric field intensity over a path. In this case, the path begins at the "−" terminal and ends at the "+" terminal, crossing the gap that defines the antenna terminals. Thus:

$$\widetilde{V}_{OC} = -\int_{gap} \widetilde{\mathbf{E}}_{gap} \cdot d\mathbf{l} \tag{10.99}$$

where $\widetilde{\mathbf{E}}_{gap}$ is the electric field in the gap. The problem with this approach is that the value of $\widetilde{\mathbf{E}}_{gap}$ is not readily available. It is not simply $\widetilde{\mathbf{E}}^i$, because the antenna structure (in particular, the electromagnetic boundary conditions) modify the electric field in the vicinity of the antenna.[4]

[4] Also, if this were true, then the antenna itself would not matter;

Fortunately, we can bypass this obstacle using the principle of reciprocity. In a reciprocity-based strategy, we establish a relationship between two scenarios that take place within the same electromagnetic system. The first scenario is shown in Figure 10.16. In this scenario, we have two dipoles. The first dipole is precisely the dipole of interest (Figure 10.15), *except* that a current $\widetilde{I}_1^t$ is applied to the antenna terminals. This gives rise to a current distribution $\widetilde{I}(z)$ (SI base units of A) along the dipole, and subsequently the dipole radiates the electric field (Section 9.6):

$$\widetilde{\mathbf{E}}_1(\mathbf{r}) \approx \hat{\theta} j \frac{\eta}{2} \frac{e^{-j\beta r}}{r} (\sin\theta) \cdot \left[\frac{1}{\lambda} \int_{-L/2}^{+L/2} \widetilde{I}(z') e^{+j\beta z' \cos\theta} dz' \right] \quad (10.100)$$

The second antenna is a $\hat{\theta}$-aligned Hertzian dipole in the far field, which receives $\widetilde{\mathbf{E}}_1$. (For a refresher on the properties of Hertzian dipoles, see Section 9.4. A key point is that Hertzian dipoles are vanishingly small.) Specifically, we measure (conceptually, at least) the open-circuit potential $\widetilde{V}_2^r$ at the terminals of the Hertzian dipole. We select a Hertzian dipole for this purpose because – in contrast to essentially all

only the relative spacing and orientation of the antenna terminals would matter!

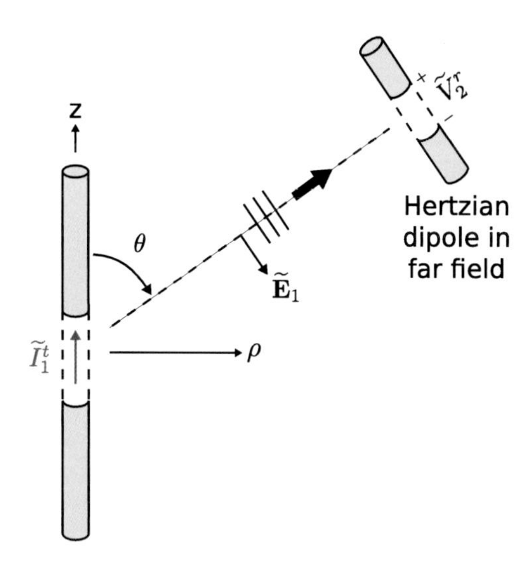

© C. Wang CC BY-SA 4.0

Figure 10.16: The dipole of interest driven by current $\widetilde{I}_1^t$ radiates electric field $\widetilde{\mathbf{E}}_1$, resulting in open-circuit potential $\widetilde{V}_2^r$ at the terminals of a Hertzian dipole in the far field.

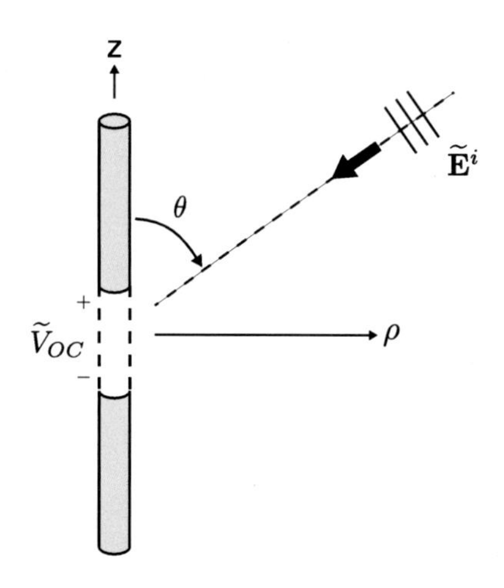

© C. Wang CC BY-SA 4.0

Figure 10.15: A potential is induced at the terminals of a thin straight dipole in response to an incident plane wave.

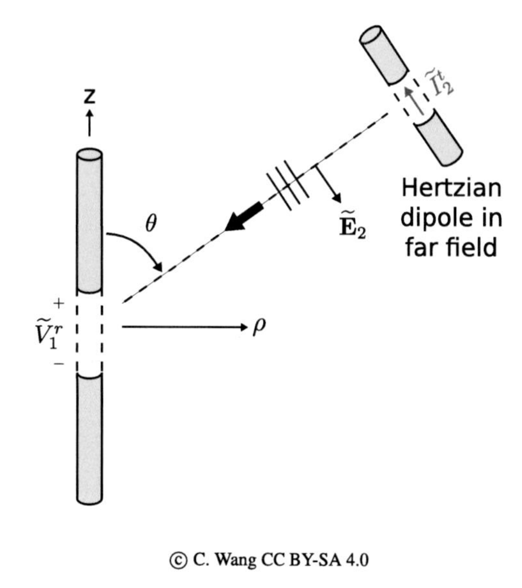

© C. Wang CC BY-SA 4.0

Figure 10.17: The Hertzian dipole driven by current $\widetilde{I}_2^t$ radiates electric field $\widetilde{\mathbf{E}}_2$, resulting in open-circuit potential $\widetilde{V}_1^r$ at the terminals of the dipole of interest.

other antennas – it is simple to determine the open circuit potential. As explained earlier:

$$\widetilde{V}_2^r = -\int_{gap} \widetilde{\mathbf{E}}_{gap} \cdot d\mathbf{l} \quad (10.101)$$

For the Hertzian dipole, $\widetilde{\mathbf{E}}_{gap}$ *is* simply the incident electric field, since there is negligible structure (in particular, a negligible amount of material) present to modify the electric field. Thus, we have simply:

$$\widetilde{V}_2^r = -\int_{gap} \widetilde{\mathbf{E}}_1 \cdot d\mathbf{l} \quad (10.102)$$

Since the Hertzian dipole is very short and very far away from the transmitting dipole, $\widetilde{\mathbf{E}}_1$ is essentially constant over the gap. Also recall that we required the Hertzian dipole to be aligned with $\widetilde{\mathbf{E}}_1$. Choosing to integrate in a straight line across the gap, Equation 10.102 reduces to:

$$\widetilde{V}_2^r = -\widetilde{\mathbf{E}}_1(\mathbf{r}_2) \cdot \hat{\theta}\Delta l \quad (10.103)$$

where Δl is the length of the gap and $\mathbf{r}_2$ is the location of the Hertzian dipole. Substituting the expression for $\widetilde{\mathbf{E}}_1$ from Equation 10.100, we obtain:

$$\widetilde{V}_2^r \approx -j\frac{\eta}{2}\frac{e^{-j\beta r_2}}{r_2}(\sin\theta) \cdot \left[\frac{1}{\lambda}\int_{-L/2}^{+L/2} \widetilde{I}(z')e^{+j\beta z'\cos\theta}dz'\right]\Delta l \quad (10.104)$$

where $r_2 = |\mathbf{r}_2|$.

The second scenario is shown in Figure 10.17. This scenario is identical to the first scenario, with the exception that the Hertzian dipole transmits and the dipole of interest receives. The field radiated by the Hertzian dipole in response to applied current $\widetilde{I}_2^t$, evaluated at the origin, is (Section 9.4):

$$\widetilde{\mathbf{E}}_2(\mathbf{r}=0) \approx \hat{\theta}j\eta\frac{\widetilde{I}_2^t \cdot \beta\Delta l}{4\pi}(1)\frac{e^{-j\beta r_2}}{r_2} \quad (10.105)$$

The "$\sin\theta$" factor in the general expression is equal to 1 in this case, since, as shown in Figure 10.17, the origin is located broadside (i.e., at $\pi/2$ rad) relative to the axis of the Hertzian dipole. Also note that because the Hertzian dipole is presumed to be in the far field, $\mathbf{E}_2$ may be interpreted as a plane wave in the region of the receiving dipole of interest.

Now we ask: What is the induced potential $\widetilde{V}_1^r$ in the dipole of interest? Once again, Equation 10.99 is not much help, because the electric field in the gap is not known. However, we do know that $\widetilde{V}_1^r$ should be proportional to $\widetilde{\mathbf{E}}_2(\mathbf{r}=0)$, since this is presumed to be a linear system. Based on this much information alone, there must be some vector $\mathbf{l}_e = \hat{\mathbf{l}}l_e$ for which

$$\widetilde{V}_1^r = \widetilde{\mathbf{E}}_2(\mathbf{r}=0) \cdot \mathbf{l}_e \quad (10.106)$$

This does not uniquely define either the unit vector $\hat{\mathbf{l}}$ nor the scalar part l_e, since a change in the definition of the former can be compensated by a change in the definition of the latter and vice-versa. So at this point we invoke the standard definition of $\mathbf{l}_e$ as the *vector effective length*, introduced in Section 10.9. Thus, $\hat{\mathbf{l}}$ is defined to be the direction in which an electric field *transmitted* from the antenna would be polarized. In the present example, $\hat{\mathbf{l}} = -\hat{\theta}$, where the minus sign reflects the fact that positive terminal potential results in terminal current which flows in the $-\hat{\mathbf{z}}$ direction. Thus, Equation 10.106 becomes:

$$\widetilde{V}_1^r = -\widetilde{\mathbf{E}}_2(\mathbf{r}=0) \cdot \hat{\theta}l_e \quad (10.107)$$

We may go a bit further and substitute the expression for $\widetilde{\mathbf{E}}_2(\mathbf{r}=0)$ from Equation 10.105:

$$\widetilde{V}_1^r \approx -j\eta\frac{\widetilde{I}_2^t \cdot \beta\Delta l}{4\pi}\frac{e^{-j\beta r_2}}{r_2}l_e \quad (10.108)$$

Now we invoke reciprocity. As a two-port linear time-invariant system, it must be true that:

$$\widetilde{I}_1^t\widetilde{V}_1^r = \widetilde{I}_2^t\widetilde{V}_2^r \quad (10.109)$$

Thus:

$$\widetilde{V}_1^r = \frac{\widetilde{I}_2^t}{\widetilde{I}_1^t}\widetilde{V}_2^r \quad (10.110)$$

Substituting the expression for $\widetilde{V}_2^r$ from Equation 10.104:

$$\widetilde{V}_1^r \approx -\frac{\widetilde{I}_2^t}{\widetilde{I}_1^t} \cdot j\frac{\eta}{2}\frac{e^{-j\beta r_2}}{r_2}(\sin\theta) \cdot \left[\frac{1}{\lambda}\int_{-L/2}^{+L/2} \widetilde{I}(z')e^{+j\beta z'\cos\theta}dz'\right]\Delta l \quad (10.111)$$

Thus, reciprocity has provided a second expression for $\widetilde{V}_1^r$. We may solve for l_e by setting this expression equal to the expression from Equation 10.108, yielding

$$l_e \approx \frac{2\pi}{\beta \widetilde{I}_1^t} \left[\frac{1}{\lambda} \int_{-L/2}^{+L/2} \widetilde{I}(z') e^{+j\beta z' \cos\theta} dz' \right] \sin\theta \tag{10.112}$$

Noting that $\beta = 2\pi/\lambda$, this simplifies to:

$$l_e \approx \left[\frac{1}{\widetilde{I}_1^t} \int_{-L/2}^{+L/2} \widetilde{I}(z') e^{+j\beta z' \cos\theta} dz' \right] \sin\theta \tag{10.113}$$

Thus, you can calculate l_e using the following procedure:

1. Apply a current $\widetilde{I}_1^t$ to the dipole of interest.
2. Determine the resulting current distribution $\widetilde{I}(z)$ along the length of the dipole. (Note that precisely this is done for the electrically-short dipole in Section 9.5 and for the half-wave dipole in Section 9.7.)
3. Integrate $\widetilde{I}(z)$ over the length of the dipole as indicated in Equation 10.113. Then divide ("normalize") by $\widetilde{I}_1^t$ (which is simply $\widetilde{I}(0)$). Note that the result is independent of the excitation $\widetilde{I}_1^t$, as expected since this is a linear system.
4. Multiply by $\sin\theta$.

We have now determined that the open-circuit terminal potential $\widetilde{V}_{OC}$ in response to an incident electric field $\widetilde{\mathbf{E}}^i$ is

$$\boxed{\widetilde{V}_{OC} = \widetilde{\mathbf{E}}^i \cdot \mathbf{l}_e} \tag{10.114}$$

where $\mathbf{l}_e = \hat{\mathbf{l}} l_e$ is the vector effective length defined previously.

This result is remarkable. In plain English, we have found that:

> The potential induced in a dipole is the co-polarized component of the incident electric field times a normalized integral of the *transmit* current distribution over the length of the dipole, times sine of the angle between the dipole axis and the direction of incidence.

In other words, the reciprocity property of linear systems allows this property of a receiving antenna to be determined relatively easily if the transmit characteristics of the antenna are known.

Example 10.9. Effective length of a thin electrically-short dipole (ESD).

A explained in Section 9.5, the current distribution on a thin ESD is

$$\widetilde{I}(z) \approx I_0 \left(1 - \frac{2}{L} |z| \right) \tag{10.115}$$

where L is the length of the dipole and I_0 is the terminal current. Applying Equation 10.113, we find:

$$l_e \approx \left[\frac{1}{I_0} \int_{-L/2}^{+L/2} I_0 \left(1 - \frac{2}{L} |z'| \right) e^{+j\beta z' \cos\theta} dz' \right] \cdot \sin\theta \tag{10.116}$$

Recall $\beta = 2\pi/\lambda$, so $\beta z' = 2\pi\,(z'/\lambda)$. Since this is an *electrically-short* dipole, $z' \ll \lambda$ over the entire integral, and subsequently we may assume $e^{+j\beta z' \cos\theta} \approx 1$ over the entire integral. Thus:

$$l_e \approx \left[\int_{-L/2}^{+L/2} \left(1 - \frac{2}{L} |z'| \right) dz' \right] \sin\theta \tag{10.117}$$

The integral is easily solved using standard methods, or simply recognize that the "area under the curve" in this case is simply one-half "base" (L) times "height" (1). Either way, we find

$$l_e \approx \frac{L}{2} \sin\theta \tag{10.118}$$

Example 10.7 (Section 10.9) demonstrates how Equation 10.114 with the vector effective length determined in the preceding example is used to obtain the induced potential.

10.12 Equivalent Circuit Model for Reception, Redux

[m0216]

Section 10.9 provides an informal derivation of an equivalent circuit model for a receiving antenna. This model is shown in Figure 10.18. The derivation of this model was informal and incomplete because the open-circuit potential $\mathbf{E}^i \cdot \mathbf{l}_e$ and source impedance Z_A were not rigorously derived in that section. While the open-circuit potential was derived in Section 10.11 ("Potential Induced in a Dipole"), the source impedance has not yet been addressed. In this section, the source impedance is derived, which completes the formal derivation of the model. Before reading this section, a review of Section 10.10 ("Reciprocity") is recommended.

The starting point for a formal derivation is the two-port model shown in Figure 10.19. If the two-port is passive, linear, and time-invariant, then the potential v_2 is a linear function of potentials and currents present at ports 1 and 2. Furthermore, v_1 must be proportional to i_1, and similarly v_2 must be proportional to i_2, so any pair of "inputs" consisting of either potentials or currents completely determines the two remaining potentials or currents. Thus, we may write:

$$v_2 = Z_{21}i_1 + Z_{22}i_2 \tag{10.119}$$

where Z_{11} and Z_{12} are, for the moment, simply constants of proportionality. However, note that Z_{11} and Z_{12} have SI base units of Ω, and so we refer to these quantities as impedances. Similarly we may write:

$$v_1 = Z_{11}i_1 + Z_{12}i_2 \tag{10.120}$$

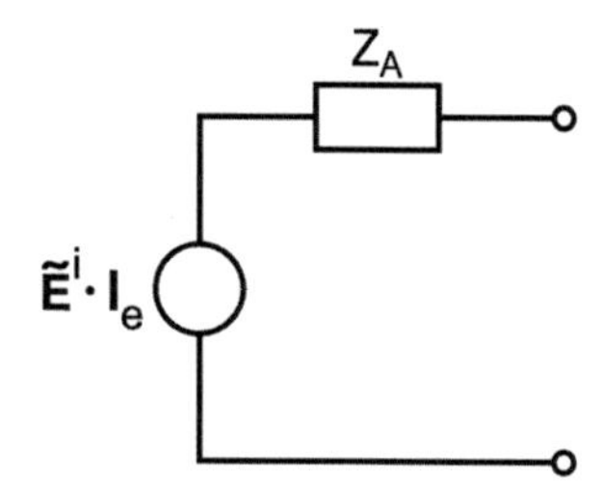

© S. Lally CC BY-SA 4.0

Figure 10.18: Thévenin equivalent circuit model for an antenna in the presence of an incident electric field $\mathbf{E}^i$.

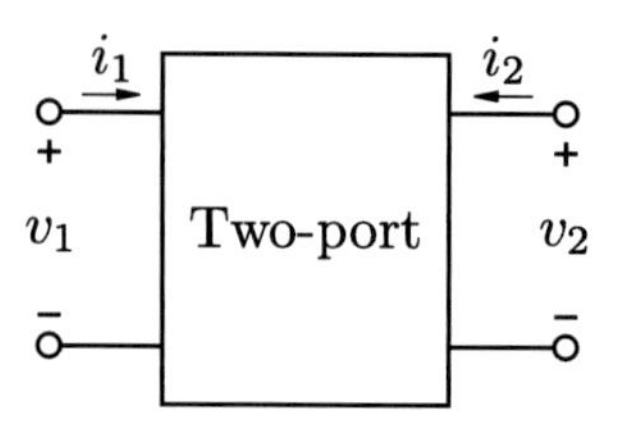

Inductiveload, public domain (modified)

Figure 10.19: Two-port system.

We can develop expressions for Z_{12} and Z_{21} as follows. First, note that $v_1 = Z_{12}i_2$ when $i_1 = 0$. Therefore, we may define Z_{12} as follows:

$$Z_{12} \triangleq \left.\frac{v_1}{i_2}\right|_{i_1=0} \tag{10.121}$$

The simplest way to make $i_1 = 0$ (leaving i_2 as the sole "input") is to leave port 1 open-circuited. In previous sections, we invoked special notation for these circumstances. In particular, we defined $\widetilde{I}_2^t$ as i_2 in phasor representation, with the superscript "t" ("transmitter") indicating that this is the sole "input"; and $\widetilde{V}_1^r$ as v_1 in phasor representation, with the superscript "r" ("receiver") signaling that port 1 is both open-circuited and the "output." Applying this notation, we note:

$$Z_{12} = \frac{\widetilde{V}_1^r}{\widetilde{I}_2^t} \tag{10.122}$$

Similarly:

$$Z_{21} = \frac{\widetilde{V}_2^r}{\widetilde{I}_1^t} \tag{10.123}$$

In Section 10.10 ("Reciprocity"), we established that a pair of antennas could be represented as a passive linear time-invariant two-port, with v_1 and i_1 representing the potential and current at the terminals of one antenna ("antenna 1"), and v_2 and i_2 representing the potential and current at the terminals of another antenna ("antenna 2"). Therefore for any pair of antennas, quantities Z_{11}, Z_{12}, Z_{22}, and Z_{21}

can be identified that completely determine the relationship between the port potentials and currents.

We also established in Section 10.10 that:

$$\widetilde{I}_1^t \widetilde{V}_1^r = \widetilde{I}_2^t \widetilde{V}_2^r \tag{10.124}$$

Therefore,

$$\frac{\widetilde{V}_1^r}{\widetilde{I}_2^t} = \frac{\widetilde{V}_2^r}{\widetilde{I}_1^t} \tag{10.125}$$

Referring to Equations 10.122 and 10.123, we see that Equation 10.125 requires that:

$$Z_{12} = Z_{21} \tag{10.126}$$

This is a key point. Even though we derived this equality by open-circuiting ports one at a time, the equality must hold generally since Equations 10.119 and 10.120 must apply – with the same values of Z_{12} and Z_{21} – regardless of the particular values of the port potentials and currents.

We are now ready to determine the Thévenin equivalent circuit for a receiving antenna. Let port 1 correspond to the transmitting antenna; that is, i_1 is $\widetilde{I}_1^t$. Let port 2 correspond to an open-circuited receiving antenna; thus, $i_2 = 0$ and v_2 is $\widetilde{V}_2^r$. Now applying Equation 10.119:

$$\begin{aligned} v_2 &= Z_{21} i_1 + Z_{22} i_2 \\ &= \left(\widetilde{V}_2^r / \widetilde{I}_1^t\right) \widetilde{I}_1^t + Z_{22} \cdot 0 \\ &= \widetilde{V}_2^r \end{aligned} \tag{10.127}$$

We previously determined $\widetilde{V}_2^r$ from electromagnetic considerations to be (Section 10.11):

$$\widetilde{V}_2^r = \widetilde{\mathbf{E}}^i \cdot \mathbf{l}_e \tag{10.128}$$

where $\widetilde{\mathbf{E}}^i$ is the field incident on the receiving antenna, and $\mathbf{l}_e$ is the vector effective length as defined in Section 10.11. Thus, the voltage source in the Thévenin equivalent circuit for the receive antenna is simply $\widetilde{\mathbf{E}}^i \cdot \mathbf{l}_e$, as shown in Figure 10.18.

The other component in the Thévenin equivalent circuit is the series impedance. From basic circuit theory, this impedance is the ratio of v_2 when port 2 is open-circuited (i.e., $\widetilde{V}_2^r$) to i_2 when port 2 is short-circuited. This value of i_2 can be obtained using Equation 10.119 with $v_2 = 0$:

$$0 = Z_{21} \widetilde{I}_1^t + Z_{22} i_2 \tag{10.129}$$

Therefore:

$$i_2 = -\frac{Z_{21}}{Z_{22}} \widetilde{I}_1^t \tag{10.130}$$

Now using Equation 10.123 to eliminate $\widetilde{I}_1^t$, we obtain:

$$i_2 = -\frac{\widetilde{V}_2^r}{Z_{22}} \tag{10.131}$$

Note that the reference direction for i_2 as defined in Figure 10.19 is opposite the reference direction for short-circuit current. That is, given the polarity of v_2 shown in Figure 10.19, the reference direction of current flow through a passive load attached to this port is from "+" to "−" through the load. Therefore, the source impedance, calculated as the ratio of the open-circuit potential to the short circuit current, is:

$$\frac{\widetilde{V}_2^r}{+\widetilde{V}_2^r / Z_{22}} = Z_{22} \tag{10.132}$$

We have found that the series impedance Z_A in the Thévenin equivalent circuit is equal to Z_{22} in the two-port model.

To determine Z_{22}, let us apply a current $i_2 = \widetilde{I}_2^t$ to port 2 (i.e., antenna 2). Equation 10.119 indicates that we should see:

$$v_2 = Z_{21} i_1 + Z_{22} \widetilde{I}_2^t \tag{10.133}$$

Solving for Z_{22}:

$$Z_{22} = \frac{v_2}{\widetilde{I}_2^t} - Z_{21} \frac{i_1}{\widetilde{I}_2^t} \tag{10.134}$$

Note that the first term on the right is precisely the impedance of antenna 2 *in transmission*. The second term in Equation 10.134 describes a contribution to Z_{22} from antenna 1. However, our immediate interest is in the equivalent circuit for reception of an electric field $\widetilde{\mathbf{E}}^i$ in the absence of any other antenna. We can have it both ways by imagining that $\widetilde{\mathbf{E}}^i$ is generated by antenna 1, but also that antenna 1 is far enough away to make Z_{21} – the factor that determines the effect of antenna 1 on antenna 2 – negligible. Then we see from Equation 10.134 that Z_{22} is the impedance of antenna 2 when transmitting.

Summarizing:

> The Thévenin equivalent circuit for an antenna in the presence of an incident electric field $\widetilde{\mathbf{E}}^i$ is shown in Figure 10.18. The series impedance Z_A in this model is equal to the impedance of the antenna in transmission.

Mutual coupling. This concludes the derivation, but raises a follow-up question: What if antenna 2 is present and *not* sufficiently far away that Z_{21} can be assumed to be negligible? In this case, we refer to antenna 1 and antenna 2 as being "coupled," and refer to the effect of the presence of antenna 1 on antenna 2 as *coupling*. Often, this issue is referred to as *mutual coupling*, since the coupling affects both antennas in a reciprocal fashion. It is rare for coupling to be significant between antennas on opposite ends of a radio link. This is apparent from common experience. For example, changes to a receive antenna are not normally seen to affect the electric field incident at other locations. However, coupling becomes important when the antenna system is a *dense array*; i.e., multiple antennas separated by distances less than a few wavelengths. It is common for coupling among the antennas in a dense array to be significant. Such arrays can be analyzed using a generalized version of the theory presented in this section.

Additional Reading:

- "Thévenin's Theorem" on Wikipedia.

10.13 Effective Aperture

[m0218]

When working with systems involving receiving antennas, it is convenient to have a single parameter that relates incident power (as opposed to incident electric field) to the power delivered to the receiver electronics. This parameter is commonly known as the *effective aperture* or *antenna aperture*.

From elementary circuit theory, the power delivered to a load Z_L is maximized when the load is conjugate matched to the antenna impedance; i.e., when $Z_L = Z_A^*$ where Z_A is the impedance of the antenna. Thus, a convenient definition for effective aperture A_e employs the relationship:

$$P_{R,max} \triangleq S_{co}^i A_e \tag{10.135}$$

where S_{co}^i is the incident power density (SI base units of W/m^2) that is co-polarized with the antenna, and $P_{R,max}$ is the power delivered to a load that is conjugate matched to the antenna impedance. Summarizing:

> *Effective aperture* (SI base units of m^2) is the ratio of power delivered by an antenna to a conjugate matched load, to the incident co-polarized power density.

As defined, a method for calculation of effective aperture is not obvious, except perhaps through direct measurement. In fact, there are at least three ways we can calculate effective aperture: (a) via effective length, (b) via thermodynamics, and (c) via reciprocity. Each of these methods yields some insight and are considered in turn.

Effective aperture via effective length. The potential and current at the load of the receive antenna can be determined using the equivalent circuit model shown in Figure 10.20, using the Thévenin equivalent circuit model for the antenna developed in Section 10.9. In this model, the voltage source is determined by the incident electric field intensity $\widetilde{\mathbf{E}}^i$ and the vector effective length $\mathbf{l_e} = \hat{\mathbf{l}}_e l_e$ of the antenna. We determine the associated effective aperture as follows. Consider a co-polarized sinusoidally-varying plane wave $\widetilde{\mathbf{E}}^i_{co}$ incident on the antenna. Further, let

$$\widetilde{\mathbf{E}}^i_{co} = E^i \hat{\mathbf{e}} \tag{10.136}$$

where $\hat{\mathbf{e}}$ is the reference direction of $\widetilde{\mathbf{E}}^i_{co}$. The co-polarized power density incident on the antenna is:

$$S^i_{co} = \frac{\left|E^i\right|^2}{2\eta} \tag{10.137}$$

where η is the wave impedance of the medium (e.g., $\cong 377\ \Omega$ for an antenna in free space). In response, the time-average power delivered to the load is

$$P_R = \frac{1}{2}\text{Re}\left\{\widetilde{V}_L \widetilde{I}^*_L\right\} \tag{10.138}$$

where $\widetilde{V}_L$ and $\widetilde{I}_L$ are the potential and current phasors, respectively, at the load. We may determine $\widetilde{V}_L$ and $\widetilde{I}_L$ from the equivalent circuit model of Figure 10.20 using basic circuit theory. First, note that the magnitude and phase of the voltage source is:

$$\widetilde{\mathbf{E}}^i_{co} \cdot \mathbf{l}_e = E^i l_e \left(\hat{\mathbf{e}} \cdot \hat{\mathbf{l}}_e\right) \tag{10.139}$$

and since we have defined $\hat{\mathbf{l}}_e$ to be equal to $\hat{\mathbf{e}}$,

$$\widetilde{\mathbf{E}}^i_{co} \cdot \mathbf{l}_e = E^i l_e \tag{10.140}$$

Next, note that the load impedance creates a voltage divider with the source (antenna) impedance such that

$$\widetilde{V}_L = \left(E^i l_e\right) \frac{Z_L}{Z_A + Z_L} \tag{10.141}$$

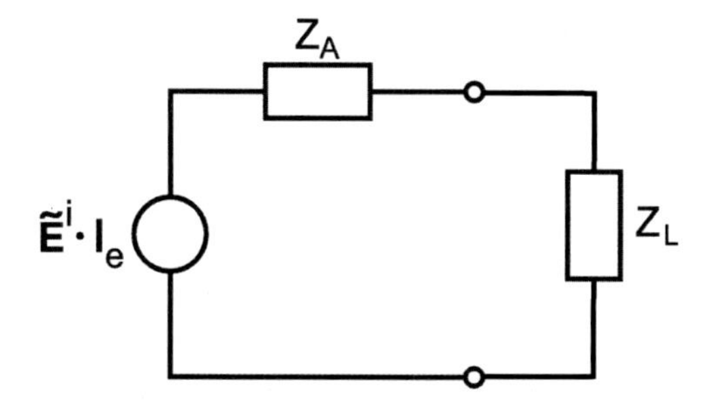

© S. Lally CC BY-SA 4.0 (modified)

Figure 10.20: Equivalent circuit model for an antenna in the presence of an incident electric field $\widetilde{\mathbf{E}}^i$, terminated into a load impedance Z_L.

Similarly, $\widetilde{I}_L$ is the voltage source output divided by the total series resistance:

$$\widetilde{I}_L = \frac{E^i l_e}{Z_A + Z_L} \tag{10.142}$$

Substituting these expressions into Equation 10.138, we obtain:

$$P_R = \frac{1}{2}\left|E^i l_e\right|^2 \frac{R_L}{\left|Z_A + Z_L\right|^2} \tag{10.143}$$

Let us identify the real and imaginary components of Z_A and Z_L explicitly, as follows:

$$Z_A = R_A + jX_A \tag{10.144}$$

$$Z_L = R_L + jX_L \tag{10.145}$$

Further, let us assume that loss internal to the antenna is negligible, so $R_A \approx R_{rad}$. If Z_L is conjugate matched for maximum power transfer, then $Z_L = Z^*_A = R_{rad} - jX_A$. Therefore:

$$\begin{aligned} P_{R,max} &= \frac{1}{2}\left|E^i l_e\right|^2 \frac{R_{rad}}{\left|Z_A + Z^*_A\right|^2} \\ &= \frac{1}{2}\left|E^i l_e\right|^2 \frac{R_{rad}}{\left|2R_{rad}\right|^2} \\ &= \frac{\left|E^i l_e\right|^2}{8R_{rad}} \end{aligned} \tag{10.146}$$

Now using Equations 10.135, 10.137, and 10.146, we find:

$$A_e = \frac{\left|E^i l_e\right|^2 / 8R_{rad}}{\left|E^i\right|^2 / 2\eta} \tag{10.147}$$

which reduces to:

$$\boxed{A_e = \frac{\eta\left|l_e\right|^2}{4R_{rad}}} \tag{10.148}$$

It is not surprising that effective aperture should be proportional to the square of the magnitude of effective length. However, we see that the medium and the radiation resistance of the antenna also play a role.

Effective length and radiation resistance are easy to calculate for wire antennas, so it is natural to use Equation 10.148 to calculate the effective apertures of wire antennas. For the electrically-short dipole (ESD) of length L, $l_e \approx (L/2)\sin\theta$ and $R_{rad} \approx 20\pi^2 (L/\lambda)^2$. Thus, we find the effective aperture assuming free space (i.e., $\eta = \eta_0$) is:

$$A_e \approx 0.119\lambda^2 \left|\sin\theta\right|^2 \quad \text{(lossless ESD)} \tag{10.149}$$

Remarkably, the effective aperture of the ESD does not depend on its length. In fact, it depends only on the frequency of operation.

Also worth noting is that *maximum* effective aperture (i.e., the effective aperture in the $\theta = \pi/2$ direction) is

$$\boxed{A_e \approx 0.119\lambda^2} \quad \text{(lossless ESD, max.)} \tag{10.150}$$

Dipoles which are not electrically-short exhibit radiation resistance which is proportional to L^p, where $p > 2$. Therefore, the effective aperture of non-electrically-short dipoles *does* increase with L, as expected. However, this increase is not dramatic unless L is significantly greater than $\lambda/2$. Here's an example:

Example 10.10. Effective aperture of a half-wave dipole.

The electrically-thin half-wave dipole exhibits radiation resistance $\cong 73~\Omega$ and effective length λ/π. Assuming the dipole is lossless and in free space, Equation 10.148 yields:

$$A_e \approx 0.131\lambda^2 \quad \text{(half-wave dipole, max.)} \tag{10.151}$$

Again, this is the effective aperture for a wave incident from broadside to the dipole.

Effective aperture via thermodynamics. A useful insight into the concept of effective aperture can be deduced by asking the following question: How much power is received by an antenna when waves of equal power density arrive from all directions simultaneously? This question is surprisingly easy to answer using basic principles of thermodynamics. Thermodynamics is a field of physics that addresses heat and its relation to radiation and electrical energy. No previous experience with thermodynamics is assumed in this derivation.

Consider the scenario depicted in Figure 10.21. In this scenario, the antenna is completely enclosed in a chamber whose walls do not affect the behavior of the antenna and which have uniform temperature T. The load (still conjugate matched to the antenna) is completely enclosed by a separate but identical chamber, also at temperature T.

Consider the load chamber first. Heat causes random acceleration of constituent charge carriers in the load, giving rise to a randomly-varying current at the load terminals. (This is known as *Johnson-Nyquist noise.*) This current, flowing through the load, gives rise to a potential; therefore, the load – despite being a passive device – is actually a source of power. The power associated with this noise is:

$$P_{load} = kTB \tag{10.152}$$

where $k \cong 1.38 \times 10^{-23}$ J/K is *Boltzmann's constant* and B is the bandwidth within which P_{load} is measured.

Similarly, the antenna is a source of noise power P_{ant}. P_{ant} can also be interpreted as captured *thermal radiation* – that is, electromagnetic waves stimulated by the random acceleration of charged particles comprising the chamber walls. These waves radiate from the walls and travel to the antenna. The *Rayleigh-Jeans law* of thermodynamics tells us that this radiation should have power density (i.e., SI base units of W/m^2) equal to

$$\frac{2kT}{\lambda^2}B \tag{10.153}$$

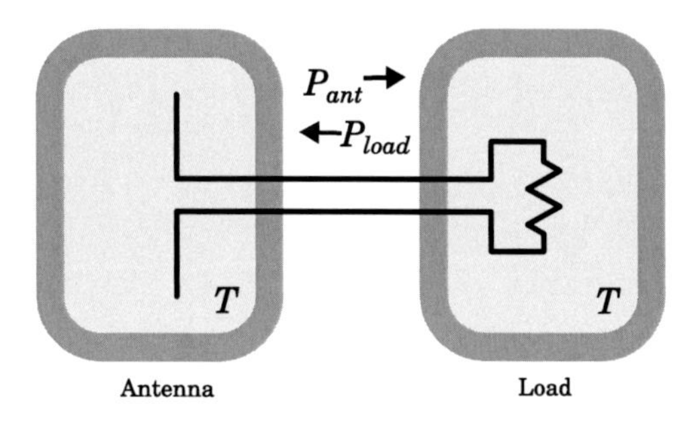

Chetvorno, public domain (modified)

Figure 10.21: Thermodynamic analysis of the power exchanged between an antenna and its load.

per steradian of solid angle.[5] The total power accessible to the antenna is one-half this amount, since an antenna is sensitive to only one polarization at a time, whereas the thermal radiation is equally distributed among any two orthogonal polarizations. P_A is the remaining power, obtained by integrating over all 4π steradians. Therefore, the antenna captures total power equal to[6]

$$\begin{aligned} P_{ant} &= \oint A_e(\theta',\phi')\left(\frac{1}{2}\frac{2kT}{\lambda^2}B\right)\sin\theta' d\theta' d\phi' \\ &= \left(\frac{kT}{\lambda^2}B\right)\oint A_e(\theta',\phi')\sin\theta' d\theta' d\phi' \end{aligned} \tag{10.154}$$

Given the conditions of the experiment, and in particular since the antenna chamber and the load chamber are at the same temperature, the antenna and load are in *thermodynamic equilibrium*. A consequence of this equilibrium is that power P_{ant} captured by the antenna and delivered to the load must be equal to power P_{load} generated by the load and delivered to the antenna; i.e.,

$$P_{ant} = P_{load} \tag{10.155}$$

Combining Equations 10.152, 10.154, and 10.155, we obtain:

$$\left(\frac{kT}{\lambda^2}B\right)\oint A_e(\theta',\phi')\sin\theta' d\theta' d\phi' = kTB \tag{10.156}$$

which reduces to:

$$\oint A_e(\theta',\phi')\sin\theta' d\theta' d\phi' = \lambda^2 \tag{10.157}$$

Let $\langle A_e \rangle$ be the *mean* effective aperture of the antenna; i.e., A_e averaged over all possible directions. This average is simply Equation 10.157 divided by the 4π sr of solid angle comprising all possible directions. Thus:

$$\langle A_e \rangle = \frac{\lambda^2}{4\pi} \tag{10.158}$$

Recall that a *isotropic* antenna is one which has the same effective aperture in every direction. Such antennas do not exist in practice, but the concept of an isotropic antenna is quite useful as we shall soon see. Since the effective aperture of an isotropic antenna must be the same as its mean effective aperture, we find:

$$\boxed{A_e = \frac{\lambda^2}{4\pi} \approx 0.080\lambda^2 \quad \text{(isotropic antenna)}} \tag{10.159}$$

Note further that this must be the *minimum possible* value of the maximum effective aperture for *any* antenna.

Effective aperture via reciprocity. The fact that all antennas have maximum effective aperture greater than that of an isotropic antenna makes the isotropic antenna a logical benchmark against which to compare the effective aperture of antennas. We can characterize the effective aperture of any antenna as being some unitless real-valued constant D times the effective aperture of an isotropic antenna; i.e.:

$$\boxed{A_e \triangleq D\frac{\lambda^2}{4\pi} \quad \text{(any antenna)}} \tag{10.160}$$

where D must be greater than or equal to 1.

Astute readers might notice that D seems a lot like *directivity*. Directivity is defined in Section 10.7 as the factor by which a *transmitting* antenna increases the power density of its radiation over that of an isotropic antenna. Let us once again consider the ESD, for which we previously determined (via the effective length concept) that $A_e \cong 0.119\lambda^2$ in the direction in which it is maximum. Applying Equation 10.160 to the ESD, we find:

$$D \triangleq A_e\frac{4\pi}{\lambda^2} \cong 1.50 \quad \text{(ESD, max.)} \tag{10.161}$$

Sure enough, D is equal to the directivity of the ESD in the transmit case.

This result turns out to be generally true; that is:

> The effective aperture of *any* antenna is given by Equation 10.160 where D is the directivity of the antenna when transmitting.

A derivation of this result for the general case is possible using analysis similar to the thermodynamics

[5] Full disclosure: This is an approximation to the exact expression, but is very accurate at radio frequencies. See "Additional Reading" at the end of this section for additional details.

[6] Recall $\sin\theta' d\theta' d\phi'$ is the differential element of solid angle.

presented earlier, or using the reciprocity theorem developed in Section 10.10.

The fact that effective aperture is easily calculated from transmit directivity is an enormously useful tool in antenna engineering. Without this tool, determination of effective aperture is limited to direct measurement or calculation via effective length; and effective length is generally difficult to calculate for antennas which are not well-described as distributions of current along a line. It is usually far easier to calculate the directivity of an antenna when transmitting, and then use Equation 10.160 to obtain effective aperture for receive operation.

Note that this principle is itself an expression of reciprocity. That is, one may fairly say that "directivity" is not exclusively a transmit concept nor a receive concept, but rather is a single quantifiable characteristic of an antenna that applies in both the transmit and receive case. Recall that radiation patterns are used to quantify the way (transmit) directivity varies with direction. Suddenly, we have found that precisely the same patterns apply to the receive case! Summarizing:

> As long as the conditions required for formal reciprocity are satisfied, the directivity of a receiving antenna (defined via Equation 10.160) is equal to directivity of the same antenna when transmitting, and patterns describing receive directivity are equal to those for transmit directivity.

Finally, we note that the equivalence of transmit and receive directivity can, again via Equation 10.160, be used to define an effective aperture for the transmit case. In other words, we can define the effective aperture of a transmitting antenna to be $\lambda^2/4\pi$ times the directivity of the antenna. There is no new physics at work here; we are simply taking advantage of the fact that the concepts of effective aperture and directivity describe essentially the same characteristic of an antenna, and that this characteristic is the same for both transmit and receive operation.

Additional Reading:

- "Antenna aperture" on Wikipedia.
- "Boltzmann constant" on Wikipedia.
- "Rayleigh-Jeans law" on Wikipedia.
- "Johnson-Nyquist noise" on Wikipedia.
- "Thermodynamics" on Wikipedia.

10.14 Friis Transmission Equation

[m0219]

A common task in radio systems applications is to determine the power delivered to a receiver due to a distant transmitter. The scenario is shown in Figure 10.22: A transmitter delivers power P_T to an antenna which has gain G_T in the direction of the receiver. The receiver's antenna has gain G_R. As always, antenna gain is equal to directivity times radiation efficiency, so G_T and G_R account for losses internal to the antenna, but not losses due to impedance mismatch.

A simple expression for P_R can be derived as follows. First, let us assume "free space conditions"; that is, let us assume that the intervening terrain exhibits negligible absorption, reflection, or other scattering of the transmitted signal. In this case, the spatial power density at range R from the transmitter which radiates this power through a *lossless and isotropic* antenna would be:

$$\frac{P_T}{4\pi R^2} \tag{10.162}$$

that is, total transmitted power divided by the area of a sphere of radius R through which all the power must flow. The *actual* power density S^i is this amount times the gain of the transmit antenna, i.e.:

$$S^i = \frac{P_T}{4\pi R^2} G_T \tag{10.163}$$

The maximum received power is the incident co-polarized power density times the effective aperture A_e of the receive antenna:

$$\begin{aligned} P_{R,max} &= A_e S^i_{co} \\ &= A_e \frac{P_T}{4\pi R^2} G_T \end{aligned} \tag{10.164}$$

This assumes that the receive antenna is co-polarized with the incident electric field, and that the receiver is conjugate-matched to the antenna. The effective aperture can also be expressed in terms of the gain G_R of the receive antenna:

$$A_e = \frac{\lambda^2}{4\pi} G_R \tag{10.165}$$

Thus, Equation 10.164 may be written in the following form:

$$\boxed{P_{R,max} = P_T G_T \left(\frac{\lambda}{4\pi R}\right)^2 G_R} \tag{10.166}$$

This is the *Friis transmission equation*. Summarizing:

> The *Friis transmission equation* (Equation 10.166) gives the power delivered to a conjugate-matched receiver in response to a distant transmitter, assuming co-polarized antennas and free space conditions.

The factor $(\lambda/4\pi R)^2$ appearing in the Friis transmission equation is referred to as *free space path gain*. More often this is expressed as the reciprocal quantity:

$$\boxed{L_p \triangleq \left(\frac{\lambda}{4\pi R}\right)^{-2}} \tag{10.167}$$

which is known as *free space path loss*. Thus, Equation 10.166 may be expressed as follows:

$$P_{R,max} = P_T G_T L_p^{-1} G_R \tag{10.168}$$

The utility of the concept of path loss is that it may also be determined for conditions which are different from free space. The Friis transmission equation still applies; one simply uses the appropriate (and probably significantly different) value of L_p.

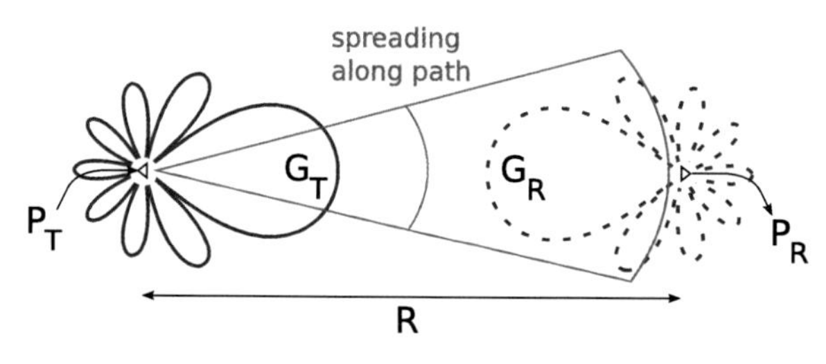

Figure 10.22: Radio link accounting for antenna gains and spreading of the transmitted wave.

A common misconception is that path loss is equal to the reduction in power density due to spreading along the path between antennas, and therefore this "spreading loss" increases with frequency. In fact, the reduction in power density due to spreading between any two distances $R_1 < R_2$ is:

$$\frac{P_T/4\pi R_1^2}{P_T/4\pi R_2^2} = \left(\frac{R_1}{R_2}\right)^2 \tag{10.169}$$

which is clearly independent of frequency. The path loss L_p, in contrast, depends only on the total distance R and does depend on frequency. The dependence on frequency reflects the dependence of the effective aperture on wavelength. Thus, path loss is not loss in the traditional sense, but rather accounts for a combination of spreading and the λ^2 dependence of effective aperture that is common to all receiving antennas.

Finally, note that Equation 10.168 is merely the simplest form of the Friis transmission equation. Commonly encountered alternative forms include forms in which G_T and/or G_R are instead represented by the associated effective apertures, and forms in which the effects of antenna impedance mismatch and/or cross-polarization are taken into account.

Example 10.11. 6 GHz point-to-point link.

Terrestrial telecommunications systems commonly aggregate large numbers of individual communications links into a single high-bandwidth link. This is often implemented as a radio link between dish-type antennas having gain of about 27 dBi (that's dB relative to a lossless isotropic antenna) mounted on very tall towers and operating at frequencies around 6 GHz. Assuming the minimum acceptable receive power is -120 dBm (that's -120 dB relative to 1 mW; i.e., 10^{-15} W) and the required range is 30 km, what is the minimum acceptable transmit power?

Solution. From the problem statement:

$$G_T = G_R = 10^{27/10} \cong 501 \tag{10.170}$$

$$\lambda = \frac{c}{f} \cong \frac{3 \times 10^8 \text{ m/s}}{6 \times 10^9 \text{ Hz}} \cong 5.00 \text{ cm} \tag{10.171}$$

$R = 30$ km, and $P_R \geq 10^{-15}$ W. We assume that the height and high directivity of the antennas yield conditions sufficiently close to free space. We further assume conjugate-matching at the receiver, and that the antennas are co-polarized. Under these conditions, $P_R = P_{R,max}$ and Equation 10.166 applies. We find:

$$\begin{aligned} P_T &\geq \frac{P_{R,max}}{G_T\left(\lambda/4\pi R\right)^2 G_R} \\ &\cong 2.26 \times 10^{-7} \text{ W} \\ &\cong 2.26 \times 10^{-4} \text{ mW} \\ &\cong \underline{-36.5 \text{ dBm}} \end{aligned} \tag{10.172}$$

Additional Reading:

- "Free-space path loss" on Wikipedia.
- "Friis transmission equation" on Wikipedia.

[m0211]

Image Credits

Fig. 10.1: © Offaperry (S. Lally), https://commons.wikimedia.org/wiki/File:Standing_Wave_Creation.svg, CC BY-SA 4.0 (https://creativecommons.org/licenses/by-sa/4.0/).

Fig. 10.2: © Offaperry (S. Lally), https://commons.wikimedia.org/wiki/File:Electrically-Short_Dipole.svg, CC BY-SA 4.0 (https://creativecommons.org/licenses/by-sa/4.0/).

Fig. 10.3: © Offaperry (S. Lally), https://commons.wikimedia.org/wiki/File:Zero-Length_Dipole_Open_Circuit.svg, CC BY-SA 4.0 (https://creativecommons.org/licenses/by-sa/4.0/).

Fig. 10.4: © Offaperry (S. Lally), https://commons.wikimedia.org/wiki/File:Transmitting_Antenna_Circuit.svg, CC BY-SA 4.0 (https://creativecommons.org/licenses/by-sa/4.0/).

Fig. 10.5: © Offaperry (S. Lally), https://commons.wikimedia.org/wiki/File:Magnitude_of_the_Radiated_Field.svg, CC BY-SA 4.0 (https://creativecommons.org/licenses/by-sa/4.0/).

Fig. 10.6: © Offaperry (S. Lally), https://commons.wikimedia.org/wiki/File:FHplaneMag.svg, CC BY-SA 4.0 (https://creativecommons.org/licenses/by-sa/4.0/).

Fig. 10.7: © T. Truckle, https://en.wikipedia.org/wiki/File:Sidelobes_en.svg, CC BY-SA 4.0 (https://creativecommons.org/licenses/by-sa/4.0/). Modified.

Fig. 10.8: © Offaperry (S. Lally), https://commons.wikimedia.org/wiki/File:Half-Power_Beamwidth.svg, CC BY-SA 4.0 (https://creativecommons.org/licenses/by-sa/4.0/).

Fig. 10.9: © Offaperry (S. Lally), https://commons.wikimedia.org/wiki/File:Antenna_Equivalent_Circuit.svg, CC BY-SA 4.0 (https://creativecommons.org/licenses/by-sa/4.0/). Modified.

Fig. 10.10: Inductiveload, https://commons.wikimedia.org/wiki/File:Two_Port_Circuit.svg, public domain. Modified.

Fig. 10.11: © Sevenchw (C. Wang), https://commons.wikimedia.org/wiki/File:An_electromagnetic_system_consisting_of_a_current_distribution_radiating_an_electric_field.svg, CC BY-SA 4.0 (https://creativecommons.org/licenses/by-sa/4.0/).

Fig. 10.12: © Sevenchw (C. Wang), https://commons.wikimedia.org/wiki/File:An_electromagnetic_system_consisting_of_a_different_current_distribution_radiating_an_electric_field.svg, CC BY-SA 4.0 (https://creativecommons.org/licenses/by-sa/4.0/).

Fig. 10.13: © Sevenchw (C. Wang), https://commons.wikimedia.org/wiki/File:A_two-port_consisting_of_two_dipole_antennas.svg, CC BY-SA 4.0 (https://creativecommons.org/licenses/by-sa/4.0/).

Fig. 10.14: © Sevenchw (C. Wang), https://commons.wikimedia.org/wiki/File:The_port_1_antenna_a_transmitting_and_b_receiving.svg, CC BY-SA 4.0 (https://creativecommons.org/licenses/by-sa/4.0/).

Fig. 10.15: © Sevenchw (C. Wang), https://commons.wikimedia.org/wiki/File:Thin_straight_dipole_respond_to_incident_plane_wave.svg, CC BY-SA 4.0 (https://creativecommons.org/licenses/by-sa/4.0/).

Fig. 10.16: © Sevenchw (C. Wang), https://commons.wikimedia.org/wiki/File:Dipole_of_interest_driven_by_current.svg, CC BY-SA 4.0 (https://creativecommons.org/licenses/by-sa/4.0/).

Fig. 10.17: © Sevenchw (C. Wang), https://commons.wikimedia.org/wiki/File:Hertzian_dipole_drive_by_current.svg, CC BY-SA 4.0 (https://creativecommons.org/licenses/by-sa/4.0/).

Fig. 10.18: © Offaperry (S. Lally), https://commons.wikimedia.org/wiki/File:Antenna_Equivalent_Circuit.svg, CC BY-SA 4.0 (https://creativecommons.org/licenses/by-sa/4.0/).

Fig. 10.19: Inductiveload, https://commons.wikimedia.org/wiki/File:Two_Port_Circuit.svg, public domain. Modified.

Fig. 10.20: © Offaperry (S. Lally), https://commons.wikimedia.org/wiki/File:Antenna_Equivalent_Circuit.svg, CC BY-SA 4.0 (https://creativecommons.org/licenses/by-sa/4.0/). Modified.

Fig. 10.21: Chetvorno, https://en.wikipedia.org/wiki/File:Antenna_and_resistor_in_cavity.svg, public domain. Modified.

Appendix A

Constitutive Parameters of Some Common Materials

A.1 Permittivity of Some Common Materials

[m0135]

The values below are relative permittivity $\epsilon_r \triangleq \epsilon/\epsilon_0$ for a few materials that are commonly encountered in electrical engineering applications, and for which permittivity emerges as a consideration. Note that "relative permittivity" is sometimes referred to as *dielectric constant*.

Here we consider only the physical (real-valued) permittivity, which is the real part of the complex permittivity (typically indicated as ϵ' or ϵ_r') for materials exhibiting significant loss.

Permittivity varies significantly as a function of frequency. The values below are representative of frequencies from a few kHz to about 1 GHz. The values given are also representative of optical frequencies for materials such as silica that are used in optical applications. Permittivity also varies as a function of temperature. In applications where precision better than about 10% is required, primary references accounting for frequency and temperature should be consulted. The values presented here are gathered from a variety of references, including those indicated in "Additional References."

Free Space (vacuum): $\epsilon_r \triangleq 1$

Solid Dielectrics:

Material	ϵ_r	Common uses
Styrofoam[1]	1.1	
Teflon[2]	2.1	
Polyethylene	2.3	coaxial cable
Polypropylene	2.3	
Silica	2.4	optical fiber[3]
Polystyrene	2.6	
Polycarbonate	2.8	
Rogers RO3003	3.0	PCB substrate
FR4 (glass epoxy laminate)	4.5	PCB substrate

[1] Properly known as *extruded polystyrene foam* (XPS).
[2] Properly known as *polytetrafluoroethylene* (PTFE).
[3] Typically doped with small amounts of other materials to slightly raise or lower the index of refraction ($= \sqrt{\epsilon_r}$).

Non-conducting spacing materials used in discrete capacitors exhibit ϵ_r ranging from about 5 to 50.

Semiconductors commonly appearing in electronics – including carbon, silicon, geranium, indium phosphide, and so on – typically exhibit ϵ_r in the range 5–15.

Glass exhibits ϵ_r in the range 4–10, depending on composition.

Gasses, including air, typically exhibit $\epsilon_r \cong 1$ to within a tiny fraction of a percent.

Liquid water typically exhibits ϵ_r in the range 72–81. Distilled water exhibits $\epsilon_r \approx 81$ at room temperature, whereas sea water tends to be at the

© 2020 S.W. Ellingson CC BY SA 4.0. https://doi.org/10.21061/electromagnetics-vol-2

lower end of the range.

Other liquids typically exhibit ϵ_r in the range 10–90, with considerable variation as a function of temperature and frequency. Animal flesh and blood consists primarily of liquid matter and so also exhibits permittivity in this range.

Soil typically exhibits ϵ_r in the range 2.5–3.5 when dry and higher when wet. The permittivity of soil varies considerably depending on composition.

Additional Reading:

- *CRC Handbook of Chemistry and Physics.*
- "Relative permittivity" on Wikipedia.
- "Miscellaneous Dielectric Constants" on microwaves101.com.

A.2 Permeability of Some Common Materials

[m0136]

The values below are relative permeability $\mu_r \triangleq \mu/\mu_0$ for a few materials that are commonly encountered in electrical engineering applications, and for which μ_r is significantly different from 1. These materials are predominantly ferromagnetic metals and (in the case of ferrites) materials containing significant ferromagnetic metal content. Nearly all other materials exhibit μ_r that is not significantly different from that of free space.

The values presented here are gathered from a variety of references, including those indicated in "Additional References" at the end of this section. Be aware that permeability may vary significantly with frequency; values given here are applicable to the frequency ranges for applications in which these materials are typically used. Also be aware that materials exhibiting high permeability are also typically non-linear; that is, permeability depends on the magnitude of the magnetic field. Again, values reported here are those applicable to applications in which these materials are typically used.

Free Space (vacuum): $\mu_r \triangleq 1$.

Iron (also referred to by the chemical notation "Fe") appears as a principal ingredient in many materials and alloys employed in electrical structures and devices. Iron exhibits μ_r that is very high, but which decreases with decreasing purity. 99.95% pure iron exhibits $\mu_r \sim 200,000$. This decreases to ~ 5000 at 99.8% purity and is typically below 100 for purity less than 99%.

Steel is an iron alloy that comes in many forms, with a correspondingly broad range of permeabilities. *Electrical steel*, commonly used in electrical machinery and transformers when high permeability is desired, exhibits $\mu_r \sim 4000$. *Stainless steel*, encompassing a broad range of alloys used in mechanical applications, exhibits μ_r in the range 750–1800. *Carbon steel*, including a broad class of alloys commonly used in structural applications, exhibits μ_r on the order of 100.

Ferrites include a broad range of ceramic materials that are combined with iron and various combinations of other metals and are used as magnets and magnetic devices in various electrical systems. Common ferrites exhibit μ_r in the range 16–640.

Additional Reading:

- *CRC Handbook of Chemistry and Physics.*
- "Magnetic Materials" on microwaves101.com.
- "Permeability (electromagnetism)" on Wikipedia.
- "Iron" on Wikipedia.
- "Electrical steel" on Wikipedia.
- "Ferrite (magnet)" on Wikipedia.

A.3 Conductivity of Some Common Materials

[m0137]

The values below are conductivity σ for a few materials that are commonly encountered in electrical engineering applications, and for which conductivity emerges as a consideration.

Note that materials in some applications are described instead in terms of *resistivity*, which is simply the reciprocal of conductivity.

Conductivity may vary significantly as a function of frequency. The values below are representative of frequencies from a few kHz to a few GHz. Conductivity also varies as a function of temperature. In applications where precise values are required, primary references accounting for frequency and temperature should be consulted. The values presented here are gathered from a variety of references, including those indicated in "Additional References" at the end of this section.

Free Space (vacuum): $\sigma \triangleq 0$.

Commonly encountered elements:

Material	σ (S/m)
Copper	5.8×10^7
Gold	4.4×10^7
Aluminum	3.7×10^7
Iron	1.0×10^7
Platinum	0.9×10^7
Carbon	1.3×10^5
Silicon	4.4×10^{-4}

Water exhibits σ ranging from about 6 μS/m for highly distilled water (thus, a very poor conductor) to about 5 S/m for seawater (thus, a relatively good conductor), varying also with temperature and pressure. Tap water is typically in the range of 5–50 mS/m, depending on the level of impurities present.

Soil typically exhibits σ in the range 10^{-4} S/m for dry soil to about 10^{-1} S/m for wet soil, varying also due to chemical composition.

Non-conductors. Most other materials that are not well-described as conductors or semiconductors and are dry exhibit $\sigma < 10^{-12}$ S/m. Most materials that are considered to be *insulators*, including air and common dielectrics, exhibit $\sigma < 10^{-15}$ S/m, often by several orders of magnitude.

Additional Reading:

- *CRC Handbook of Chemistry and Physics.*
- "Conductivity (electrolytic)" on Wikipedia.
- "Electrical resistivity and conductivity" on Wikipedia.
- "Soil resistivity" on Wikipedia.

Appendix B

Mathematical Formulas

B.1 Trigonometry

[m0138]

$$e^{j\theta} = \cos\theta + j\sin\theta \tag{B.1}$$

$$\cos\theta = \frac{1}{2}\left(e^{j\theta} + e^{-j\theta}\right) \tag{B.2}$$

$$\sin\theta = \frac{1}{j2}\left(e^{j\theta} - e^{-j\theta}\right) \tag{B.3}$$

$$\cos^2\theta = \frac{1}{2} + \frac{1}{2}\cos 2\theta \tag{B.4}$$

$$\sin^2\theta = \frac{1}{2} - \frac{1}{2}\cos 2\theta \tag{B.5}$$

$$\sin(a \pm b) = \sin a \cos b \pm \cos a \sin b \tag{B.6}$$

$$\cos(a \pm b) = \cos a \cos b \mp \sin a \sin b \tag{B.7}$$

Hyperbolic trigonometric functions:

$$\sinh\theta = \frac{1}{2}\left(e^{+\theta} - e^{-\theta}\right) \tag{B.8}$$

$$\cosh\theta = \frac{1}{2}\left(e^{+\theta} + e^{-\theta}\right) \tag{B.9}$$

B.2 Vector Operators

[m0139]

This section contains a summary of vector operators expressed in each of the three major coordinate systems:

- Cartesian (x,y,z)
- cylindrical (ρ,ϕ,z)
- spherical (r,θ,ϕ)

Associated basis vectors are identified using a caret (ˆ) over the symbol. The vector operand $\mathbf{A}$ is expressed in terms of components in the basis directions as follows:

- Cartesian: $\mathbf{A} = \hat{\mathbf{x}}A_x + \hat{\mathbf{y}}A_y + \hat{\mathbf{z}}A_z$
- cylindrical: $\mathbf{A} = \hat{\rho}A_\rho + \hat{\phi}A_\phi + \hat{\mathbf{z}}A_z$
- spherical: $\mathbf{A} = \hat{\mathbf{r}}A_r + \hat{\theta}A_\theta + \hat{\phi}A_\phi$

Gradient

Gradient in Cartesian coordinates:

$$\nabla f = \hat{\mathbf{x}}\frac{\partial f}{\partial x} + \hat{\mathbf{y}}\frac{\partial f}{\partial y} + \hat{\mathbf{z}}\frac{\partial f}{\partial z} \tag{B.10}$$

Gradient in cylindrical coordinates:

$$\nabla f = \hat{\rho}\frac{\partial f}{\partial \rho} + \hat{\phi}\frac{1}{\rho}\frac{\partial f}{\partial \phi} + \hat{\mathbf{z}}\frac{\partial f}{\partial z} \tag{B.11}$$

Electromagnetics Vol. 2. © 2020 S.W. Ellingson CC BY SA 4.0. https://doi.org/10.21061/electromagnetics-vol-2

Gradient in spherical coordinates:

$$\nabla f = \hat{\mathbf{r}}\frac{\partial f}{\partial r} + \hat{\theta}\frac{1}{r}\frac{\partial f}{\partial \theta} + \hat{\phi}\frac{1}{r\sin\theta}\frac{\partial f}{\partial \phi} \tag{B.12}$$

Divergence

Divergence in Cartesian coordinates:

$$\nabla \cdot \mathbf{A} = \frac{\partial A_x}{\partial x} + \frac{\partial A_y}{\partial y} + \frac{\partial A_z}{\partial z} \tag{B.13}$$

Divergence in cylindrical coordinates:

$$\nabla \cdot \mathbf{A} = \frac{1}{\rho}\frac{\partial}{\partial \rho}(\rho A_\rho) + \frac{1}{\rho}\frac{\partial A_\phi}{\partial \phi} + \frac{\partial A_z}{\partial z} \tag{B.14}$$

Divergence in spherical coordinates:

$$\begin{aligned}\nabla \cdot \mathbf{A} = &\ \frac{1}{r^2}\frac{\partial}{\partial r}\left(r^2 A_r\right) \\ &+ \frac{1}{r\sin\theta}\frac{\partial}{\partial \theta}(A_\theta \sin\theta) \\ &+ \frac{1}{r\sin\theta}\frac{\partial A_\phi}{\partial \phi}\end{aligned} \tag{B.15}$$

Curl

Curl in Cartesian coordinates:

$$\begin{aligned}\nabla \times \mathbf{A} = &\ \hat{\mathbf{x}}\left(\frac{\partial A_z}{\partial y} - \frac{\partial A_y}{\partial z}\right) \\ &+ \hat{\mathbf{y}}\left(\frac{\partial A_x}{\partial z} - \frac{\partial A_z}{\partial x}\right) \\ &+ \hat{\mathbf{z}}\left(\frac{\partial A_y}{\partial x} - \frac{\partial A_x}{\partial y}\right)\end{aligned} \tag{B.16}$$

Curl in cylindrical coordinates:

$$\begin{aligned}\nabla \times \mathbf{A} = &\ \hat{\rho}\left(\frac{1}{\rho}\frac{\partial A_z}{\partial \phi} - \frac{\partial A_\phi}{\partial z}\right) \\ &+ \hat{\phi}\left(\frac{\partial A_\rho}{\partial z} - \frac{\partial A_z}{\partial \rho}\right) \\ &+ \hat{\mathbf{z}}\frac{1}{\rho}\left[\frac{\partial}{\partial \rho}(\rho A_\phi) - \frac{\partial A_\rho}{\partial \phi}\right]\end{aligned} \tag{B.17}$$

Curl in spherical coordinates:

$$\begin{aligned}\nabla \times \mathbf{A} = &\ \hat{\mathbf{r}}\frac{1}{r\sin\theta}\left[\frac{\partial}{\partial \theta}(A_\phi \sin\theta) - \frac{\partial A_\theta}{\partial \phi}\right] \\ &+ \hat{\theta}\frac{1}{r}\left[\frac{1}{\sin\theta}\frac{\partial A_r}{\partial \phi} - \frac{\partial}{\partial r}(rA_\phi)\right] \\ &+ \hat{\phi}\frac{1}{r}\left[\frac{\partial}{\partial r}(rA_\theta) - \frac{\partial A_r}{\partial \theta}\right]\end{aligned} \tag{B.18}$$

Laplacian

Laplacian in Cartesian coordinates:

$$\nabla^2 f = \frac{\partial^2 f}{\partial x^2} + \frac{\partial^2 f}{\partial y^2} + \frac{\partial^2 f}{\partial z^2} \tag{B.19}$$

Laplacian in cylindrical coordinates:

$$\nabla^2 f = \frac{1}{\rho}\frac{\partial}{\partial \rho}\left(\rho\frac{\partial f}{\partial \rho}\right) + \frac{1}{\rho^2}\frac{\partial^2 f}{\partial \phi^2} + \frac{\partial^2 f}{\partial z^2} \tag{B.20}$$

Laplacian in spherical coordinates:

$$\begin{aligned}\nabla^2 f = &\ \frac{1}{r^2}\frac{\partial}{\partial r}\left(r^2\frac{\partial f}{\partial r}\right) \\ &+ \frac{1}{r^2\sin\theta}\frac{\partial}{\partial \theta}\left(\frac{\partial f}{\partial \theta}\sin\theta\right) \\ &+ \frac{1}{r^2\sin^2\theta}\frac{\partial^2 f}{\partial \phi^2}\end{aligned} \tag{B.21}$$

B.3 Vector Identities

[m0140]

Algebraic Identities

$$\mathbf{A} \cdot (\mathbf{B} \times \mathbf{C}) = \mathbf{B} \cdot (\mathbf{C} \times \mathbf{A}) = \mathbf{C} \cdot (\mathbf{A} \times \mathbf{B}) \tag{B.22}$$

$$\mathbf{A} \times (\mathbf{B} \times \mathbf{C}) = \mathbf{B}\,(\mathbf{A} \cdot \mathbf{C}) - \mathbf{C}\,(\mathbf{A} \cdot \mathbf{B}) \tag{B.23}$$

Identities Involving Differential Operators

$$\nabla \cdot (\nabla \times \mathbf{A}) = 0 \tag{B.24}$$

$$\nabla \times (\nabla f) = 0 \tag{B.25}$$

$$\nabla \times (f\mathbf{A}) = f\,(\nabla \times \mathbf{A}) + (\nabla f) \times \mathbf{A} \tag{B.26}$$

$$\nabla \cdot (\mathbf{A} \times \mathbf{B}) = \mathbf{B} \cdot (\nabla \times \mathbf{A}) - \mathbf{A} \cdot (\nabla \times \mathbf{B}) \tag{B.27}$$

$$\nabla \cdot (\nabla f) = \nabla^2 f \tag{B.28}$$

$$\nabla \times \nabla \times \mathbf{A} = \nabla\,(\nabla \cdot \mathbf{A}) - \nabla^2 \mathbf{A} \tag{B.29}$$

$$\nabla^2 \mathbf{A} = \nabla\,(\nabla \cdot \mathbf{A}) - \nabla \times (\nabla \times \mathbf{A}) \tag{B.30}$$

Divergence Theorem: Given a closed surface $\mathcal{S}$ enclosing a contiguous volume $\mathcal{V}$,

$$\int_{\mathcal{V}} (\nabla \cdot \mathbf{A})\, dv = \oint_{\mathcal{S}} \mathbf{A} \cdot d\mathbf{s} \tag{B.31}$$

where the surface normal $d\mathbf{s}$ is pointing out of the volume.

Stokes' Theorem: Given a closed curve $\mathcal{C}$ bounding a contiguous surface $\mathcal{S}$,

$$\int_{\mathcal{S}} (\nabla \times \mathbf{A}) \cdot d\mathbf{s} = \oint_{\mathcal{C}} \mathbf{A} \cdot d\mathbf{l} \tag{B.32}$$

where the direction of the surface normal $d\mathbf{s}$ is related to the direction of integration along $\mathcal{C}$ by the "right hand rule."

Appendix C

Physical Constants

[m0141]

The speed of light in free space (c), which is the phase velocity of any electromagnetic radiation in free space, is $\cong 2.9979 \times 10^8$ m/s. This is commonly rounded up to 3×10^8 m/s. This rounding incurs error of $\cong 0.07\%$, which is usually much less than other errors present in electrical engineering calculations.

The charge of an electron is $\cong -1.602 \times 10^{-19}$ C. The constant $e \triangleq +1.602176634 \times 10^{-19}$ C is known as the "elementary charge," so the charge of the electron is said to be $-e$.

The permittivity of free space (ϵ_0) is $\cong 8.854 \times 10^{-12}$ F/m.

The permeability of free space (μ_0) is $4\pi \times 10^{-7}$ H/m.

The wave impedance of free space (η_0) is the ratio of the magnitude of the electric field intensity to that of the magnetic field intensity in free space and is $\sqrt{\mu_0/\epsilon_0} \cong 376.7\ \Omega$. This is also sometimes referred to as the *intrinsic impedance of free space*.

Boltzmann's constant is $\cong 1.381 \times 10^{-23}$ J/K, the amount of energy associated with a change of one degree of temperature. This is typically assigned the symbol k (unfortunately, the same symbol often used to represent *wavenumber*).

 © 2020 S.W. Ellingson CC BY SA 4.0. https://doi.org/10.21061/electromagnetics-vol-2

Index

Made in the USA
Las Vegas, NV
01 July 2023